MACHINE SHOP
Theory and Practice

BY

ALBERT M. WAGENER
INSTRUCTOR
TRADE AND TECHNICAL TRAINING DIVISION
APPRENTICE SCHOOL, FORD MOTOR COMPANY
DEARBORN, MICHIGAN

AND

HARLAN R. ARTHUR
SUPERVISOR
TRADE AND TECHNICAL TRAINING DIVISION
APPRENTICE SCHOOL, FORD MOTOR COMPANY
DEARBORN, MICHIGAN

SECOND EDITION

VAN NOSTRAND REINHOLD COMPANY
NEW YORK   CINCINNATI   TORONTO
LONDON   MELBOURNE

VAN NOSTRAND REINHOLD COMPANY REGIONAL OFFICES:
Cincinnati   New York   Chicago   Millbrae   Dallas

VAN NOSTRAND REINHOLD COMPANY FOREIGN OFFICES:
London   Toronto   Melbourne

Copyright © 1950 by Litton Educational Publishing, Inc.

MANUFACTURED IN THE UNITED STATES OF AMERICA

Published by VAN NOSTRAND REINHOLD COMPANY
450 West 33rd Street, New York, N.Y.   10001

Published simultaneously in Canada by
D. VAN NOSTRAND COMPANY (Canada), LTD.

30 29 28 27 26 25 24 23 22 21 20 19

To

FREDERICK E. SEARLE,

WHOSE DEVOTED INTEREST IN THE
PRACTICAL EDUCATION OF YOUTH HAS
BEEN A CONTINUAL INSPIRATION TO US,
THIS TEXT IS RESPECTFULLY DEDICATED

IN APPRECIATION

The following manufacturers have been very generous in supplying photographs, electrotypes, and descriptive literature in the compilation of this text. We take this opportunity to express our gratitude for their interest and cooperation in this undertaking.

●

FIRM	ADDRESS
Armstrong Bros. Tool Co.	Chicago, Ill.
Atlas Press Co.	Kalamazoo, Mich.
Brown & Sharpe Mfg. Co.	Providence, R. I.
Cincinnati Milling Machine and Cincinnati Grinders Inc.	Cincinnati, Ohio
Gould & Eberhardt	Newark, N. J.
Heald Machine Co.	Worcester, Mass.
Kearney & Trecker	Milwaukee, Wis.
Nicholson File Co.	Providence, R. I.
Norton Company	Worcester, Mass.
Pratt & Whitney	West Hartford, Conn.
Rivett Lathe & Grinder Co.	Brighton, Mass.
The Blancharl Machine Co.	Cambridge, Mass.
The Bullard Machine Co.	Bridgeport, Conn.
The Cincinnati Shaper Co.	Cincinnati, Ohio
The Lufkin Rule Co.	Saginaw, Mich.
The Monarch Machine Tool Co.	Sidney, Ohio
The L. S. Starrett Co.	Athol, Mass.
The Taft-Peirce Manufacturing Co.	Woonsocket, R. I.
O. S. Walker Co.	Worcester, Mass.
The Warner & Swasey Co.	Cleveland, Ohio
J. H. Williams & Co.	Buffalo, N. Y.

PREFACE TO SECOND EDITION

The past several years have witnessed the introduction of new design in some of the basic tool machines. New pictures, diagrams, illustrative sketches, and certain revisions of content have been incorporated in this second edition to reflect the new developments, and some of the old material has been deleted. Many sketches and drawings have been redrawn for better clarity.

New exercises for practice in reading the basic precision measuring tools have been added which will assist the student and instructor to understand thoroughly and easily the principles involved.

Basic shop safety has been briefly outlined and inserted as preliminary instruction to the actual text material.

The authors have just completed an entirely new Workbook to accompany this revised edition. The Workbook is totally objective throughout. All sections of the text are covered by multiple-choice, true-false, or completion type questions accompanied by illustrative diagrams and drawings.

A. M. W.
H. R. A.

TABLE OF CONTENTS

GENERAL SAFETY SUGGESTIONS

Safety in the shop depends upon the instructor, the student, and the conditions of the shop equipment. A safe instructor is one who knows and practices safe methods of instruction. A safe student is always aware of the need for proper mental alertness and the proper execution of instructions. A safe shop is always well lighted and kept in good housekeeping order. It shows evidence of safety guards properly placed, covering all moving gears, belts and protruding moving parts to a height of six feet.

Many important safety factors depend upon the clothing worn in the shop and the manner in which it is worn. From top to toe it is worthy of special mention. It is good practice to wear a small "watch" cap or "skull" cap to protect the hair and scalp. Long neckties should never be allowed to hang loosely; they should, in fact, be removed. Always roll up the sleeves above the elbow to prevent entanglement with moving parts of the work or the machine. A snugly fitted apron is preferred to a shop coat. It is unwise and unsafe to carry shop "towels" or cleaning rags in trouser pockets. It is not safe to wear thinly soled shoes in the shop because of the danger of stepping on sharp chips. Always remove finger rings before starting to work in the shop. Be sure to wear safety goggles when working on or near any job where flying chips or particles may strike the face.

It is always dangerous to operate a machine of any kind unless you have been properly instructed. Never attempt to make repairs to electrical or mechanical equipment without approval of your instructor. When changing a set-up on a machine always be sure the machine is "dead," that is, make sure you have "pulled the switch."

When making inspections or taking test measurements on any work-piece that is being machined, be sure that you wait for the work to come to a complete rest. For instance, do not attempt to insert a plug gage in a hole while the work is in motion.

Always use a chip paddle to remove chips from the lathe. Never use your fingers for this operation; painful laceration might result.

If at any time you should injure yourself so that blood shows go immediately to the First Aid Station after notifying your instructor. Proper attention can prevent serious infection.

Machine guards are installed for your protection, so don't remove them under any circumstances.

Don't use equipment or tools that are not safe. For example, don't use a chisel with a mushroom head; grind it to restore it to safe conditions.

It is smart and safe to be ready to start on time properly attired. Last-minute rushes may mean many lost moments.

Chapter 1

RULES AND SCALES

DEFINITIONS
Rule . . . Scale

TYPES OF RULES AND SCALES AND THEIR USES
Graduations — numbers . . . Flexible . . . Narrow steel rule . . . Hook rules . . . Reading the rule . . . Shrink scales . . . Decimal scales

DEFINITIONS

The interchangeable use of the terms "rule" and "scale" by mechanics in industry has led to a considerable amount of confusion. A **rule** is a strip of wood, metal, or other suitable material graduated into units of measurement which can be used to measure the **actual** dimensions of an object. A **scale** is a strip of wood, metal, or other suitable material graduated into representative units which can be used to check or lay off **representative** measurement. The six- or twelve-inch graduated blade used by a machinist or toolmaker in his work is a rule, because he checks actual measurement with it. The shrink blades used by a patternmaker or coremaker in his work are scales because he checks representative measurement with them; that is, he must make the patterns sufficiently large, so that after the casting has cooled it will have shrunk to the right size.

Thus far, few textbooks or catalogues have made attempts to distinguish clearly and correctly between these two terms. On the contrary, there has been a feeling that by employing the terminology of the man in the shop—however incorrect—the books and catalogues would have greater appeal. Recently, however, a movement has been started to correct improper terminology as generally used by men in industry, and authors of textbooks and catalogues are gradually making the necessary corrections.

TYPES OF RULES AND SCALES AND THEIR USES

Rules are made in a variety of lengths, widths, and thicknesses, and several styles of **graduations,** each one having a particular advantage or desirable qualities. Of the graduations used on rules, the one most common is the No. 4. These graduations consist of one face graduated to read in 64ths and 32nds of an inch, the other graduated to read in

FIG. 1–1.   Rule with No. 4 graduations.

16ths and 8ths of an inch. These rules are usually about 3/64" thick and vary in width, depending on the length, from 1/2" to 1-1/4", and in the common lengths are not flexible. See Fig. 1–1.

Mechanics who work to close limits prefer the **"flexible"** rule. These rules are made in a variety of lengths and widths. The width varies from 1/2" to 3/4" depending on the length and generally they are graduated on one side only with No. 10 graduations which consist of one edge graduated in 32nds of an inch and the other edge graduated in 64ths of an inch. These rules are extremely flexible, which make them adaptable to work which heavier rules could not do. Fig. 1–2 shows one of these rules.

FIG. 1–2.   Rule with No. 10 graduations.

The **narrow steel rule** shown in Fig. 1–3 is found to be convenient for measuring

FIG. 1–3.   Narrow depth rule.

the depths of narrow slots or small deep holes. It is about 3/16″ wide and about 1/25″ thick. It is graduated on one edge of each side, either in 32nds and 64ths of an inch or in 64ths and 100ths of an inch.

The **hook rules** shown in Figs. 1–4 and 1–5 are found very convenient for taking measurements through the holes of gears or pulleys, the distance from an inside under-

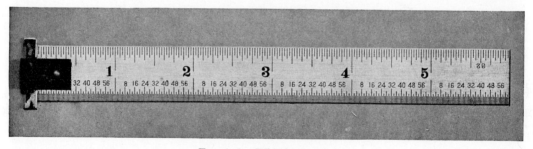

FIG. 1–4.   Narrow hook rule.

FIG. 1–5.   Wide hook rule.

cut to the face of the work, or from points where the mechanic cannot see if the edge of the rule is flush with the edge of the work.

To learn to read the rule all that is necessary is to become familiar with the graduations on it, notice what the graduations are, and how they are grouped to form

FIG. 1–6.   Obverse side.

FIG. 1–7.   Reverse side.

different values. Figs. 1–6 and 1–7 show the obverse and reverse sides of a rule having No. 4 graduations; that is, graduations of 8ths and 16ths of an inch on one side, and

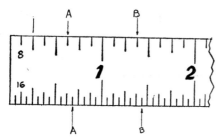

FIG. 1–8. Witness lines for practice reading.

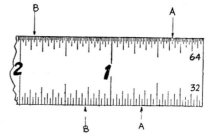

FIG. 1–9. Witness lines for practice reading.

32nds and 64ths of an inch on the other. Familiarize yourself with these graduations and then practice reading the dimensions on Figs. 1–8 and 1–9.

Scales, as mentioned before, are used for checking or laying off representative measurement. They are used by the draftsman in drawing and also by patternmakers and coremakers. The draftsman uses it for making drawings to a certain scale size, while the patternmaker uses it for making patterns a certain amount oversize to take care of the shrinkage of the metal when it cools off. For example, cast-iron has a shrinkage of nearly 1/8″ to the foot; therefore, a 12″ **shrink scale** for cast iron would actually be 12-1/8″ long. It can readily be understood from this that any fractional part of a foot would have a proportionate amount of this shrinkage, or the one-inch graduations would actually be 1-1/96″ long. In purchasing a new steel rule, the buyer should inspect it carefully to make sure that he gets what he wants.

FIG. 1–10. Shrink scale.

Fig. 1–10 shows a picture of a **shrink scale** and at first glance might be mistaken for an ordinary rule; however, close observation shows it to be clearly marked "SHRINK 1/8 TO FOOT." Other shrink scales are marked in a similar manner.

SHRINKAGE OF VARIOUS METALS IN CASTING

Iron pipe	1/8 in.	Malleable iron	1/8 in.
Steel	1/4 in.	Aluminum	3/16 in.
Copper	3/16 in.	Lead	5/16 in.
Thick brass	5/32 in.	Thin brass	3/16 in.

Certain industrial organizations have adopted a **decimal** system for specifying dimensions on blue prints, which replaces the fractional system. Under the new decimal system it is understood that a two-place decimal dimension will carry the same degree of accuracy as the former method; that is, plus or minus .010 variation from the size specified. It is further understood that the dimension should end in an even figure so as to eliminate the third decimal place in case the figure would have to be divided by two. For example, the diameter of a hole instead of being given as 1.250 would be given as either 1.24 or 1.26.

The system has considerable merit because it makes the dimensions easier for the mechanic to work to and saves time for inspectors, designers, and draftsmen, as well as keeping a drawing or blue print more uniform.

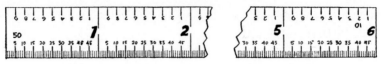

FIG. 1–11.   Rule graduated in tenths and fiftieths.

Fig. 1–11 shows a machinist's rule graduated in tenths, (1/10), and fiftieths, (1/50), to conform to the new system.

Depth gage. Fig. 1–12 shows a depth gage which is designed to permit semi-precision measurements of the depth of slots, blind holes, and similar stepped dimensions. The head of this gage is 2″ wide and 1/8″ thick. The head is removable and can be used independently.

Protractor and depth gage. The gage illustrated in Fig. 1–13 is a semi-precision tool used by machinists and draftsmen for laying out or checking angles. The protractor is graduated in steps of one degree. This tool can also be used as a depth gage similar to the one shown in Fig. 1–12.

FIG. 1–13.
Protractor and
depth gage.

FIG. 1–12.
Depth gage.

EXERCISES

Example 1.

How many fourths in 1.750″?

Solution.

$$1.750 = 1\tfrac{3}{4} = \tfrac{7}{4}$$

Answer   Seven

Example 2.

How many sixteenths in 4.3125″?

Solution.

$$4.3125 = 4\tfrac{5}{16} = \tfrac{69}{16}$$

Answer   Sixty-nine

Example 3.

What is the value of 3/4 plus 1/64?

Solution.

$$\tfrac{3}{4} = \tfrac{48}{64} \qquad \tfrac{48}{64} + \tfrac{1}{64} = \tfrac{49}{64}$$

Answer $\tfrac{49}{64}$

Example 4.

What is the value of 1-7/8 minus 3/32?

Solution.

$$1\tfrac{7}{8} = 1\tfrac{28}{32} \qquad 1\tfrac{28}{32} - \tfrac{3}{32} = 1\tfrac{25}{32} \qquad\qquad\qquad Answer \quad 1\tfrac{25}{32}$$

Example 5.

How much must be allowed for shrinkage in casting thick brass to a dimension of 8″? Answer to be nearest fraction in decimal equivalent table.

Solution.

Shrinkage for thick brass is 5/32″ per foot.

$$8 \text{ inches} = \frac{8}{12} = \frac{2}{3} \text{ feet} \qquad \frac{2}{3} \times \frac{5}{32} = \frac{5''}{48} \text{ shrinkage}$$
$$16$$

$$\tfrac{5}{48} = 5 \div 48 = .104 = \tfrac{7}{64} \text{ (approximately)} \qquad\qquad Answer \quad \tfrac{7}{64}$$

PROBLEMS

1. How many eighths in 1.625?

2. How many sixty-fourths in 2.250?

3. How many thirty-seconds in 3.0625?

4. What is the value of 2-5/8 plus 3/64?

5. What is the value of 15/16 minus 1/64?

6. How many thirty-seconds in 1-3/4 minus 1/32?

7. One inch less 5/64 is how many sixty-fourths?

8. What would be the allowance in casting a lead pipe 15″ long? Answer to be nearest fraction in decimal equivalent table.

9. An aluminum casting is 20.75″ long when it is cast. How long will it be after it cools? Answer to be nearest fraction in decimal equivalent table.

10. If a steel casting shrinks 7/8″, how long was it before it cooled?

REVIEW QUESTIONS

1. What is the difference between a rule and a scale?

2. What is meant by a No. 4 graduation; No. 10 graduation?

3. A hook rule is useful for taking measurements under what conditions?

4. What is a shrink scale?

5. How is a decimal scale graduated?

6. In a vertical column make a list of the consecutive fractions from zero to one inch in steps of one sixteenth of an inch.

7. Write the decimal equivalent corrected to four decimal places opposite each fraction in the above example.

8. What is the decimal value of 1/32?

9. What is the decimal value of 1/64?

10. Can you suggest an easy way to remember the decimal value of such fractions as 17/32, 9/64, 31/32?

Chapter 2

SEMI=PRECISION AND COMMON PRECISION TOOLS

DEFINITIONS
Precision tools . . . Non-precision tools . . . Semi-precision tools

SEMI-PRECISION TOOLS
Combination square . . . Dividers . . . Trammel . . . Calipers — Outside, Inside, Hermaphrodite . . . Telescoping gages . . . Screw pitch gage . . . Radius gage . . . Thickness gage . . . Surface gage . . . Parallels — Adjustable, Non-adjustable . . . V-Block . . . Planer gage . . . Solid square

PRECISION TOOLS
Micrometers . . . Principle of the micrometer . . . To read the micrometer . . . Screw thread micrometer . . . Inside micrometer . . . Depth micrometer . . . Tube micrometer . . . Verniers — principle . . . Height gage . . . Vernier caliper . . . Vernier depth gage . . . Gear tooth Vernier caliper . . . Universal Vernier bevel protractor . . . How to read the protractor

INDICATING GAGES
Dial indicator . . . Universal indicator

DEFINITIONS

Precision tools are those which possess the quality of exactness or a high degree of accuracy. Tools such as pliers, wrenches, screw-drivers, etc., are of the **non-precision** type, because they are used for rough work and therefore do not possess the quality of

FIG. 2–1.   Blade and combination.

exactness. Tools such as the combination square and its attachments, dividers, screw pitch gages, and the like, are of the **semi-precision** type, because they possess a moderate degree of accuracy and exactness. Tools such as micrometers, protractors, vernier tools and indicators are of the **precision** class because they possess a high degree of accuracy and because of their reliability in taking nearly exact measurements.

SEMI-PRECISION TOOLS

The **combination square** is a tool that can be used for a variety of purposes. When new its accuracy may be such as to place it in the precision class. However, since the head can be made to slide along the blade, it does not retain its accuracy for a very

FIG. 2–2. Bevel protractor and blade.

long time, particularly if it is put to much use. This tool with its attachments, however, does fill a very important place in every machinist's or toolmaker's kit. The **head** may be slid along the **blade,** and locked in position by the knurled nut, as shown in

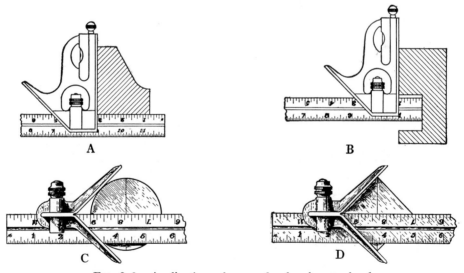

FIG. 2–3. Applications of square head and center head.

Fig. 2–1, or the blade may be removed entirely for use as a rule, since it is marked with No. 4 graduations. The head of the combination contains a spirit level and also a handy scriber point, and is so made that one side forms a 45-degree angle with the blade. This set has a wide range of uses, a few of which are shown in Fig. 2–3 A, B, C, and D.

The **center head** shown in Fig. 2–1, can be substituted for the square head and used to locate the center of shafting or other cylindrical pieces. Another attachment of this set is the **bevel protractor.** This is held firmly at any point along the blade and contains a revolving turret graduated in degrees from 0° to 180°. This head contains a spirit level which makes it useful as an inclinometer.

Dividers are used for measuring between points, for transferring or laying out distances, or for scribing arcs of circles. Fig. 2–4 shows the standard machinist's or toolmaker's dividers and some of its uses. The **legs** are usually round and drawn to a fine point; they are hinged at the head end on a hardened **stud,** the opening and closing of the legs being controlled by the **knurled nut** and the **screw.** The

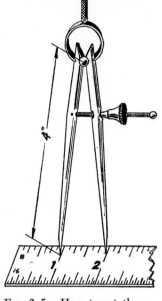

FIG. 2–5. How to set the divider to a rule.

FIG. 2–4. Dividers.

spring keeps the legs under tension at all times except when opened completely. The **knurled grip** makes for easy operation, especially when scribing arcs or circles. When not in use, spring tools of this nature should be opened up to relieve the spring tension, thus preserving the spring life. The size of this tool is governed by the distance from the pivot to the end of the point, not by the maximum distance to which it may be opened. The sizes generally run from 2 to 6 inches, although larger sizes are made.

When distances too great to be measured or laid out by the dividers are encountered, the **trammel,** Fig. 2–7, is

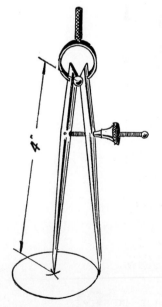

FIG. 2–6. Scribing a circle with the divider.

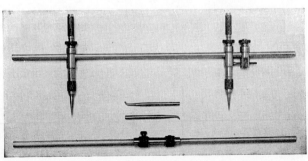

FIG. 2–7. Trammel set.

used. This tool consists of a long, round, steel **beam** with a flat on one side and two **sliding heads** designed to slide along the bar and clamp on its flat side. One of these **heads** is equipped with a **micrometer screw adjustment.** This makes it possible to make fine adjustments of the point. The heads are equipped with spring collets for adjustments of the points in or out as may be necessary.

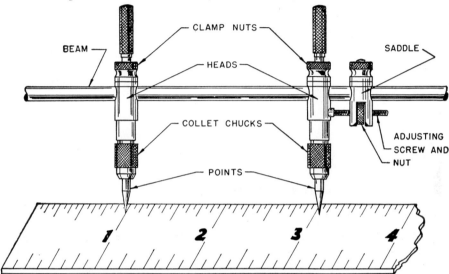

FIG. 2–8.   Setting a trammel to a rule.

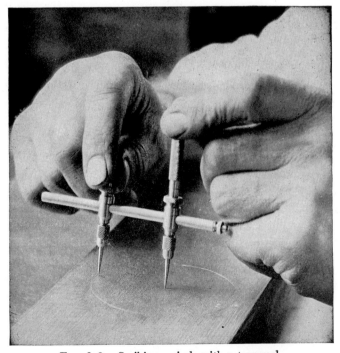

FIG. 2–9.   Scribing a circle with a trammel.

Calipers are tools similar to dividers except that the legs are curved either in or out, depending on whether they are used for taking inside or outside measurements, and the ends are rounded off instead of being pointed. These tools are used for **taking** measurements across flat or curved surfaces, but must be used in conjunction **with** some standard of comparison such as a rule or micrometer. Figs. 2–11 and 2–13 **show** how the outside and inside calipers are set to a rule.

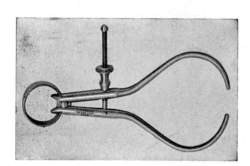

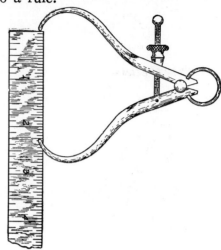

FIG. 2–10. Outside caliper.

FIG. 2–11. Setting an outside caliper to a rule

Fig. 2–14 shows how the **outside caliper** is used on the work. Notice that **the** caliper legs must be centered exactly on the center-line of the work and be in a **plane** perpendicular to the axis of the work. In this position the caliper is moved in and **out,** keeping one leg tangent to the work, and adjusting the remaining leg until the **point**

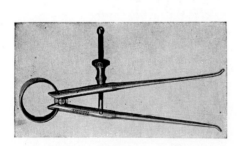

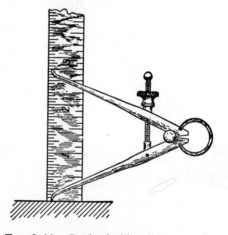

FIG. 2–12. Inside caliper.

FIG. 2–13. Setting inside caliper to a rule.

just touches the work on the opposite side; this process is called **"getting the feel,"** or **"getting the touch."** It must be remembered that accuracy in the use of this tool is dependent on the sensitivity of the feel or touch, and the student should take **great** care in acquiring it. This will take time, but persistent practice will produce **excellent** results.

Fig. 2–15 illustrates the use of the **inside caliper.** This tool is used much the same as the outside caliper, but occupies a more prominent place, because it is used more frequently. This is due to the fact that it can be used readily in conjunction with the vernier caliper or micrometer caliper for acquiring a much more accurate reading than can be had with an outside caliper. In using

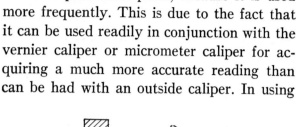

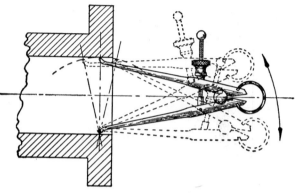

FIG. 2–14.   Using the outside caliper.

FIG. 2–15.   Using the inside caliper.

this caliper, hold the stationary leg down on the bottom side of the hole, and while moving it with a rocking motion, adjust the other leg to the proper feel, that is, until it just barely touches the wall at a point diametrically opposite the other leg. The measurement may then be transferred for reading to a rule or micrometer caliper as shown in Fig. 2–16. In transferring the measurement to a micrometer, the same amount of caution must be exercised as was used in getting the feel of the hole.

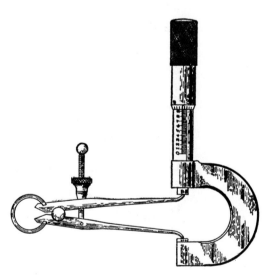

FIG. 2–16.   Transferring a caliper setting to a
micrometer.

FIG. 2–17.   Hermaphrodite caliper.

The **hermaphrodite caliper,** Fig. 2–17, resembles an ordinary inside caliper except that one leg has the end hooked in for making contact on the work. The other leg is like that of a divider, since it is drawn to a sharp point. This tool is used for scribing lines parallel with a given surface or for locating centers in cylindrical work.

See Figs. 2–19 and 2–20. To set the hermaphrodite caliper, the scriber point should be moved back so that it comes just inside the hooked leg. Then, with the hooked leg set on the end of the rule, the scriber point is hinged out until it coincides with the required graduation on the rule as shown in Fig. 2–18.

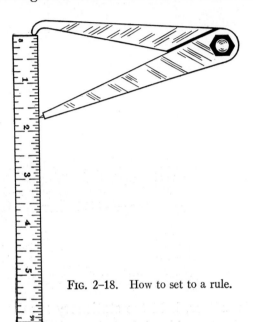

FIG. 2–18. How to set to a rule.

FIG. 2–19. Locating the center.

FIG. 2–20. Scribing lines parallel to a given surface.

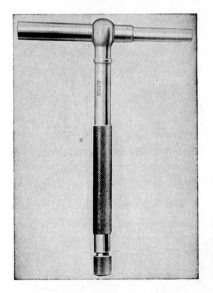

FIG. 2–21. Telescoping gage.

Telescoping gages are instruments by means of which nearly exact sizes of holes or slots can be transferred to a micrometer caliper or other suitable standard of comparison. This tool is widely used in internal cylindrical grinding, rather than an ordinary caliper, because of the speed, accuracy and simplicity of adjustment. The ends of the telescoping heads are ground with a spherical radius equal to the radius of the smallest hole in which it can be used. Fig. 2–21 shows one of these gages; Fig. 2–22 gives the range of each different size. Fig. 2–23 shows how this instrument is used. To use it, compress the **head** and lock it by turning the **knurled nut.** Insert the gaging end in the hole to be gaged, unlock the head and it will expand to the diameter of the hole; next, get the feel, or touch, the same as with a caliper, then lock the plunger in position, after which the reading may be transferred to a micrometer caliper by gaging it over the ends of the head.

NO.	GAGE CLOSED	GAGE OPEN
A	1/2 IN.	3/4 IN.
B	3/4 IN.	1 1/4 IN.
C	1 1/4 IN.	2 1/8 IN.
D	2 1/8 IN.	3 1/2 IN.
E	3 1/2 IN.	6 IN.

FIG. 2–22.   Table of sizes.

FIG. 2–23 A.   Small-hole gage.

Fig. 2–23 A shows a small-hole gage. It is made in four sizes as follows:

Size "A"—Range 0.125″ to 0.200″
Size "B"—Range 0.200″ to 0.300″
Size "C"—Range 0.300″ to 0.400″
Size "D"—Range 0.400″ to 0.500″

Unlike the telescoping gage the small knurled nut on the handle end is used to pull a taper-headed draw bar into the gaging end which causes the split ball to expand to fill the hole. The hole size is then transferred to a common micrometer caliper.

FIG. 2–23.   Using the telescoping gage.

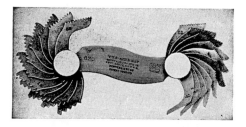

FIG. 2–24.   Screw pitch gage.

The **screw pitch** gage, Fig. 2–24, an instrument frequently confused with a thread gage, is used in checking the number of threads per inch on a screw, bolt or nut. If the pitch of a thread is not known, it may be readily determined by comparing it with one of the standards of the screw pitch gage. On the edge of thin leaves, teeth are cut corresponding to standard thread sections. The free end of the leaf is generally stamped to show the number of threads per inch and the decimal value for the double depth of the thread. See Fig. 2–25.

To use the screw pitch gage, place successive leaves over the thread until one of them is found to coincide or mesh with the thread, then the number of threads per

FIG. 2–25. Use of screw pitch gage.

inch can be read directly from the stamping on the leaf. These gages are made for the American National Coarse and National Fine threads, Whitworth threads, and the International Standard or Metric form of threads.

The **radius** or **fillet gage,** Fig. 2–26, is a standard form of template used for gaging regular concave or convex surfaces. It contains a series of leaves having standard radii ground and lapped on the ends and sides. Another type consists of individual leaves which progress from 1/32″ up to 9/32″ by 64ths, and from 9/32″ to 1/2″ by 32nds. The size of the radius is stamped on the leaf for ready reference. Figs.

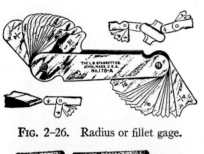

FIG. 2–26. Radius or fillet gage.

FIG. 2–26-B.
Using concave side
of gage.

FIG. 2–26-C.
Using concave
side of gage.

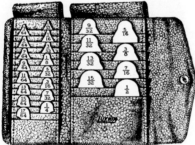

FIG. 2–26 A. Radius gages.

FIG. 2–26-D.
Using convex side
of gage.

FIG. 2–26-E.
Using convex
side of gage.

2–26 A, B, C, D, and E show these gages and some applications.

The **thickness gage,** frequently called a **"feeler gage,"** shown in Fig. 2–27, contains a series of leaves varying in thickness from one-half a thousandth up. They are made in a variety of lengths and thicknesses, making it possible to get many combinations in thousandths of an inch. This gage is particularly useful to machinists, toolmakers, or machine repair men in gaging narrow slots or clearances, or for adjusting gaps for valves.

FIG. 2–27. Thickness gage.

The **center gage,** sometimes called a **"thread gage,"** is used as a standard of comparison for threading tools. It is used for comparing the shape of the threading tool bit with an accurately ground and lapped "V" on the edge of the gage. It is also used for setting the tool in the tool post of the lathe, so that the center line of the V-point is perpendicular to the axis of rotation of the screw blank, and for testing the included angle of lathe, grinder, or other machine centers. These gages are made for

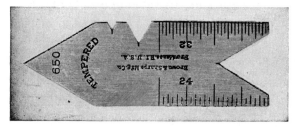

FIG. 2–28. Obverse side of center gage.

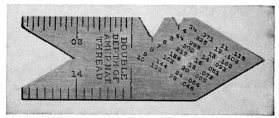

FIG. 2–29. Reverse side of center gage.

American National threads, English Standard threads and for the Metric System. Two views of this gage, Figs. 2–28 and 2–29, show the graduations on the edges for checking the number of threads per inch. One side of the point is engraved to show

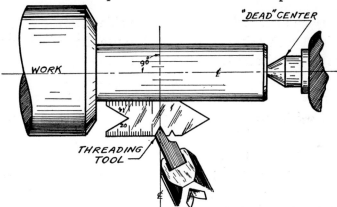

FIG. 2–30. Setting external threading tool with center gage.

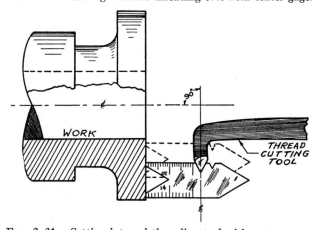

FIG. 2–31. Setting internal threading tool with center gage.

the size of tap drills for 60-degree V-threads and shows in thousandths of an inch the double depth of commonly used threads. Figs. 2–30 and 2–31 illustrate methods of using the gage for setting a thread chasing tool for external or internal threads.

A **surface gage** is an instrument used for scribing lines at given heights or for transferring heights from one job to another. This gage, shown in Fig. 2–32, consists of a **base,** and an upright **rod,** to which is attached a **scriber point** held by a **clamp.** The upright may be pivoted from a horizontal plane through an angle in excess of 270°. This tool can be used for scribing lines on vertical surfaces, horizontal surfaces, or can

be used as a semi-precision height gage. When used at the bench for layout purposes, the work and gage are both placed on a plane surface known as a bench plate; in this manner the scriber point can be set to a definite height by means of a rule or any other suitable standard measuring device. The grooved base of the surface gage is provided for scribing lines concentric with a given hole. The "V" rests on a plug or mandrel and the scriber point is adjusted for the height; then by rotating the surface gage on the plug or mandrel, a line is scribed at the correct distance from the center of the hole.

FIG. 2–32.
Surface gage.

The base contains four **friction pins** which may be pushed down to bear against the edge of a surface plate or the side of a slot in the planer, mill, or shaper table for doing liner work. If it is desired to use the surface gage for small work the spindle may be removed and the scriber needle inserted in a hole provided for it in the base pivot where it can be readily adjusted for fine work.

Parallels are of two kinds, **adjustable** and **non-adjustable.** The non-adjustable types, shown in Fig. 2–33, are bars of steel especially hardened to give a minimum of warp and are ground and lapped to standard widths and thicknesses. These parallels are used in checking or laying out work at the bench; they are also used in conjunction with the milling machine and shaper vises for setting up work, and on grinders and lathes for setting up work either on the face plate or chucks. Their accuracy is sufficiently close to permit their use as gages in checking slots or keyways at the surface grinder or milling machine.

FIG. 2–33. Hardened and ground non-adjustable parallels.

The **adjustable parallel,** shown in Fig. 2–34, is composed of two wedges or inclined planes, dove-tailed together so that one part may be slid along the other and in so doing change the width of the parallel. This tool is used in Fig. 2–35 in connection with the milling machine, shaper, and planer vises

FIG. 2–34. Adjustable parallel.

FIG. 2–35. Using adjustable parallel.

for setting up the work. It is also used for leveling up work on the planer, mill, and drill press. Perhaps one of the greatest uses for this tool, when it is new, is that of an adjustable gage, because it may be adjusted and locked to micrometer measurements for checking slots or keyways. Letters are used to designate the sizes as follows:

LETTER	LENGTH	THICKNESS	CAPACITY					
A	1-3/4	9/32	From	3/8	inch to	1/2	inch	
B	2-1/8	9/32	"	1/2	" "	11/16	"	
C	2-11/16	9/32	"	11/16	" "	15/16	"	
D	3-9/16	9/32	"	15/16	" "	1-5/16	"	
E	4-3/16	9/32	"	1-5/16	" "	1-3/4	"	
F	5-1/16	9/32	"	1-3/4	" "	2-1/4	"	

The **"V-block,"** shown in Fig. 2–36, is a hardened and ground block of steel. The sides of the "V" form a 90-degree angle and are central with the sides of the block.

FIG. 2–36. V-Blocks.

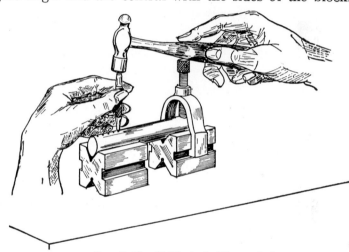

FIG. 2–37. V-Blocks holding a shaft.

Slots cut in both sides enable the use of a clamp for securely holding the work. The opposite sides are ground parallel with each other, and each face square with the adjacent faces. These blocks are used to hold cylindrical work, for laying it out, for locating and drilling holes in cylindrical work, or for holding cylindrical work in a vise, or for various other operations on cylindrical work. Fig. 2–37 shows V-blocks holding a shaft which has been laid out.

Fig. 2–38 shows a **planer** or **shaper gage.** This gage is similar to the adjustable parallel shown in Fig. 2–34. It is composed of two inclined planes. Like the adjustable parallel, it may be set by means of a micrometer or height gage and used as a gage for checking slots from 3/8″ wide up to 8-1/4″ wide. This gage was primarily designed as an aid to the shaper or planer operator, to assist in setting the cutting

FIG. 2–38. Planer gage.

tool to the proper depth. By setting this gage with a micrometer or surface gage to the thickness of the work and then bringing the cutting tool in contact with it, the first cut can be relied upon to give the proper thickness of work. This naturally eliminates the slow method of cut and try which ordinarily prevails, and saves much time and effort in completing a given job. Fig. 2–39 shows how the plane gage is used on the planer while Fig. 2–40 shows the use of it for checking slots.

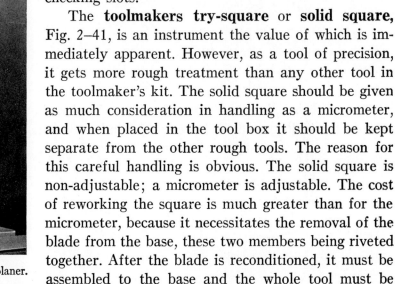

The **toolmakers try-square** or **solid square,** Fig. 2–41, is an instrument the value of which is immediately apparent. However, as a tool of precision, it gets more rough treatment than any other tool in the toolmaker's kit. The solid square should be given as much consideration in handling as a micrometer, and when placed in the tool box it should be kept separate from the other rough tools. The reason for this careful handling is obvious. The solid square is non-adjustable; a micrometer is adjustable. The cost of reworking the square is much greater than for the micrometer, because it necessitates the removal of the blade from the base, these two members being riveted together. After the blade is reconditioned, it must be assembled to the base and the whole tool must be

Fig. 2–39.   Using planer gage on planer.

re-lapped to a master cylinder and surface plate. Micrometer parts such as screws, anvils, and thimbles can be replaced at a very nominal cost, as compared to the cost in time required to recondition a square. In using the square, great care must be

Fig. 2–40.   Using a planer gage for checking slots.

Fig. 2–41.   Solid square.

observed to avoid dropping it. The square is truly a precision instrument and if given the proper treatment will provide a lifetime of service. This tool is used for testing two adjacent faces of a piece of work to determine if they are perpendicular or at 90° to each other; in fact, it may be used to determine the squareness of any two related parts of a piece of work.

PRECISION TOOLS

Micrometers. The word micrometer is derived from two Greek words. **Micro,** meaning small, little, or insignificant; **meter,** meaning a measure, or system of measurement. From these derivations it is readily understood that the word micrometer means small or fine measurements and when applied to a tool or instrument means a mechanism for gaging small or fine measurements.

The **micrometer caliper,** Fig. 2–42, is perhaps the most commonly used precision instrument in the toolroom or machine shop. It is composed of a **frame** in the shape of the letter "U." At one end of this frame is a contact block called the **anvil. A spindle,** with a screw adjustment, operates through the other end of the frame. On the outside of the frame a **sleeve** is rigidly attached which encloses the spindle. This sleeve telescopes into a **thimble** which is rigidly attached to the extreme outer end of the spindle. The spindle being threaded is thus completely enclosed by the sleeve and thimble. Fig. 2–42 shows the micrometer and its working parts.

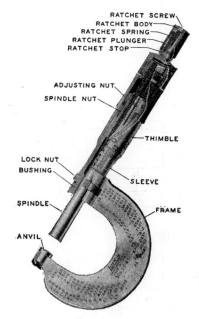

FIG. 2–42. Micrometer showing parts labeled.

In **using the micrometer,** the thimble is rotated by the thumb and fingers, moving the screw and spindle with it. The screw has forty threads per inch, so that one revolution of the thimble moves the spindle 1/40″ or .025. These revolutions of the thimble are plainly marked as graduations on the sleeve. The frame end of the thimble is beveled and graduated into twenty-five equally spaced divisions, each division being 1/25th of a revolution, representing 1/25th of .025, or one one-thousandth of an inch (.001″). When the micrometer caliper is completely closed, the zero mark on the thimble should coincide with the zero mark on the sleeve. If the micrometer is opened one graduation on the thimble, the reading would be .001″ or one one-thousandth of an inch; if the thimble is turned farther until the tenth line on the thimble coincides with a line on the sleeve, the micrometer would be opened 10/25ths of .025 or .010.

To read the micrometer caliper, read the visible vertical lines on the sleeve starting from the zero, remembering that each division is .025. To this add the number of divisions on the thimble, reading from the zero on the thimble to the line which coincides with the horizontal line on the sleeve. This should be the total reading or the distance from the end of the spindle to the face of the anvil.

In the sketches shown below, practice reading the settings and if possible procure a micrometer caliper and practice with it to acquire the proper sense of feel or touch.

The common micrometer caliper cannot be used for taking measurements finer than one one-thousandth of an inch (.001″). Later models have a vernier added to the sleeve so that measurements as fine as one ten-thousandth (.0001) may be taken. This consists of ten equally spaced divisions placed longitudinally on the sleeve, which occupy the same space as nine divisions on the thimble. The difference between one of the ten longitudinal divisions and one of the nine divisions on the thimble is one-tenth of a space on the thimble. Since one space on the thimble represents one one-thousandth, then one longitudinal space on the sleeve will represent one ten-thousandth (.0001).

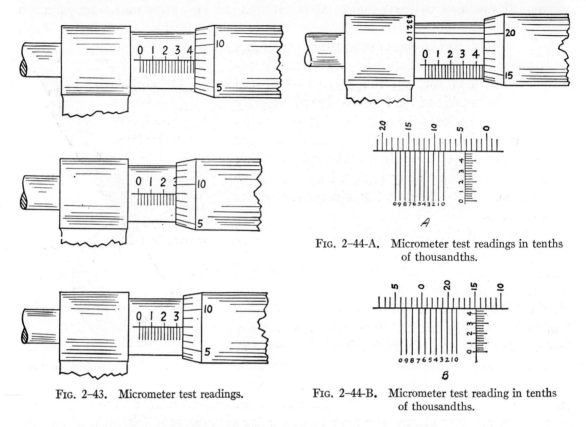

FIG. 2–44-A. Micrometer test readings in tenths of thousandths.

FIG. 2–44-B. Micrometer test reading in tenths of thousandths.

FIG. 2–43. Micrometer test readings.

Example 1.

In the sketch shown at *A*, Fig. 2–44, the twelfth line from the zero on the thimble coincides with the number 4 line on the sleeve, so the reading would be .504 on the sleeve and thimble and, .0004 on the sleeve, longitudinally, making the reading .504 + .0004 or .5044.

Example 2.

Sketch *B* shows the reading on the sleeve and thimble to be .439 and on the sleeve, longitudinally, line number 9 coincides with a line on the thimble; therefore the complete reading is .439 + .0009 or .4399.

To become proficient at reading the micrometer, one should practice with an actual instrument, measuring several different sizes of stock, until the size can be read as easily as reading the written words.

Screw thread micrometer calipers, Fig. 2–45, used for checking the pitch diameters of screw threads, are similar to the common micrometer in that they are read the same and have the same principle of operation. The spindle is ground to a point having a conical angle of 60°. The anvil, instead of being flat, has a 60-degree "V" which fits the thread. Some of these anvils are movable, while others are rigidly fixed in the frame. In measuring screw threads, the angle of the point on the spindle and the sides of the "V" on the anvil come in contact with the machined surface of the thread, so that the reading of the micrometer indicates the pitch diameter of the screw, or the full size less the single depth of the thread. In Fig. 2–46 the spindle point is

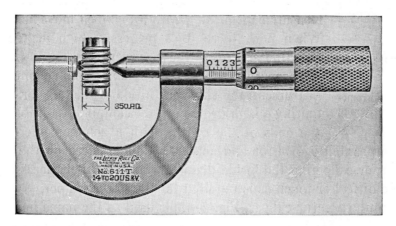

FIG. 2–45.   Application of screw thread micrometer caliper.

shown closed in the "V" of the anvil. With the micrometer in this position the reading is zero, so that readings are taken the same as on a regular micrometer caliper. These micrometers may be secured for checking American National Fine or Coarse threads

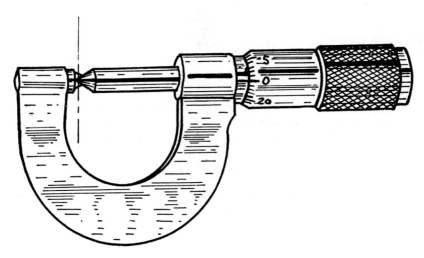

FIG. 2–46.   Screw thread micrometer closed.

or for the British Whitworth Standard thread. The one-inch micrometers are made to check threads within four ranges, that is, 8 to 13 threads per inch, 14 to 20 threads, 22 to 30, and 32 to 40 threads per inch.

The **inside micrometer** caliper, Fig. 2–47, is used for checking internal and lineal measurements; it is also used for setting calipers, or with special equipment, as **a** height gage. The thimble is graduated to read in thousandths of an inch, and the screw has a total movement of either 1/2″ or 1″ depending on the capacity of the set.

In the smaller set, the measuring rods enable a maximum measurement of 8″, and the screw has a movement of only 1/2″. In the larger sets, the rods make possible a maximum measurement of 32″, with a one-inch movement of the screw. When new, these tools possess a high degree of accuracy, but after much use the accuracy is seriously impaired by the wear on the end of the rod and thimble pin. In using this instrument for checking inside diameters, or dimensions requiring a high degree of precision, it is desirable to check over the ends of the caliper with a common micrometer caliper; this offsets the possibility of error and acts as a double check on the instrument. In using this tool for calipering the inside diameters of holes, it is necessary to exercise the same sense of feel or touch as is required for the inside caliper.

FIG. 2–47. Inside microme- ter caliper with measuring rods.

The **depth micrometer** caliper, Fig. 2–48, is used as the name implies, for taking micrometer readings of depths of pockets, grooves, recesses, and so forth. The thimble is graduated to read in thousandths of an inch, but the sleeve is graduated in a direction

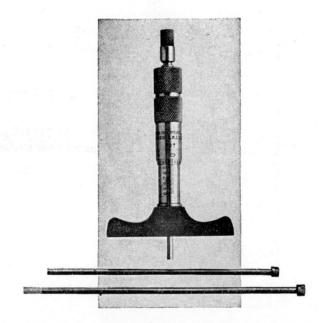

FIG. 2–48. Depth micrometer with measuring rods.

exactly opposite to that of the common micrometer caliper. Fig. 2–49 shows a comparison of the two kinds of sleeves. Notice that on the common micrometer the reading starts at the frame and progresses out toward the end; whereas, on the sleeve of the depth micrometer, the reading starts out at the end and progresses in toward the base or frame. Otherwise the readings are the same. In inserting the different measuring rods through the screw, care must be exercised to see that the shoulder on the cap-end of the rod is free from dirt, and seating properly. After the rod is inserted, it is good practice to check the instrument for correct reading. This can be done by placing the base of the micrometer on a surface checking plate and screwing the rod down flush

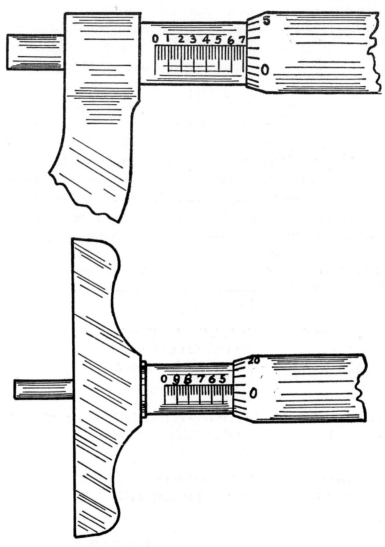

FIG. 2–49.   Comparison of common micrometer sleeve and depth micrometer sleeve.

with the base. If, when the rod is flush with the base, the zero mark on the thimble coincides with the zero mark on the sleeve, then the instrument is not out of adjustment. If these zero marks do not coincide, the tool should be placed in competent hands for adjustment.

The **tube micrometer,** shown in Fig. 2–50, is used for measuring the thickness of the wall of tubing, bushings, and similar work and is read the same as the standard micrometer. Generally the anvil is made to fit in a hole 3/8″ in diameter or larger and will take measurements up to 3/4″ deep.

Ball points, consisting of a sleeve open at one end and closed by a .250 diameter ball, are designed to fit over the anvil and thimble of the micrometer. These are used in connection with the micrometer for taking measurements over concave surfaces, or individual concave radii. When one of these points is used, .250 must be subtracted from the reading. When two points are used .500 must be subtracted.

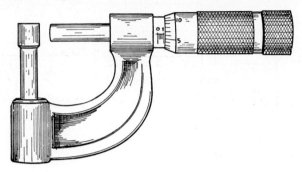

Fig. 2–50.   Tube micrometer.

EXERCISES

Example 1.

What would the micrometer reading be if the edge of the thimble uncovered the third line past the .200 mark on the sleeve and if the eleventh line on the thimble coincides?

Solution.

Each line on the sleeve equals .025, therefore three lines would be .075 and the sleeve reading = .200 + .075 or .275. Since each line on the thimble represents .001, then eleven lines will represent .011 and the complete reading is .275 + .011 = .286

Answer .286

Example 2.

What is the micrometer reading when the edge of the thimble uncovers the first line past the .400 mark on the sleeve and the twelfth line on the thimble coincides?

Solution.

One line past the .400 mark gives a sleeve reading of .425. Twelve lines on the thimble would represent .012. Therefore the total reading is .425 + .012 or .437

Answer .437

PROBLEMS

The following drawings are presented for practice in reading the common micrometer and the depth micrometer. Problems 1 and 2 are 0″ to 1″ micrometer readings; problems 3 to 5 inclusive are 1″ to 2″ micrometer readings; problems 6 to 8 inclusive are 2″ to 3″ micrometer readings; and problems 9 to 11 inclusive are 0″ to 1″ depth micrometer readings.

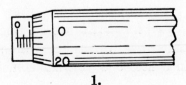

1.

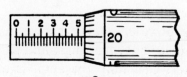

2.

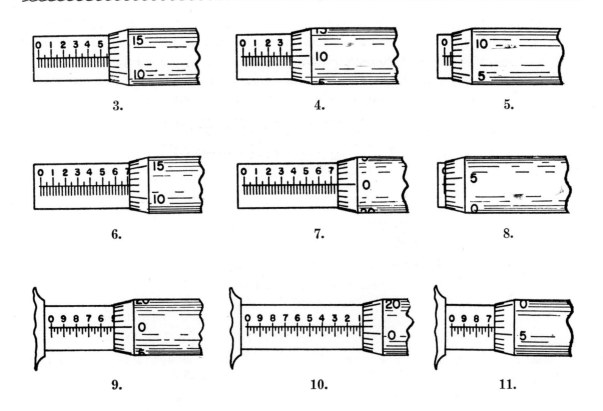

3.   4.   5.

6.   7.   8.

9.   10.   11.

VERNIERS

The name **"Vernier"** as applied to several precision tools is derived from the name of the man who discovered this principle. Pierre Vernier, a French scientist and mathematician, reasoned that the eye can not discern the exact distance between two given lines but can tell when two lines coincide or fall on each other so as to form one straight line. On this fact he developed the vernier principle which is applied to micrometers, calipers, protractors, and similar instruments.

Generally, there are **two systems** for graduating vernier calipers. On one type the smallest division on the blade is .020, while the smallest division on the plate is .019. On the other type the smallest division on the blade is .025 while the smallest division on the plate is .024. In either case the difference between the graduations is .001. The inch graduation on the blade is divided into 40 equal spaces, each space being equal to 1/40″, or .025. When the zero on the plate coincides with the zero on the blade, the 25th mark on the plate coincides with the .600 mark on the blade; thus the 25 equal spaces on the plate equal .600. Therefore, one space on the plate will equal 1/25th of .600 or .024. However, since the difference between a space on the plate and a space on the blade is .001, it is convenient to think of the graduations on the plate as being .001. Fig. 2–51 illustrates the graduations of the plate as compared to the graduations on the blade. **To read the vernier,** read the blade up to the zero on the plate, then move down and read along the plate until a line is found to coincide with a line on the blade.

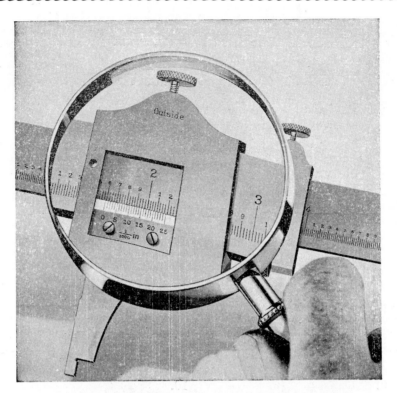

FIG. 2–51. Enlarged view of vernier plate and section of blade.

Example. (See the setting in Fig. 2–51.)

Reading the blade, notice that the zero on the plate has just passed the 1.575 mark; reading along the plate, notice that the 14th line coincides with a line on the blade; therefore, the complete reading is 1.575 + .014 or 1.589.

The vernier height gage, Fig. 2–52; vernier caliper, Fig. 2–53; depth gage, Fig. 2–54; and the gear tooth calipers, Fig. 2–55, are all read the same; that is, the graduations on the plate represent .001. However, there are two sizes of gear tooth calipers; on one the graduations on the blade are equal to .020, while on the larger one the smallest graduations are equal to .025.

The **vernier height gage,** Fig. 2–52, is used for locating centers, for measuring heights over plugs or toolmaker's buttons, or in layout work for accurately scribing lines in relation to a given face or surface. In using this tool, caution must be exercised to see that readings are taken from the proper side of the blade. One side is graduated for readings taken from the base of the instrument and the graduations start at one inch. This side should be read when the instrument is used as a height gage. The reverse side is graduated, starting with zero, to be read when the instrument is used as an outside caliper.

The **vernier caliper,** Fig. 2–53, is used for taking either outside or inside measurements, being graduated on both sides of the blade. The width of the nibs, when closed, varies according to the capacity of the instrument from .250 to .500. Prick punch marks, accurately located on the blade and slide, are provided for setting dividers as an aid to transferring measurements. Here again, care must be exercised in reading the instrument, or an error equal to the width of the nibs might result.

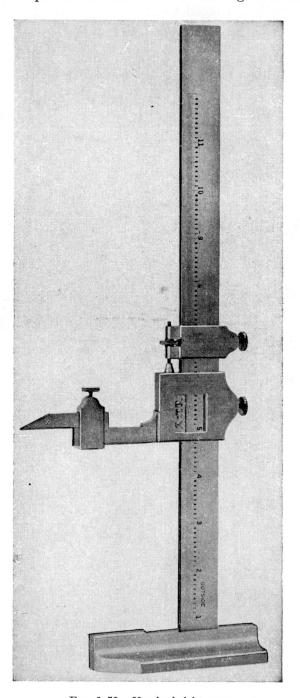

Fig. 2–52. Vernier height gage.

The **vernier depth gage,** Fig. 2–54, is used in much the same manner as the depth micrometer. The accuracy of this tool is more permanent than the depth micrometer due to the fact that it does not depend on mechanical movement for taking measurements. One side of the blade is graduated to read in 64ths of an inch, while on the other side the smallest graduation is equal to .025. This instrument is read the same as the other verniers.

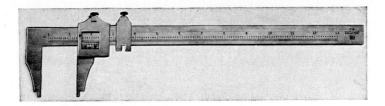

FIG. 2–53.   Vernier caliper.

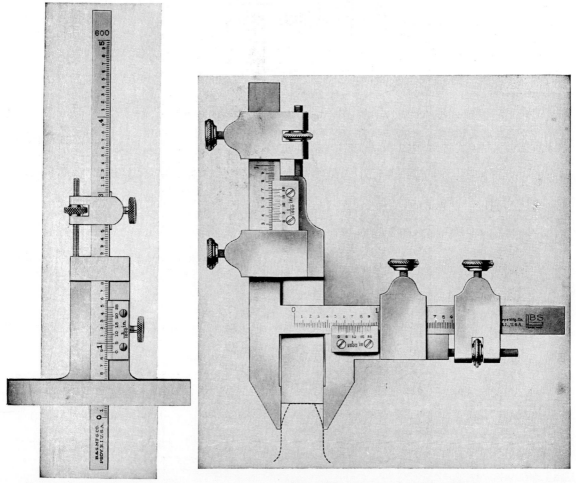

FIG. 2–54.   Vernier depth gage.   FIG. 2–55.   Gear tooth vernier caliper.

The **gear tooth vernier caliper,** Fig. 2–55, is used for taking measurements in connection with gear teeth, gear cutters, hobs, and the like. It is used for checking the chordal thickness and corrected addendum of gear teeth.

To test the tooth thickness with a gear tooth vernier caliper, the addendum beam is set for the corrected addendum. After the burrs have been stoned from the end of the tooth, the addendum beam is set on the end of the teeth as illustrated in Fig. 2–56. The caliper jaws are adjusted to the thickness of the tooth by means of the knurled nut, then the chordal thickness can be read directly from the horizontal blade.

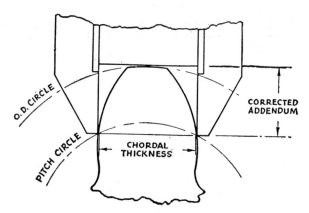

FIG. 2–56.   Application of a gear tooth vernier caliper.

CAUTION. Make certain that the vernier graduations are read correctly. On the smaller size the finest graduation on the blade is .020, while on the larger size the smallest graduation is .025. It must be remembered that this instrument checks the corrected addendum and chordal thickness of the tooth only, it **does not** check the pitch diameter of the gear.

EXERCISES

Example 1.

What will be the vernier caliper reading for an outside measurement if the zero on the vernier plate has passed the third line to the right of the .600 mark and the nineteenth line on the plate coincides with a line on the blade?

Solution.

Each line on the blade equals .025; therefore, if the zero on the plate has passed the third line to the right of the .600 mark, the reading for the blade is .675. Each line on the vernier plate represents .001 so that if the nineteenth line on the plate coincides with a line on the blade, the zero mark has passed the .675 mark by .019; therefore the complete reading is .675 + .019 or .694

Answer .694

Example 2.

What will be the vernier caliper reading for an inside measurement if the zero on the plate has passed the second line to the left of the 1.900 mark on the blade and the eleventh line on the vernier plate coincides with a line on the blade?

Solution.

Two lines to the left of the 1.900 mark on the blade gives a reading of 1.850. Since the eleventh line on the plate coincides with a line on the blade, the zero mark on the plate is .011 past the 1.850 and the total reading is 1.850 + .011 or 1.861

Answer 1.861

PROBLEMS

The following sketches are provided to give exercise in reading vernier calipers and height gages.

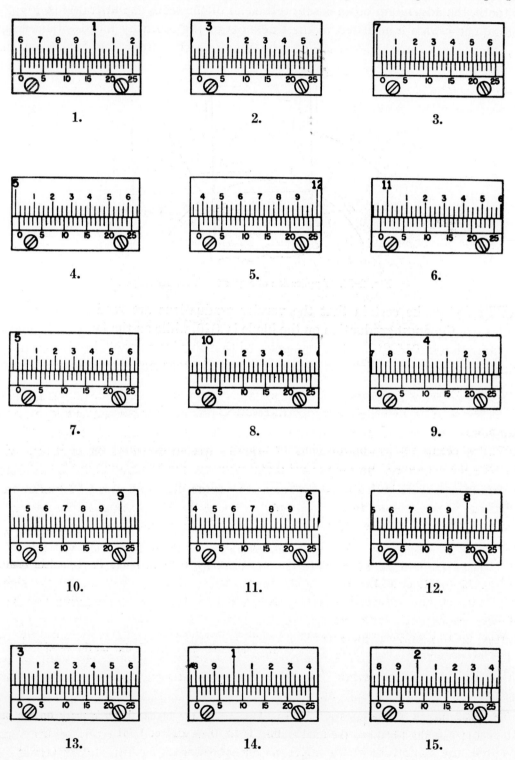

1.

2.

3.

4.

5.

6.

7.

8.

9.

10.

11.

12.

13.

14.

15.

A protractor is an instrument for measuring or laying out angles.

The **universal vernier bevel protractor,** Fig. 2–57, is a precision instrument used in the tool room or machine shop for accurately measuring angles in degrees and minutes. This instrument is composed of a dial, graduated in degrees, which is an integral part of the stock. It is equipped with two blades, 7″ and 12″ long. They may be clamped tightly against the dial by means of an eccentric stud which locks them against the side of a slot in the dial. The blade may be slid along its entire length or turned through any angle and clamped at that point. One side of this instrument is

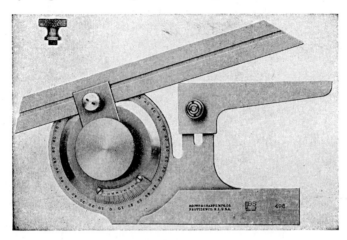

FIG. 2–57.   Universal vernier bevel protractor.

flat which makes it convenient for laying it on flat work, increasing its range of usefulness. A vernier is mounted on the center plate in such a manner that its edge overlaps the graduations on the dial. The graduations on the dial make a complete circle or 360°. The vernier is graduated into 12 equally spaced divisions on each side of the zero. When the zero on the vernier coincides with the zero on the dial, the 12th line on the vernier coincides with the 23-degree mark on the dial, thus these 12 marks on the vernier are actually equal to 23°. Therefore, one of the 12 divisions on the vernier will equal 1/12th of 23 degrees (23 degrees equals 1380 minutes) or 115 minutes. Again, looking at the protractor with the two zero lines coinciding, it is found that if the vernier were moved slowly, the *number one* line on the vernier would meet the *number two* line on the dial, or the 120-minute mark; thus, when the first line to the right or left of zero on the vernier is made to coincide with the next consecutive line on the dial, the vernier or blade has moved the difference between 120 minutes and 115 minutes, or 5 minutes. The graduations on the vernier, therefore, are actually equal to 115 minutes, but for convenience of use it is practical to think of them as being 5 minutes. It is for that reason that every third line, starting from the zero, is marked consecutively 15, 30, 45, and 60.

To read the protractor, note the direction of travel of the vernier around the plate with respect to the zero on the plate, then read the dial up to the zero on the vernier. This gives the magnitude of the angle in degrees. Now move down to the vernier plate and read the number of minutes, proceeding in the same direction as for the dial reading, until two lines are found to coincide. This gives the reading in degrees and minutes.

In reading any vernier tool, the secret of getting an accurate reading lies in how the user holds it, and whether or not a reading glass is used. To get an accurate reading, the instrument should be held perpendicularly with respect to the line of vision, with the user's back turned to the light so that the light rays cause the graduations to stand out clearly.

PROBLEMS

The sketches shown below are provided to illustrate the reading of vernier bevel protractor gages.

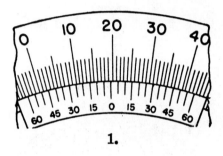

1.

2.

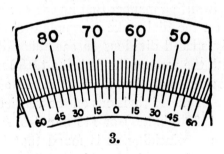

3.

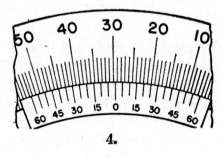

4.

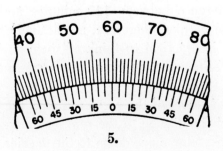

5.

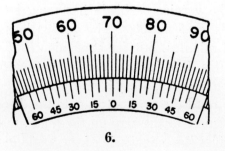

6.

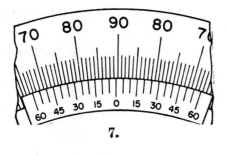

7.

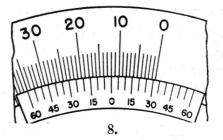

8.

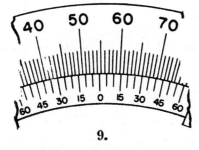

9.

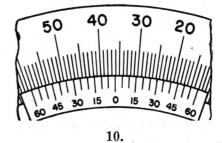

10.

INDICATING GAGES

An **indicating gage** is one that shows visually the variations in dimensions as they pertain to uniformity of size or shape. The amount of variation is generally indicated on a dial or graduated fan-shaped scale.

Indicating gages are made in a variety of shapes, sizes, and principles. The common **dial** type, shown in Fig. 2–58, works on the gear and rack principle; that is, the plunger has gear teeth cut on it which actuates a pinion attached to the pointer shaft; thus, any movement of the plunger causes a corresponding movement of the pointer. The reading, in thousandths or ten-thousandths, is taken visually from the numbered dial. This indicator is used more frequently for checking external surfaces than for internal ones, and has many uses both in the tool room and on production.

The **universal junior indicator,** Fig. 2–59, is operated on the lever principle. In this gage the contact point actuates a pointer which visually indicates on a fan-

FIG. 2–58. Common dial type indicating gage.

shaped dial the amount of movement of the point. The scale on this dial is graduated to give a total reading of .010, which is considerably less than the total reading possible with the dial indicator. The indicator is small, compact, and easy to handle, and for this reason generally makes up a part of every toolmaker's kit.

Fig. 2–60 shows a Universal test indicator which can be used for testing external surfaces or internal surfaces. It is sufficiently long and slender to allow it to be used for indicating holes that are quite deep. To use this indicator bring the contact point

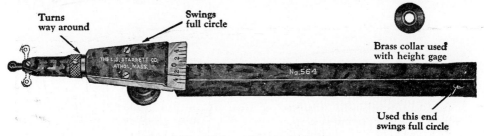

FIG. 2–59. Universal junior indicator.

against the work so that the needle registers at "O"; then, as the work is moved under the indicator, or the indicator along the work, any variation will show on the fan-shaped dial, which gives a maximum reading of .015″ either side of zero.

FIG. 2–60. Universal test indicator.

FIG. 2–61. "Last Word" indicator.

This small dial type indicator, Fig. 2–61, is very sensitive and easy to read. It can be used in conjunction with a height gage, surface gage or with any of the common tool room machines and has a range of .030″.

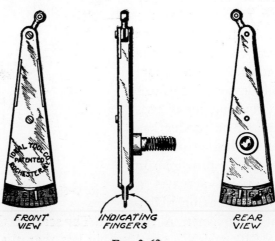

FIG. 2–62.

REVIEW QUESTIONS

1. Name three semi-precision tools.
2. Name several precision tools.
3. What factors determine the classification of a tool as being precision or semi-precision?
4. What are the principal parts of a combination square?
5. How are dividers used?
6. Trammels are used for what purpose?
7. What is meant by the expression, "getting the touch"?
8. What are the advantages of telescoping gages over inside calipers?
9. Describe the use of the hermaphrodite caliper in locating the center of a shaft.
10. How is a screw pitch gage used?
11. What is a radius gage?
12. What is a thickness gage?
13. Name several uses of a center gage.
14. For what purpose is a surface gage used?
15. How many kinds of parallels are there?
16. Describe a V-block.
17. What range of sizes can be used on a planer or shaper gage?
18. Discuss the care of a solid square.
19. Name the important parts of a micrometer.
20. How many threads per inch are there on the screw of a micrometer?
21. What is the decimal value of 1/40"?
22. What part of an inch is 1/25th of 1/40"?
23. How many separate readings are necessary in determining a reading to four decimal places?
24. What dimension on a screw does a screw thread micrometer measure?
25. Discuss the use of an inside micrometer.
26. How does the sleeve of a depth micrometer differ from a common micrometer with respect to graduations?
27. How much must be subtracted from the micrometer reading when ball points are used?
28. Discuss the vernier principle.
29. Name six tools commonly used in the machine shop which employ a vernier.
30. What dimensions of a gear tooth are checked by a gear tooth vernier?
31. What is the value of each graduation on the vernier of a vernier bevel protractor?
32. What are indicating gages?

Chapter 3

SHAPER—PLANER

SHAPER

HISTORY: Development — DESCRIPTION: Classes — CRANK SHAPER: Bull Wheel
IMPORTANT PARTS: Names — DESCRIPTION
Ram . . . Base . . . Crossrail . . . Table feeding mechanism . . . Saddle . . . Table . . . Rapid traverse hand feed . . . Automatic power feed . . . Shaper vise . . . Tool head . . . Speed control mechanism . . . Bull wheel

SHAPER OPERATION
To set the length of stroke . . . To set the position of the stroke . . . Holding the work . . . Clamp or vise . . . Shaping a block of rectangular form . . . To shape an inside square corner . . . In shaping a job to layout . . . Angular work . . . To cut a dovetail . . . Compound angles . . . Work operations and solution of a compound angle . . . Work operations square wedge

WORK DIFFICULTIES
Chattering tool . . . Warping of work . . . Checking the squareness of vise

SPEEDS AND FEEDS
Factors involved . . . Tables of strokes per minute . . . Formula to determine speeds

CUTTING TOOLS
Compared to lathe tools . . . Tools commonly used . . . Do's and Don'ts

VERTICAL SHAPER (SLOTTER)

DEFINITION
Holding the work . . . Setting length of stroke . . . Position of the stroke . . . Work difficulties

PLANER

DEFINITION
Difference between shaper and planer . . . History . . . Size . . . Planer parts, names of principal parts . . . Bed . . . Columns . . . Crossrail . . . Table . . . Tool head . . . Table drive . . . Feeds . . . Holding the work . . . Clamping hints

HISTORY

The shaper was originally intended as a woodworking machine. The first one was designed by Sir Mark I. Brunel, a Norman Frenchman, who came to the United States as a refugee from France about 1793. The idea for the design of the shaper came to him while he was attending a dinner at Alexander Hamilton's home. At this dinner he met an English industrialist by the name of Dilabigarre, who had the responsibility of making blocks (pulleys or sheaves) for English sailing vessels and had been experiencing considerable difficulty in forming the mortices. Dilabigarre presented his problem to Brunel, who after much thought suggested that the mortices could probably be cut three or four at a time if the proper machinery could be developed. After many reverses, Brunel's plans finally materialized in 1797. He produced the first successful shaper while he was located at Fort Montgomery in the highlands of the Hudson River in New York State.

The metal working shaper was not developed until 1836. It was invented by James Nasmyth, an Englishman, whose family and ancestors were of an artistic, as well as mechanical, turn of mind. This machine was only one of a long list of important machines which Nasmyth invented. His metal working shaper was popularly known for a long time as "Nasmyth's Steel Arm," and did much to encourage the metal working industry.

DESCRIPTION

The metal working shaper, as it is used today, is a machine in which the metal removing tool is moved by a ram which travels in a horizontal plane with a reciprocating motion. Its size is determined by the size of the largest cube which can be machined on it. This machine was originally intended to produce plane surfaces, either angular, horizontal, or vertical, but with skillful manipulation may be used for producing either concave or convex surfaces. The work is usually held in a vise which is bolted to a box-like table. This table may be moved vertically or horizontally.

There are two classes of shapers in use today, the **"Crank"** shaper and the **"Geared"** shaper. Of the two, the crank shaper is most commonly used, and is made in either Standard or Universal type. The difference between these two lies in the fact that the Universal type has a vise that can be swiveled out of a horizontal plane on a swiveling work table.

CRANK SHAPER

In the crank shaper, Fig. 3–1, the ram is given its reciprocating motion by means of a rocker arm which is operated by a crank pin from the main driving gear or **"Bull Wheel,"** Fig. 3–2. The ram carries the downfeed mechanism which contains the clapper box and cutting tool and peels a chip off the work on the forward stroke.

IMPORTANT PARTS

The important parts of the shaper are: **ram, column, base, crossrail, speed control mechanism, rocker arm, and bull wheel.**

DESCRIPTION

The **ram** is a chilled iron casting of semi-cylindrical form, heavily ribbed on the inside to give strength and rigidity. It is actuated back and forth horizontally in the dovetail slide of the base by means of the **rocker arm** and the crank pin. The ram contains the stroke positioning mechanism and the downfeed mechanism.

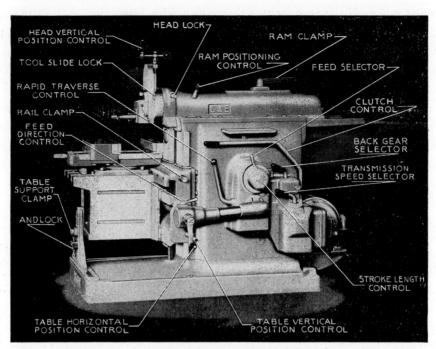

FIG. 3–1.   Standard tool room shaper (crank type).

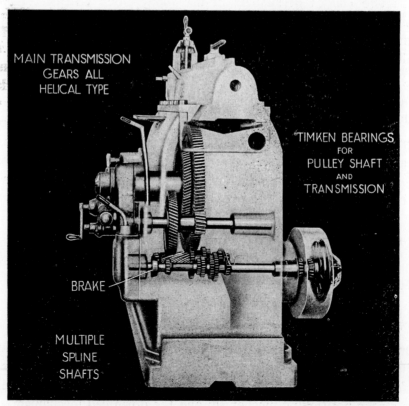

FIG. 3–2.   Phantom view of "bull wheel" and main transmission gears.

The **base** is a heavily ribbed cast iron body which gives support to the operating members of the machine. It is so designed as to reduce vibration to a minimum and has an accurately machined and scraped dovetail in the top to form a bearing slide for the ram. The front of the casting is machined to furnish two **columns** upon which the crossrail slides in its up and down movement.

The **crossrail** is a heavy, chilled, malleable casting which is attached to the columns of the base by means of gib plates and bolts. The top surface of the crossrail as well as the front surfaces are accurately machined and scraped to provide a smooth surface for the table saddle as it is fed back and forth. The crossrail contains the table elevating mechanism as well as the table traverse mechanism.

The **table feeding mechanism** consists of the pawl and ratchet mechanism, rocker screw for regulating the amount of feed for each return stroke of the ram, and the feed connecting link which connects the rocker screw to the ratchet drive and lead screw. As the rocker screw moves back and forth the connecting link moves with it, actuating the pawl and ratchet on the end of the feed screw. The feed screw is held rigidly by the **crossrail** and passes through a bronze nut in the back of the saddle. Thus any movement of the ratchet by the rocker screw causes the feed screw to move the table a definite distance.

The **saddle** is an accurately machined malleable casting which is gibbed to the crossrail and to which the table is firmly bolted. When the table is removed, the front of the saddle reveals T-slots which permit the clamping or bolting of work.

The **table** of the shaper is an accurately machined malleable iron casting of box-like construction and is bolted to the saddle. The top and sides contain T-slots which permit the clamping of work or the swivel work vise. Some of these tables are constructed so that they swivel in a vertical plane on the saddle or can be tilted up and down. When a shaper is so equipped, it is known as a Universal Shaper. The table may be moved horizontally by the use of either the rapid traverse hand feed or the automatic feed and may be adjusted vertically to provide for different thicknesses of work.

To use the **rapid traverse hand feed,** a crank is furnished which fits the squared end of the feed screw. This permits the table to be fed just as fast as the operator desires to turn the crank, or a lever controlling a high speed power traverse can be thrown to move the table in either direction relative to the operator. Movement for the automatic table feed is derived from an eccentric slot in the bull wheel. This eccentric slot makes one revolution for every revolution of the bull wheel and transmits motion by means of a shoe and series of lever arms to the rocker screw and connecting link so that the connecting link moves forward and backward on one revolution of the bull wheel.

To engage the **automatic power feed** the work is fed into the cutter by hand feed. The pawl is turned so that it engages the teeth of the ratchet on the feed screw; since the power feeding mechanism is always in motion while the shaper is running, the pawl will be moved back and forth, driving the ratchet in one direction or the other depending on how the face of the pawl contacts the ratchet. On the return stroke of the ram the feed screw is moved causing the table to be fed toward the cutter in preparation for the cutting stroke.

The **shaper vise** is a sturdy mechanism having two jaws, one stationary, the other movable, and so arranged that they may be drawn together by a screw. This vise differs from other vises since the jaws are longer and deeper and will open to accommodate work of considerable width. Generally the vise comes equipped with hardened steel jaws ground in place. These jaws should not be removed except for repair purposes. The body of the shaper vise may be swiveled in a horizontal plane from 0° to 180°; however, the usual position is to have the jaws set either parallel with the stroke of the ram or perpendicular to the stroke.

The **tool head** is a dovetail slide fastened to the front of the ram by means of T-head bolts, which permits it to be swiveled in a vertical plane from 0° to 90°. This head consists of the downfeed mechanism, clapper box, and tool post. It may be raised or lowered by hand feed to accommodate vertical cuts on the work. When making vertical or angular cuts using the downfeed mechanism, the clapper box must be swiveled away from the surface to be machined, otherwise the tool will dig into the work on the return stroke.

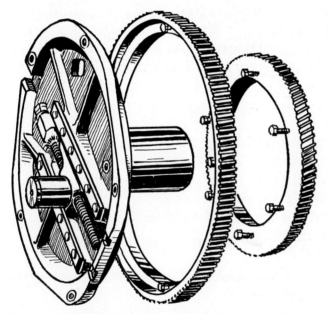

FIG. 3–3. Bull wheel showing stroke adjustment mechanism.

The **speed control mechanism** is a change gear box located on the operator's side of the shaper and is so designed that the speed of the ram and cutting tool may be changed for varying length of the work and hardness of metals. At a constant speed of the driving gear, the ram will make the same number of strokes per minute regardless of whether the stroke is 4″ or 12″. It is necessary, therefore, for the cutting tool to make three times as many strokes for the 4″ cut as it does for the 12″ cut in order to maintain the same cutting speed. This change of speed can be accomplished by engaging or disengaging gears of varying numbers of teeth by adjusting the speed control lever.

The **bull wheel** is a large cast steel gear mounted inside the shaper base or column and driven by a pinion which is motivated by the speed control mechanism. Anchored to the center of this cast steel gear is a radial slide which carries a sliding block into which the crank pin fits. The position of the sliding block is controlled by a small lead screw which is connected to the operator's side of the shaper by means of bevel gears and a square-ended shaft. Obviously the location of the sliding block with respect to the center of the bull wheel governs the length of the stroke of the ram. The farther apart these two centers are located the greater the length of the stroke. Fig. 3–4 shows the linkage between bull wheel and ram.

SHAPER OPERATION

Several factors which affect the efficient operation of a shaper are: setting the length of stroke, setting the position of the stroke, the clamping of the work, the grinding and setting of the tool bit, the speed of the ram, and the feed of the work.

To set the length of stroke on a shaper, move the ram to the extreme backward position by means of the hand wheel. Place the hand crank on the stroke setting shaft located on the operator's side of the shaper, and loosen the binding nut. Then turn the crank so that the pointer on the ram indicates on the scale the length of the work plus 5/8″, then tighten the binding nut.

The reason that 5/8″ was added to the length of the stroke was to provide clearance for the cutter.

To set the position of the stroke, move the ram to the extreme forward position by means of the hand wheel. Place the hand crank on the stroke positioning shaft located on the top front of

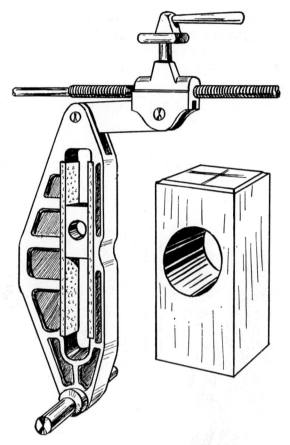

Fig. 3–4.   Linkage between bull wheel and ram.

the ram, and loosen the binder lever. Turn the crank so that the cutting tool clears the front of the work by 1/8″, then tighten the binder lever.

The **stroke** of the shaper is the distance the ram travels in either a backward or forward direction. On the forward stroke of a crank shaper the cutting tool peels a chip off the work; therefore the forward stroke is known as the cutting stroke and is slower than the return stroke. The reason that the cutting stroke is slower is not because of the resistance offered by the work to the cutting tool, but because of the location of the crank pin at the extremity of each stroke. The rocker arm which is actuated by the crank pin assumes an angular position at the end of each stroke which causes the crank pin to assume a position below the horizontal centerline of the bull wheel. From the accompanying sketch, Fig. 3–5, it can be seen that the crank pin has to travel through about three-fifths of a circle for the cutting stroke and two-fifths for the return stroke; since both strokes are the same length it is very obvious that the ram will return to its original starting position in one-fifth less time than it went forward.

Before starting any job on a shaper it is very necessary to have a complete understanding of the blue print and the shaper operations which the job requires. Make sure that there is sufficient stock to do the job according to the blue print. See that all tools are clear of the ram and cutting tool, that the machine is well lubricated and that all table and vise saddle bolts are tight.

While operating the shaper keep your mind on the work at hand. Don't go away from the machine and leave it running or don't engage in conversation fellow workers who are operating machines.

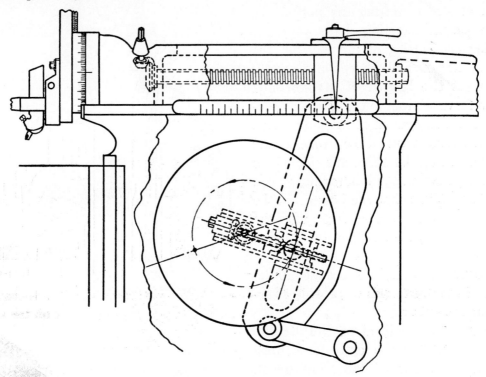

FIG. 3–5.   Sketch explaining rapid return stroke.

Holding work. Work may be held on a shaper by clamping it to the table or by means of a vise. Before putting the work in the vise make sure that the vise is free from any obstruction which might keep the work from seating properly. Make sure that burrs or rough edges left from former machining operations are removed from the work.

In seating the work in the vise it is not necessary to pound it severely with a hammer or mallet. Generally, if a mallet must be used at all, light taps are all that is necessary. A good practice is to put narrow pieces of ordinary scratch pad paper under each corner of the work, then, by pulling gently on each piece, it can be determined whether or not the work is seating properly.

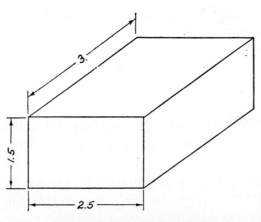

FIG. 3–6.   Rectangular block.

In shaping a block of rectangular form, as shown in Fig. 3–6, the general practice is to shape the thickness first, then the width and the length.

Procedure.

1) After the work has been properly seated in the vise, Fig. 3–7, the length of stroke should be adjusted and positioned properly for the work. The tool is then fed down by hand until it contacts the work, and the table moved crosswise; the work is then moved away, clear of the cutting tool, and the tool head is fed down to give a depth of cut sufficient to clean up the surface. With the ram moving back and forth, the work is again fed by hand to the tool and the automatic feed engaged by dropping the feed-pawl into mesh with the ratchet gear on the table lead screw.

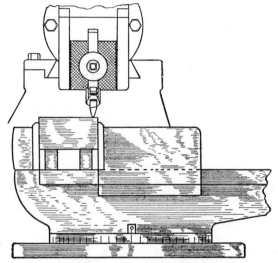

FIG. 3–7. Cleaning up the first side of the block.

2) After shaping one side to clean up, it is next necessary to shape the correct thickness and keep the faces parallel with each other. To do this place two parallels of the same size on the vise rails as shown in Fig. 3–8. Use two hold downs, Fig. 3–9, one on each side of the work, so that the finished side will be seated squarely on the parallels; then spot the cutter on the work,

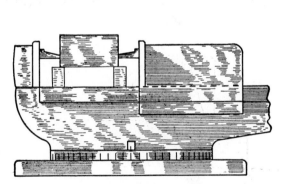

FIG. 3–8. Shaping second side parallel with first side using hold downs.

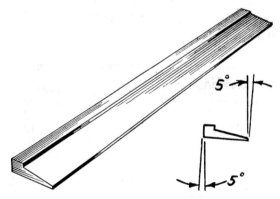

FIG. 3–9. Shaper hold down.

after which, adjust the depth of cut so as to leave about 1/32″ for finishing. After the roughing cut has been taken, increase the speed of the ram so as to give a good finish on the final cut.

3) After shaping the thickness the next operation is to shape the width square with the thickness. This is accomplished by placing one of the finished sides against the solid jaw of the vise, then putting a hold down or narrow parallel between the movable vise jaw and the other finished side of the work, as shown in Fig. 3–10. This method holds the work quite securely and keeps the vise jaws parallel.

4) After the width has been squared with the thickness, the finished side of the

width is placed down on the vise and the work held by two hold downs, one on either side of the work, as shown in Fig. 3–11.

5) When the width and thickness have been shaped square with each other and to the finished size, the next operation is to shape the length to size and square with the

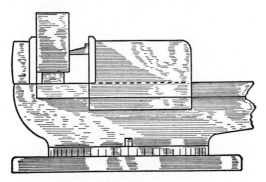

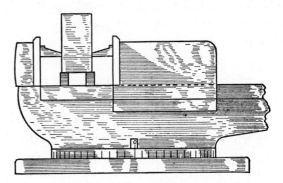

FIG. 3–10. Shaping first side of width square with thickness.

FIG. 3–11. Shaping width to size square with thickness.

width and thickness. Loosen the vise saddle bolts and swivel the vise 90° so that the vise screw is parallel with the travel of the ram. Tighten the saddle bolts and place the work in the end of the vise so that the surface to be shaped is exposed to the cutting tool and so the longest dimension of the exposed surface will be the stroke of the ram. The other end of the vise must be blocked with a parallel or piece of stock which is the same size as the work to keep the vise jaws nearly parallel so that they will better grip the work.

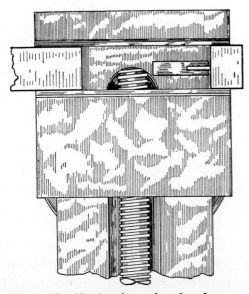

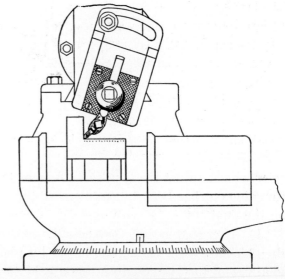

FIG. 3–12. Shaping the work to length square with width and thickness.

FIG. 3–13. Shaping an inside square corner.

6) Next place a solid square on the vise rails and against the work, adjust the work to the square and then tighten the vise securely. See Fig. 3–12. After the vise has

been tightened test the work again with the square to make sure that it has not moved.

7) Repeat the process of setting the job to shape the other end of the work square and to the correct length.

To shape an inside square corner such as that shown in Fig. 3–13, first shape the job to thickness, width, and length as previously outlined; then, with the broadest surface resting on parallels and held by hold downs, rough out the vertical surface by feeding the tool head down and taking a series of horizontal roughing cuts. When both surfaces have been roughed out to within 1/16″, tilt the clapper box towards the extreme right (operator standing in front of the machine), and adjust the tool holder so that the one tool bit can operate on both surfaces. Use a small downfeed and finish the vertical section; then finish the base.

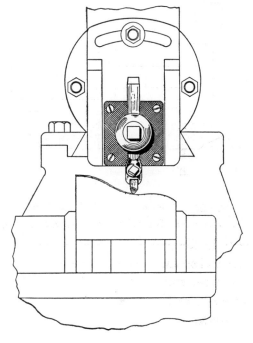

In shaping a job to layout, if much stock is to be removed, take roughing cuts to bring the job within 1/16″ to 1/32″ of the line. Then take light cuts so that the cutting tool will split the layout lines. Be very sure to leave part of the prick punch indentations in the work as **"witness"** marks.

If a job is laid out containing a **concave or convex radius** as shown in Fig. 3–14,

FIG. 3–14.   Shaping to lay out.

rough shape it to within finishing stock, working the straight line to size. Next, swivel the cutting tool slightly in a clockwise direction but leave the clapper box in a vertical position. Then feed the tool head down until the cutting tool cuts to the line, move the table by hand and feed the tool down again repeating this alternate feeding down of the tool and moving of the table until all excess stock has been removed and the radius blends in with the flat surfaces.

Angular work is shaped much the same as radial work. The sketches shown in Figs. 3–15, 3–16, and 3–17 indicate how the clapper box must be swiveled. Angular surfaces are machined either by setting the tool head, adjusting the table, or setting the work to the desired angle.

To determine the accuracy of the angular setting, a sine bar (see Figs. 13–12, 13–13, 13–14, p. 220) or bevel protractor set at the correct angle is placed in the vise in a position to correspond to that which the work will assume. Then a dial indicator, placed in the tool rest, is run over the sine bar or bevel protractor and the machine adjusted to give a zero-zero reading from one end of the gage to the other. When the correct setting is obtained the table or head is tightened and the indicator is passed over the gage again to make certain that the setting has not been disturbed by the tightening.

When the table is swiveled to produce an angle it is not necessary to swivel the

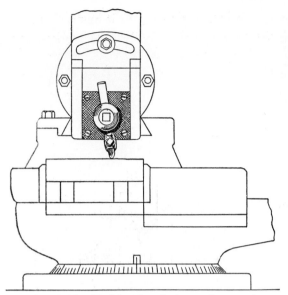

FIG. 3–15.   Tool head and clapper box set for
horizontal cut.

clapper box, but when the tool head has been swiveled, the upper part of the clapper box should be swiveled in a direction away from the surface being machined, otherwise the cutting tool will drag and produce an undercut in the work. It is an advantage at times, when a heavy cut is being taken on a horizontal surface, to have the clapper box turned in a direction away from the cut. This has a tendency to preserve the cutting edge of the tool.

To cut a dovetail, both a right- and left-hand cutting tool and tool holder are necessary and once the actual cutting of the angular sides begins, the work should not be disturbed. Surfaces 2 and 3, Fig. 3–18, should be machined first, then the tool head is swiveled to the proper angle and the tool and tool holder, corresponding to the angular side to be machined first, are put in the tool post. Care should be taken

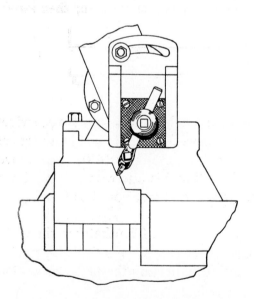

FIG. 3–16.   Tool head and clapper box set
for angular surface (left).

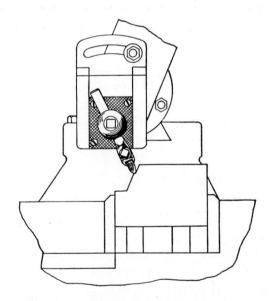

FIG. 3–17.   Tool head and clapper box set
for angular surface (right).

to keep the tool bit from digging into the work and as the layout lines are approached frequent checks should be made to insure accurate sizing of the dovetail.

Another type of work which the operator of a shaper is frequently called upon to do is the shaping of **compound angles.** A compound angle is one whose magnitude depends on the value of two other angles. The subject of compound angles is a course of study all by itself and is too involved to be presented fully in this treatise. However, a few of the more simple forms which occur frequently will be considered. In the case of the job shown in Fig. 3–20, it is assumed that the width, thickness, and length have

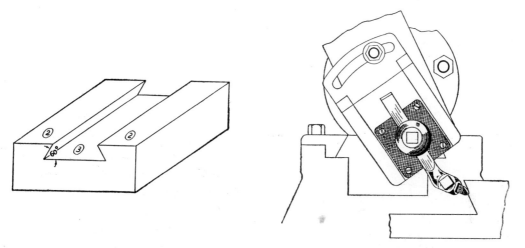

FIG. 3–18. Dovetail slide.   FIG. 3–19.   Shaping a dovetail slide.

been shaped to size and it is required to shape the plane *ABC*. With the vise set so that the screw is parallel with the travel of the ram, place the job in the vise; then swivel

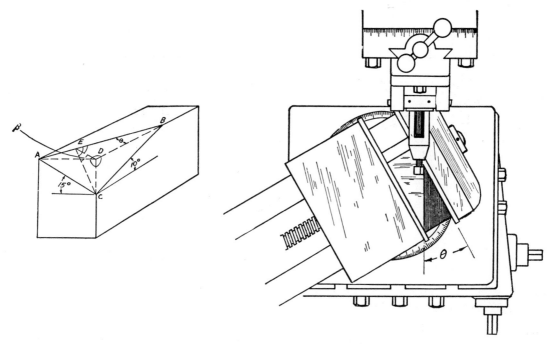

FIG. 3–20. Illustration of a simple   FIG. 3–21.   Vise swiveled through angle θ.
        compound angle.

the vise through the angle θ (theta) so that line *AB* is parallel with the travel of the ram, Fig. 3–21. Next, tilt the vise through the angle β (beta) which will put plane

ABC in a horizontal position as shown in Fig. 3–22. From the foregoing it is clearly evident that angle θ and β must be given, regardless of what other angles the draftsman puts on the blue print or sketch.

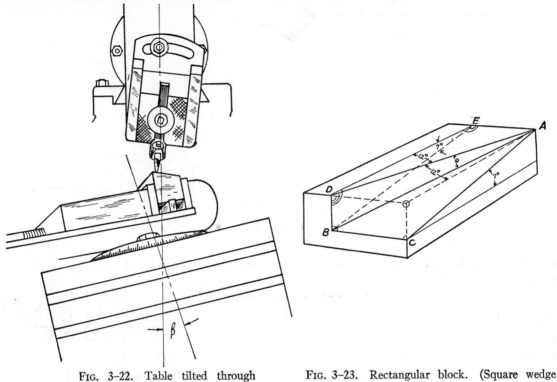

FIG. 3–22. Table tilted through angle β.

FIG. 3–23. Rectangular block. (Square wedge to be cut out.)

Example 1.

Assume that the draftsman gave angle *CAD* as 15° and angle *CBD* as 10°.

Solution.

The solution for θ and β would be as follows:

Let *CD* = 1; then *BD* is the cotangent of 10° and *AD* is the cotangent of 15°.

Therefore, the tangent of θ is equal to the cotangent of 15° divided by the cotangent of 10°, or the cotangent of 15° multiplied by the tangent of 10°.

To find the value of β let *BD* = 1. Then *DE* is equal to the sine of θ and *DC* is the tangent of 10°.

Therefore, the tangent of β will equal the tangent of 10° divided by the sine of θ, or the tangent of 10° multiplied by the cosecant of θ.

Example 2.

To do the job shown in Fig. 3–23.

Solution.

Have the vise screw parallel with the travel of the ram and locate the job in the vise. Then swivel the vise through the angle *ADE* so that line *AD* is parallel with the stroke of the ram. Next tilt the table up through the angle θ (theta) so that line *AB* is in a horizontal plane.

To find the value of angle θ, assume that angle *ADE* is given as 12° and angle *DEB* is given as 7°.

Then letting line $DE = 1$, AD will equal the secant of $12°$ and DB will equal the **tangent of** $7°$. The tangent of angle θ will equal DB divided by AD or the tangent of $7°$ divided by the secant of $12°$.

Instead of dividing by the secant of $12°$, the same result may be obtained by multiplying the tangent of $7°$ by the cosine of $12°$.

Further information relative to calculations on compound angles may be found in that excellent text, "Practical Shop Mathematics," Vol. II, by Wolfe and Phelps.

WORK DIFFICULTIES

Two conditions which cause much concern to the operator of a shaper are chattering of the work or cutting tool and warping of the work. Some of the more common causes of chattering are: the cutting tool having too much clearance, the tool suspended too far, the work improperly supported, or too much play between the ram and its ways. Chattering may be eliminated by the operator correcting any or all of the above conditions; however, a machine repair man should be called to remove the play in the ram. Warping of the work may be avoided by taking light cuts, alternately from each side, to remove internal strains.

Work being out of parallel may be caused by chips or dirt between the work and vise or by chips getting between the vise and saddle. Work being out of square may be caused by dirt or chips between the work and solid jaw of the vise, or the solid jaw may be out of square with the stroke of the ram. To determine whether or not the vise is square with the stroke of the ram, Fig. 3–24, place a dial indicator or other suitable indicating gage in the tool holder, with the point of the indicator on the face of the solid jaw; then move the table and vise at right angles to the

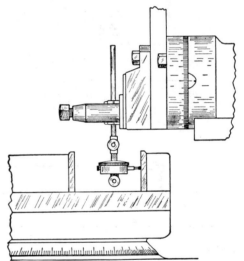

Fig. 3–24.   Checking the vise for squareness with stroke of the ram.

stroke, observing any change in the indicator setting. If the jaw is out of square, loosen the saddle bolts slightly and bump the vise in a direction to compensate for the amount of error.

To check the solid jaw of the vise for being vertically square with the stroke, place an indicating gage in the tool post, resting the point of the indicator on the edge of the blade of the square as shown in Fig. 3–25; then move the table back and forth so that any **"out-of-squareness"** will be registered by the indicator. If the vise is out of square in this position it may be due to dirt between the saddle and the table, or if the table is universal, it may be due to the fact that the table has been moved. It might also be caused by the solid jaw being worn or damaged.

To check the vise rails for being parallel with the stroke of the ram, get two parallels of the same length and width, which are equal to or greater than the width or depth of the vise. Place these parallels on the vise rails, then place an indicating gage in the tool post so that its point rests on the edge of the parallel as shown in Fig. 3–26. Now move the ram back and forth by hand, but do not let the indicator point drop off the end of the parallel, and observe the indicator needle. If the outer end of each of the parallels is low it indicates one of two things: either there is dirt under the back end of the vise, or the table sags due to wear on the table cross-head gib.

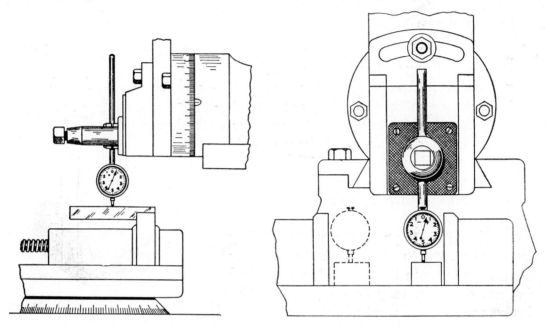

FIG. 3–25. Checking solid jaw for being vertically square with stroke.

FIG. 3–26. Checking vise rails for being parallel
with stroke of ram.

If the back end of the parallel is low or if alternate points on the two parallels do not give the same reading, it is an indication that the vise is not bearing properly on the table. These conditions may be overcome by seeing that the vise seats properly, or by having the table cross-head gib adjusted.

SPEEDS AND FEEDS

The shaper was designed for the purpose of reducing the job to the desired shape or size in a minimum of time and effort. With this idea in mind, the completion of a job requires one or more roughing cuts and a finishing cut. The greatest cut for the purpose of stock removal depends on many factors, the more important of which are: rigidity of work set up, rigidity of cutting tool mounting, machine support, how the tool bit is ground, and general machine conditions. Unfortunately, no general rule can be given for the depth of cut, feed, and speed of shaper, due to so many variable conditions.

Generally speaking it is the duty of the operator to make the machine do the work. In other words the operator must make the shaper work during the roughing cut.

The feed and depth of cut should be such as to remove as much stock as the shaper is capable of driving during the roughing operations, being consistent, of course, with the amount of material to be removed. The stroke of the ram should be set for the correct speed in FPM, setting the feed as great as possible without tearing the metal. Then feed the cutting tool down to its maximum capacity. For a finishing cut leave 1/32″ to 1/16″ of stock and then increase the speed of the ram.

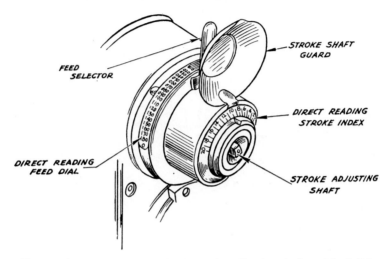

Fig. 3–27.   Gould and Eberhardt stroke adjusting shaft and feed dial.

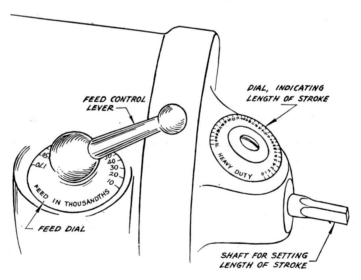

Fig. 3–28.   Cincinnati stroke adjusting shaft and feed dial.

A common error made by most mechanics is to under-estimate the ability of a machine and cutter. If the machine is operated too slowly and there is failure to make the cutter work up to capacity, then production of work comparable with the time expended is impossible. For this reason it is wise for the mechanic to determine the number of strokes per minute of the ram as a starting point; then if the machine set-up or other conditions do not warrant the speed, it can always be stepped down.

The speed at which a shaper operates is always specified as so many **"strokes per minute"** of the ram. The standard number of strokes per minute is different for various kinds of shapers. On most of the older models, the number of strokes per minute for various positions of the back gear lever and the speed change lever is not indicated on the machine; instead, the positions are marked 1-2-3-4, as shown in Fig. 3–29. On the modern shapers these positions clearly indicate the strokes per minute, as shown in Figs. 3–27 and 3–28.

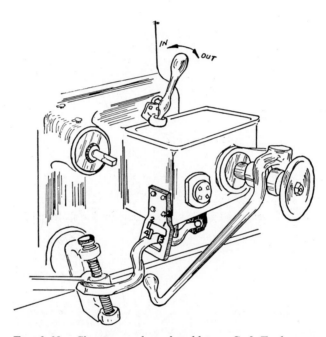

FIG. 3–29.   Change gear lever for old type G. & E. shaper.

The following chart shows the numbers of strokes per minute of the ram obtainable on one of the older Gould and Eberhardt shapers.

BACK GEAR IN		BACK GEAR OUT	
Position	Strokes per min.	Position	Strokes per min.
1	10	1	45
2	15	2	65
3	21	3	92
4	30	4	132

FIG. 3–30.   Chart of speeds obtainable, back gear in and back gear out for old-style G. & E. shaper.

Figs. 3–31 and 3–32 show the index plates from a modern 16″ Gould & Eberhardt shaper and a modern 16″ Cincinnati shaper.

Since the number of strokes per minute for the different positions of the lever is fixed, the speed in surface feet per minute will change with any change in the length of the work. Also the number of surface feet per minute for different kinds of metal demands a change in the number of strokes per minute, so that until the operator of a shaper becomes well acquainted with the action of the machine on these different metals, the two factors mentioned above must be taken into consideration in setting the machine for the correct number of strokes per minute.

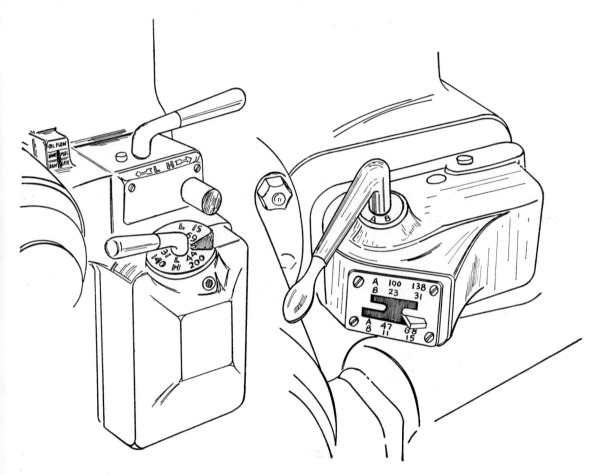

FIG. 3–31. Speeds obtainable on new style G.&E. shaper (back gear in and back gear out).

FIG. 3–32. Speeds obtainable on new style Cincinnati shaper (back gear in and back gear out).

The following formulas for determining the number of strokes per minute of the ram and the cutting speed are based on the fact that the cutting tool is in operation on the forward stroke which is only three-fifths of the time and is therefore slower than the return stroke.

$$CS = (N \times L) \div 6$$
$$N = (CS \times 6) \div L$$

where, $N =$ Number of strokes per minute of ram
$L =$ Length of stroke
$CS =$ Cutting speed of metal in **FPM**

Example 1.

For what number of strokes per minute should the ram be set to shape a block of machine steel 10″ long?

Solution.

The cutting speed for machine steel, using a high speed steel tool bit, is 115 FPM. Applying the above formula, $N = (CS \times 6) \div L$,
$$N = (115 \times 6) \div 10 = 69$$

Answer 69 strokes per minute

Example 2.

What would be the cutting speed for a block of tool steel 6″ long if the number of strokes per minute of the ram is 58?

Solution.

Using the formula $CS = (N \times L) \div 6$,
$$CS = (58 \times 6) \div 6 = 58$$

Answer 58 FPM

The cutting speeds for various metals in terms of FPM of the ram and the approximate table feeds are given below. These are given as starting points only and will depend on several different factors.

MATERIAL	SPEED	FEED
Cast Iron	50–60	.080
Machine Steel	110–120	.060
Tool Steel	60–70	.050
Chrome Non-Shrink		
High Speed Steel	40–50	.030
Nichrome		.050
Brass		
Copper	160–255	.050
Aluminum		

Most shapers are provided with what is commonly known as a back gear which can be shifted so as to increase or decrease the speed. With this arrangement it is possible to obtain a total of eight different speeds, as shown in Fig. 3–30. This is quite desirable because metals of different toughness require different speeds for more effective machining.

PROBLEMS

1. At what number of strokes per minute should the ram be set to shape a piece of cast iron 4″ long?

2. At what number of strokes per minute should the ram be set to shape a piece of aluminum 14.5″ long?

3. At what number of strokes per minute should the ram be set to shape a piece of tool steel 8-3/4″ long?

4. At what number of strokes per minute should the ram be set to shape a piece of machine steel 11-1/4″ long?

5. At what number of strokes per minute should the ram be set to shape a piece of high speed steel 7″ long?

6. What will be the cutting speed if the stroke is set at 5" and the number of strokes per minute of the ram is 92?

7. What will be the cutting speed if the stroke is set at 4" and the number of strokes per minute of the ram is 65?

8. What will be the cutting speed if the stroke is set at 8.5" and the number of strokes per minute of the ram is 21?

9. What will be the cutting speed if the stroke is set at 7" and the number of strokes per minute of the ram is 132?

10. What will be the cutting speed if the stroke is set at 11" and the number of strokes per minute of the ram is 15?

CUTTING TOOLS

The shaper tool differs from the lathe tool, Fig. 3–33, in that the shaper tool has less side and front clearance because the work feeds into it on the return stroke, whereas the lathe tool is constantly feeding into the work.

The shaper, like the lathe, is frequently called upon to make many different kinds of cuts and for this reason the operator must be able to grind the tool bits necessary to do the job. The tool post of a lathe is equipped with a rocker rest for the tool holder in order to provide a means of adjusting the tool bit

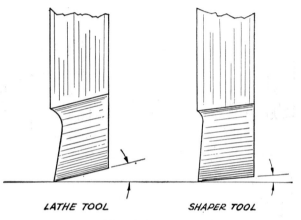

LATHE TOOL   SHAPER TOOL

FIG. 3–33. Comparison of front clearance angles between lathe and shaper tool bits.

for front clearance. The shaper tool post is not thus provided, so that the proper clearance angles must be ground. For best results these angles should not exceed 4°. If more clearance than this is given, the cutting edge of the tool will not last long, due to the lack of backing to keep it from chipping or breaking down. Less clearance than 2° will permit the tool bit to rest on the work, causing the tool to heat up quickly, leaving a poor finish on the work.

The sketches in Fig. 3–34 illustrate some of the more commonly used cutting tool shapes. Special tool shapes may have to be ground from time to time for special operations. When these occasions arise, the grinding operation will have to be governed by the requirements of the job.

In putting the tool holder in the tool post, set it so that the point of the tool projects about two inches below the bottom of the tool block. Greater distances than this may cause chattering because of insufficient support of the tool. Never have the work table so far away from the cutting tool that the tool head or tool holder will have to be given a long overhang. This practice might result in breaking the tool head slide and it puts undue strain on the tool post, slide, and clapper box.

Make sure that there is at least 2" clearance between the ram and the vise or work.

Tools commonly used. Among the precision tools commonly used on the shaper are the solid square and micrometer. This tool, the solid square, is strictly a precision tool and should be handled with the same consideration as that given to a micrometer. It should not be dropped or handled carelessly in connection with the work. It should be kept separately from other tools so that it will not be sprung, bent or nicked.

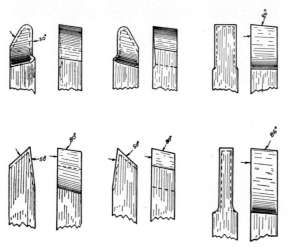

FIG. 3–34. Forms of shaper tool bits.

A surface gage is frequently used on the shaper for lining up or leveling up the work to layout lines. The scriber point may be used in connection with one of the spindles or the base, setting the point to one end of the layout and adjusting the work so that the line is horizontal.

The sine bar is used in connection with the shaping of angles whose values require a high degree of accuracy. Sine bars are available in standard lengths of 5″ and 10″.

To set the tool head or work table at the correct angle, one end of the sine bar must be raised above the other an amount equal to 5 or 10 times the sine of the angle. The tool head or work table should be swiveled to the approximate angle by means of the graduations. Then place the sine bar in position in the work vise. The indicator point should then be brought to bear on the top surface of the sine bar and the table adjusted to give a zero-zero reading from one end of the sine bar to the other.

DO'S and DON'TS

DO thoroughly understand the requirements of the job.

DO see that there is at least 2″ clearance between the ram and the vise, or work.

DO wear goggles. Remember, you can eat with false teeth, and walk with a wooden leg, but you can't see with a glass eye.

DO keep your hands away from the moving work and tool holder.

DO make sure that the tool bit clears the work at both ends before starting the ram in motion.

DO keep vise handle pointing toward floor.

DO see that all tools are clear of the working surface before starting the ram in motion.

DO make sure that the job is held securely.

DO make sure that the tool head is not down too far.

DO see that the shaper is well oiled.

DO keep your mind on your work.

DO see that the machine operates at near capacity.

DO keep shirt collar buttoned for protection against hot chips.

DON'T use ill-fitting wrenches on the shaper.

DON'T hammer the vise wrench or handle. It mars and nicks the wrench and does not materially increase the clamping pressure on the work.

DON'T walk away from the shaper and leave it running.

DON'T wear thin-soled shoes.

DON'T stand directly in front of shaper while it is in operation.

DON'T try to talk to a neighbor operator and run your machine at the same time.

DON'T forget to keep the tool head gib friction bolt tight after the head has been fed down.

DON'T try to feed the tool head down without loosening the gib friction bolt.

DON'T forget to increase the speed of the ram before taking a finishing cut. It gives a better finish and completes the job in a shorter time.

DON'T let chips accumulate in the vise screw recess; they damage the nut in the sliding jaw.

DON'T hammer on the tool head or clapper box to swivel them. Loosen the nuts sufficiently so that the head or box can be turned easily by hand.

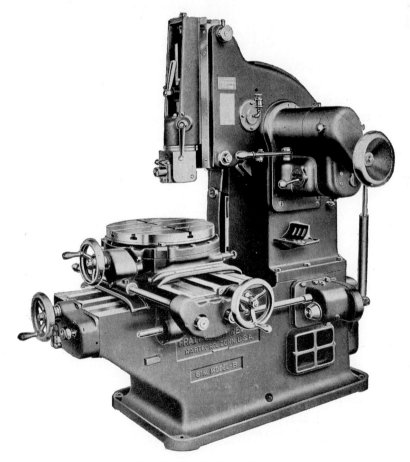

FIG. 3–35. Vertical shaper.

VERTICAL SHAPER (SLOTTER)

DEFINITION

The vertical shaper, Fig. 3–35, sometimes called a **"slotter,"** is a machine with a vertical ram which is especially adapted to slotting holes, pockets, keyways, and clearance on dies. The ram travels up and down and can be adjusted to shape angles up to 5° and has a tool head which can be swiveled through 180° in a horizontal plane. The tool head and ram of a slotter are not adjustable angularly. The work table is supported on a fixed knee and can be moved in or out longitudinally by hand or

FIG. 3–36. Work clamped to table.

power feed. When the shaping of cylindrical or semi-cylindrical forms is required, the work table may be equipped with a rotary plate which can be power driven.

Holding work. Work may be held on a vertical shaper by a vise, by clamps, or by special fixtures; it is commonly held, however, by strap clamps as shown in Fig. 3–36. The work is usually supported by rest blocks to provide for chip clearance and to give the cutter a chance to complete the stroke.

For **setting the length of stroke** of the ram, an eccentric, Fig. 3–37, is provided on the right hand side of the machine. (Operator facing machine.) By loosening the jam nuts, the eccentric may be turned to any desired position on the scale to give a stroke from "O" to the full capacity of the machine.

The **position of the stroke** is set in the same manner as on the shaper. The binder lever is loosened on the ram, and a wrench fitted to the stroke positioning screw is turned so that when the ram is at the bottom of the stroke the edge of the cutting tool will clear the work by about 1/8″. The binder lever is then tightened.

The tool head contains a clapper box designed to prevent the cutting tool from dragging against the work on the up-stroke. It is unlike the shaper clapper box since the tool seat is held out in position by a spring. The tool post passes

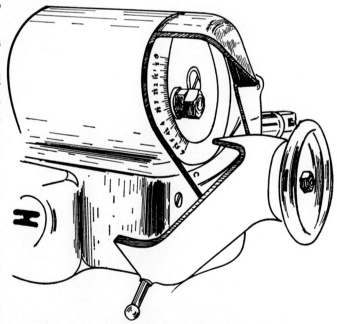

FIG. 3–37. Mechanism for setting length of stroke.

through the clapper box and grips the cutting tool or tool holder by pulling it up against the rest plate when a nut on the inside end of the tool post is tightened.

The speed chart shown in Fig. 3–38 is for the Pratt & Whitney 6″ vertical shaper and indicates the number of strokes per minute possible with the gear shift lever in the four different positions. It likewise shows the maximum cutting speed in FPM at the middle of the stroke for various stroke lengths with the gear shift lever in position 1, 2, 3, or 4, as shown in Fig. 3–39.

The cutting tool used on a vertical shaper differs from the one used on a shaper in that it is strictly an end cutting tool. The sketches shown in Figs. 3–40, 3–41, 3–42, and 3–43, represent some of the tool shapes and holders commonly used. Fig. 3–40 shows a solid forged tool used for heavy duty work. Fig. 3–41 shows a heavy duty holder using bits of various sizes and shapes, depending on the work require-

VERTICAL SHAPER CHART PRATT & WHITNEY 6 IN. MODEL			
LENGTH OF STROKE	POSITIONS OF GEARS		
	1	2	3	4
	STROKES PER MINUTE			
	33	49	76	116
	MAXIMUM CUTTING SPEED IN FEET PER MINUTE AT MIDDLE OF STROKE			
6½	40	59	92	—
6	38	56	87	—
5½	35	53	81	—
5	33	49	76	—
4½	30	45	70	—
4	28	41	64	97
3½	25	37	57	87
3	22	32	50	77
2½	19	28	43	66
2	15	23	35	54
1½	12	18	27	42
1	8	12	19	29

Fig. 3–38. Speed chart plate on vertical shaper.

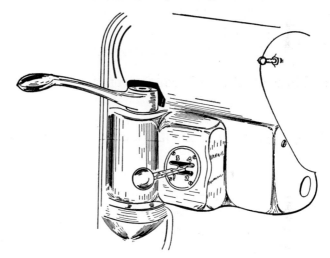

Fig. 3–39. Lever positions for speeds.

ments, and is more economical than that shown in Fig. 3–40. Fig. 3–42 shows a tool holder for such tools as shown in Fig. 3–43.

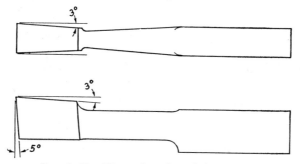

Fig. 3–40. Heavy duty forged slotter tool.

Work difficulties. Perhaps the greatest difficulty encountered with work on the vertical shaper is that the cutting tool has a tendency to spring to one side, or deviate from a vertical path. This tendency may be overcome by using a short and strong cutting tool. In the case of cutting a small keyway in a long slender hole, it is best to rough out the keyway first, then use a cutter up to size for finishing the job. One factor that goes a long way to eliminate vertical shaper trouble is to keep the tools

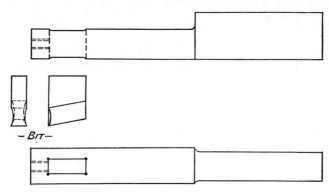

– BIT –

FIG. 3–41.   Heavy duty tool holder for bit inserts.

sharp and to see that they have the proper rake and clearance angle. If one side of the tool is sharper than the other it will naturally cut more freely and hence be apt to run toward the sharp side, thus causing the keyway to be out of parallel with the centerline of the hole. For extremely small keyways it is best to set the job up on a rotary table,

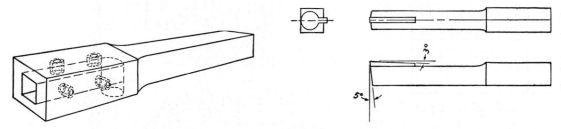

FIG. 3–42.   Heavy duty tool holder.   FIG. 3–43.   Cutters for use with heavy duty tool holder.

so that the center of the hole in which the keyway is to be cut will be on the exact center of the rotary table. Then in case the sides of the keyway do not come exactly square, the rotary table can be turned to permit cleaning up the sides of the keyway so that they will be square.

The operator of a vertical shaper is frequently called upon to shape circular sections which cannot be done conveniently on any other machine. The center of the rotary plate or table usually contains a ground hole which is exactly on center at the intersection of the T-slots. Into this hole a test plug may be placed and indicated so that the rotary table is on the exact center of the tool holder. The work may be located loosely on the rotary table and indicated so that it is on center; then the work can be clamped tightly after which the excess stock on the work may be removed to produce the correct radius.

Occasionally it is necessary to cut serrations in a flat or semi-cylindrical piece of work. Besides accurate indexing to insure correct spacing of the teeth, the cutting tool must be kept sharp and of the right shape, because frequently these serrated teeth have to mesh much the same as gear teeth do; therefore, if the teeth are not the same shape and size, the pieces will not fit together properly.

The safety rules for operating a horizontal shaper apply to a vertical shaper with these in addition:

1) Keep all tools off the work table.

2) Try out by hand the position and length of stroke before starting the ram in motion.

3) See that the tool properly clears the work on the length of the stroke.

4) Before starting the machine in motion make sure that everything is clear of the downward stroke of the ram.

PLANER

DEFINITION

A planer, Fig. 3–44, is a machine used to produce flat surfaces on work that is too large or otherwise impossible to machine on a shaper. The planer differs from the

FIG. 3–44. Planer.

shaper in that the work table moves back and forth with a reciprocating motion while the cutting tool is fed on a crossrail which straddles the table.

History. The invention of the planer cannot be credited to any particular individual, but is due to several people. Several individuals in England have been credited with the planer invention as early as 1570. However, Richard Roberts, an

Englishman, in 1817 developed a planer which was almost identical to the present day machine and to him goes most of the credit for the planer as we now know it.

Size. The size of a planer is determined by the size of the largest rectangular solid it can machine; that is, a planer with a size of 28″ × 28″ × 7′ is 28″ between the uprights, has a maximum of 28″ from the table to the crossrail and has a maximum stroke of 7′ or 84″. Planers are made in a wide variety of sizes capable of handling work from small machine castings up to large turbine parts.

Planer parts. The important parts of a planer are; the **bed, columns, crossrail, planer table, tool head,** and the **table drive.**

The **bed** supports the columns and all moving members of the machine. It is an extremely heavy, rigid casting, possessing accurately finished ways on which the table slides.

The **columns** are heavy box-like structures located on each side of the bed, connected at the top by a heavy cast member. They support the crossrail and various working parts which control the movement of the cutting tool.

The **crossrail** is a rigid casting of box-like structure which carries the saddle and tool head. It is supported by, and can be adjusted vertically on, the front finished faces of the columns, by means of vertical screws located in each of the columns. The crossrail contains the feed rod and screw for controlling the movement of the cutting tool. Since the accuracy of the surfaces produced is dependent on the accuracy at which the cutting tool is moved, it is of the utmost importance that the crossrail, when clamped, be parallel to the table. The surest way to determine this parallelism is to place an indicator in the tool post with the indicator point touching the table, then move the tool head crosswise of the machine at the same time observing any variation of the indicator needle.

The planer **table** is made of a good grade of cast iron and presents a broad surface upon which the work can be mounted. It is provided with T-slots for bolting work and contains accurately reamed holes located at convenient points for locating stops and poppets. These T-slots and holes should be kept free from nicks and burrs. Never force the shanks of the stops or poppets into the holes by driving them with a hammer since this action upsets the surface of the table and destroys its accuracy.

The **tool head** of a planer is much like that of a shaper both in construction and operation. It is provided with a feed screw for moving it with respect to the work; it can be swiveled for taking angular cuts, and it may be set over either way to provide for the clearance of the tool when taking vertical or angular cuts.

The **table drive** on a planer may be accomplished by one of two methods, either by gears or pulleys. Where gears are used entirely, a large gear known as the **"Bull"** gear is connected with a rack on the bottom side of the table and by a series of gears to the electric motor. The quick return of the table is accomplished by adjustable stops on the side of the table, which, at the end of each cutting stroke, come in contact with a shifter or lever which throws in a high speed gear in the driving train of gears. In the belt driven type two belts, one open, the other crossed, operate on loose and fixed pulleys. In this case the table travel stops come in contact with a shifter lever at the end of each stroke. When it makes contact at the end of the cutting stroke, the shifter throws the belt off the fixed pulley onto the loose one and at the same time throws the crossed belt from a loose pulley to a fixed pulley. Since the crossed belt is running faster than the open belt, the table comes back faster on the return stroke. With this arrangement the operator can use the shifter lever by hand to run the belts on loose pulleys and stop the table movement without stopping the whole machine. Provisions are made to lock the shifter lever in a neutral position to guard against accidental starting of the machine.

Feeds. The automatic in- and downfeeds of the cutting tool operate at the beginning of the cutting stroke. This is particularly true on long work. If a long flat surface is being planed, the infeed is used and is controlled by the feed screw moving the cutter head along the crossrail. If it is necessary to plane a vertical surface the automatic feed is used to operate the small feed screw in the tool head. Either one of these feeds may be accomplished by hand by turning a crank or handle on the feed screw which controls movement of the head in the direction required.

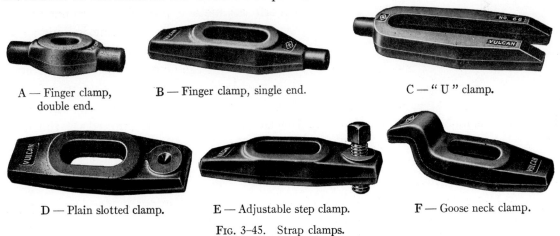

A — Finger clamp, double end. B — Finger clamp, single end. C — " U " clamp.

D — Plain slotted clamp. E — Adjustable step clamp. F — Goose neck clamp.

FIG. 3–45. Strap clamps.

Holding the work. Work is generally held on the planer by means of clamps or by toe dogs and poppets. Fig. 3–45 shows several types of strap clamps.

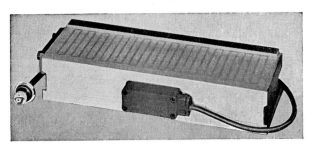

FIG. 3–46. Magnetic chuck.

Since quite a variety of work, both in size and shape, can be done on this machine, other methods of holding the work are often required. For example, if the work is of a repetitive nature, it may be desirable to use a special fixture for holding it. On the other hand, the work may be of such a nature as to require the use of jacks or packing blocks to support an overhanging section or to support a section which is not sufficiently rigid to withstand the action of the cutting tool. In some few instances a magnetic chuck is used to hold the work. A picture of this holding device is shown in Fig. 3–46.

Since the majority of jobs worked on the planer are held by clamps, the operator must frequently use considerable ingenuity in setting up the job. Clamping calls for the use of such items as bolts, studs, washers, nuts, shims, step blocks, strap clamps, jacks, toe dogs, poppets, stops, packing blocks, and C-clamps. Pictures of some of these holding devices are shown in Fig. 3–47.

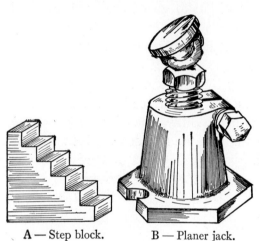

A — Step block.   B — Planer jack.

FIG. 3–47. Holding devices.

In clamping work to the planer table, especially in the case of iron castings, it is important to arrange the clamps so as not to produce undue strain on any one section. Nearly all metals can be sprung under pressure; therefore, if the clamping is done so as to produce a strain, after the piece has been machined and the clamping pressure released, the machined surface will not be true. If the work does not seat evenly on the table, the high corners must be shimmed before the clamping pressure is applied. If the high corner is too far away from the table to be shimmed, packing blocks or planer jacks may be used, but be careful, if a jack is used, not to raise it too high. Fig. 3–48 shows a planer gage. While this tool has many uses, it was primarily designed as an aid to the operator of the planer. Usually the job is seated directly on the planer table and its thickness cannot be conveniently gaged. By setting the planer gage with a micrometer to the rough finished size of the work, Fig. 3–49, the planer tool can be brought

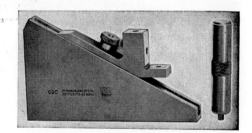

FIG. 3–48. Planer gage.

to bear on the gaging surface, Fig. 3–50, thus insuring that the tool will cut only deep enough to leave the required material for a finishing cut. The planer gage can then be set for the finished thickness of the work and the process of setting the cutting tool repeated. This eliminates the cut and try method which results when a planer gage is not used.

Clamping hints:

1) Be sure that the work is clamped securely before starting to machine it.

2) Make a habit of sighting between the work and cross head, and work and machine uprights, to see that the work clears.

3) Protect all finished surfaces by placing shims of copper, brass or fiber between the clamp and the work.

4) When placing the work in position protect the table from work scratches or marks by using rubber or cardboard pads.

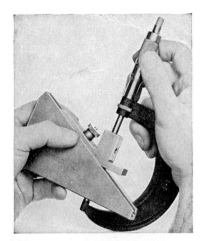

FIG. 3–49. Setting a planer gage with a micrometer.

FIG. 3–50. Setting the planer tool with a planer gage.

5) When a finished surface is placed on the table, put pieces of thin paper under the corners so that as the clamping operation progresses they can be used to determine whether or not the work is seating correctly.

6) Use a washer with every nut and bolt.

7) Don't select bolts which are too long. They might interfere with the action of the cutting tools.

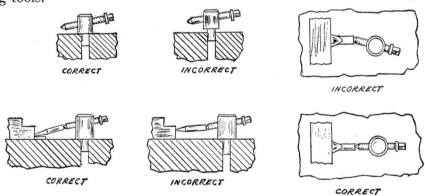

FIG. 3–51 A. Correct and incorrect use of toe dogs and poppets.

8) Don't try to use bolts that are too short. For best holding results, the nut should screw completely on the bolt, not just two or three threads.

9) Make frequent use of stops for the work to rest against. When using strap clamps or U-clamps, support the clamp parallel with the table and keep the bolt as close to the work as possible.

10) When using toe dogs and poppets for holding work, keep the toe dog in a straight line with the screw of the poppet. See Fig. 3–51 A and B.

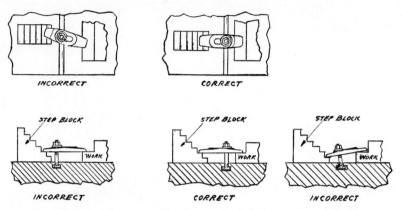

FIG. 3–51 B.   Correct and incorrect use of clamps and step blocks.

REVIEW QUESTIONS

1. Name the important parts of a shaper.
2. Discuss the principle involved in shortening or lengthening the stroke of the ram.
3. Why is 5/8″ added to the length of the stroke?
4. Outline the procedure of setting up a simple job in the shaper.
5. Discuss the procedure necessary to shape a rectangular block.
6. What is meant by shaping a job to lay out?
7. Describe a shaper hold down.
8. Discuss a few common work difficulties.
9. How is the vise checked for being square with the stroke of the ram?
10. What are the necessary steps to check the solid jaw for being vertically square with the stroke?
11. How does a shaper tool differ from a lathe tool with respect to clearance?
12. What precision tools are commonly used on a shaper?
13. What is the chief difference between a common shaper and a vertical shaper?
14. How is work held on a vertical shaper?
15. Discuss common work difficulties on a vertical shaper.
16. How does a planer differ from a shaper?
17. Name the important parts of a planer.
18. How is work held on a planer?
19. What precautions should be taken in clamping work to a planer table?
20. Give five important rules for the use of strap clamps.

Chapter 4

LATHE

HISTORY
Tree lathe

DEFINITION
Engine lathe

CLASSIFICATION
Screw machine . . . Horizontal turret lathe . . . Vertical turret lathe . . . Back-off lathe

HISTORY

The lathe as we know it today is the result of the ambition and craftsmanship of the best mechanics from the 17th century to the present time. Historically, the first

Fig. 4-1.   Tree lathe.

lathe necessitated the use of two trees, which the mechanic selected as being far enough apart to suit his needs. He bored a hole through the trunk of each tree, and through each hole drove a conical pointed wooden pin into the center of the log of wood he

67

wanted to turn. To the most conveniently located branch of one of the trees a rope was fastened, the free end of the rope he wound around the work two or three times and then tied a loop in it near the ground. This lathe required one man to manipulate the turning tool and another to supply the power. As the power man pressed down with his foot in the loop, the log would turn in one direction; then as he released the pressure, the springy branch would cause the rope to turn the log in the reverse direction.

From this crude beginning the machine developed into a pole lathe, then the counter weight lathe, then the fly wheel lathe. In the year 1797, Henry Maudslay, an English mechanic, designed and built what is said to be the first screw cutting lathe. In this lathe, the spindle was geared to the lead screw which in turn drove the carriage.

Shortly after Maudslay built his screw cutting lathe, one of them found its way into the New England States. At this time the United States was still severely hampered by English laws which prohibited the export of machinery and supplies. While these laws worked a hardship for a while, it did not take the American revolutionists very long to capitalize on Maudslay's lathe. They built similar lathes having wooden beds with strips of iron for ways. In 1836 a mechanic by the name of Putnam was building screw cutting lathes in Fitchburg, Mass. Lathes having iron beds were built as early as 1850 in New Haven, Conn. In 1853 a lathe having an all iron bed, and a back geared head, in which the spindle was connected to the lead screw by means of change gears, was built by Freeland in New York City.

By 1850 the demand for farming implements, firearms, hardware, and household utensils was so great that small factories had made their appearance all over the New England States.

By the year 1861 it was evident that war would be declared between the North and the South. This created such a new demand for machines that the United States soon led the rest of the world in their design, accuracy, and production. This leadership can be traced back directly to the lathe, for it is the only machine which is capable of reproducing itself as well as others.

DEFINITION

A lathe is a mechanical device in which the work is held and rotated against a suitable cutting tool for the purpose of producing cylindrical forms in wood, metal and other materials. Irregular forms may be produced by means of special equipment.

The term **"engine,"** in connection with the lathe, goes back to that period in history when the steam engine was used to furnish the power necessary for operating it. Thus it is that some text books and mechanics still refer to a machine shop lathe as an **"Engine Lathe."**

American manufacturers generally specify the size of a lathe by the **diameter** of the largest piece of work which can be swung over the ways, and the **total length** of the bed. European manufacturers specify the size by giving the **radius** of the largest piece of work which can be swung over the ways. For example an American made lathe with the size specified as 18″ × 14′, is one which will swing a piece of work 18″ in diameter, and has a bed the total length of which is 14′. A similar lathe of European manufacture would have the size specified as 9″ by 14′.

CLASSIFICATION

The tool room or machine shop lathe, as mentioned before, was the fore-runner of many modern specialized machines. Some of these machines are quite similar in principle, among which are the **Screw Machine, Horizontal Turret Lathe, Vertical Turret Lathe,** and the **Back-off Lathe.**

Fig. 4–2. Screw machine.

Screw machine. This machine, Fig. 4–2, was developed primarily to manufacture machine screws to relieve the machine shop lathe of that duty. As time went on new ideas were incorporated, such as a multiple head containing stations for different kinds of tools, to carry out different operations. This head can be indexed to bring each tool into position for operating on the work. It replaced the tailstock of the machine shop lathe. The spindle evolved into a special rapid chucking device to handle long bar stock, replacing the small conventional spindle and 3- or 4-jaw chuck. The compound rest gradually changed into a tool head having four different stations, each containing tools for special purposes. All of these changes came about gradually, until today the screw machine may be considered a highly specilized lathe capable of doing multiple operations on work of a repetitive nature.

The "set-up" of this machine depends on the nature of the work to be done, but once it is adjusted to the work requirements, it can be depended upon to produce piece after piece with unfailing accuracy, except for the wear on the single edged cutting tools.

Horizontal Turret Lathe. This machine is similar to the screw machine in that it has a turret, or head, containing stations for different kinds of tools. The difference

FIG. 4–3. Turret lathe.

FIG. 4–4. Vertical turret lathe.

lies in the fact that it was built for handling large, chunky pieces of work by means of a special chuck. The spindle of this machine is exceptionally large and is capable of clearing work of quite large diameters. In operation it is quite similar to the screw machine.

Vertical turret lathe. This type of lathe commonly referred to as a "Bullard" is really a horizontal turret lathe tipped up on the work head end. It is provided with an exceptionally large combination work table and 4-jaw chuck, with provisions for holding work by means of strap clamps.

The turret swivels and has six different stations for tools. Unlike the horizontal turret lathe and screw machine, the main turret can be fed across the work as well as parallel with the axis of rotation of the work. This arrangement readily adapts the vertical turret lathe to boring holes of large diameter as well as facing operations. The vertical column on the operator's side of this machine contains a four station turret for holding four different cutting tools to be used for turning the outside diameter of the work. Each of these turrets is independent in its movements both as to direction and amount of feed and both may be used on the work at the same time.

REVIEW QUESTIONS

1. Describe a tree lathe.
2. Name several types of lathes.
3. How did the term engine lathe originate?
4. How is the size of the American-made lathe specified? European-made lathe?
5. What is the chief difference between a screw machine and a turret lathe?
6. What is a vertical turret lathe?

Chapter 5

TOOL ROOM LATHES

Bench lathe . . . Tool room lathe . . . Getting acquainted with the lathe . . . Lining up centers . . . Cutting tools . . . Clearance . . . Holders . . . Grinding tool bits . . . Setting the tool . . . Cutting speed

Bench lathe. The bench lathe, Fig. 5–1, is a small tool room lathe used to facilitate the machining of small miscellaneous parts required in bench operations and is capable of producing these parts cheaply, accurately, and quickly.

FIG. 5–1.　Bench lathe.

These lathes usually have a capacity for work of 8, 9, 10, or 11″ in diameter, have beds 36″ to 40″ long, are equipped for thread cutting and can do work operations similar to those done on the standard tool room lathe.

Tool room lathe. The lathes previously mentioned have a place in large tool rooms but are not nearly as important as the lathe shown in Fig. 5–2.

This type of lathe is used far more frequently than the others because of its adaptability to a wide range of operations. It demands a much greater degree of skill to operate. To the uninitiated, the experienced lathe operator does not seem to encounter any great difficulty in starting and completing a job; however, before he could do this, he spent considerable time learning those simple fundamentals which are so essential to good workmanship. He knows that his lathe must be lubricated regularly, that he must use care to prevent marring the painted and polished surfaces, that he must keep it free of dirt, chips, and oil stains.

For good workmanship, the machine centers and sockets have to be given especially good care by keeping them clean and free from nicks and burrs. All working parts must move freely but not loosely.

Getting acquainted with the lathe. It is very important for the beginner to get acquainted with the starting and stopping lever. He should try out the various movements of the cross feed and compound to determine their action. The carriage

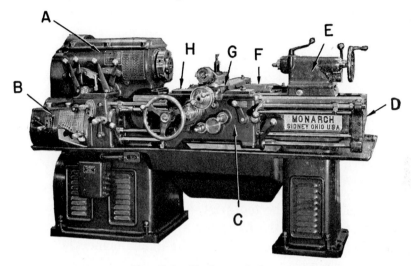

FIG. 5–2.   Tool room lathe.
Principal Assembly Units — A, Headstock.   B, Gearbox.   C, Apron.   D, Bed.   E, Tailstock.
F. Carriage.   G, Compound rest.   H, Taper attachment.

should be moved back and forth by hand and the tailstock should be moved along the ways as well as moving the quill in and out by means of the hand wheel. Notice the graduations on the dials of the control handles; try to get a good impression of their values.

Start the machine motor and learn to start and stop the spindle with the motor running. Notice where this lever is located because it will have to be used more frequently than any other. Try increasing and decreasing the spindle speed by referring to the **"plate of spindle speeds."** With the spindle revolving, engage the carriage feed and notice in which direction it moves. Try reversing the direction; stop the carriage movement and engage the power for the cross-feed slide; reverse the direction of the feed.

Move the tumbler gear lever to the extreme left and notice what effect it has on the feed. Now move it to the extreme right. Did the rate of feed increase or decrease?

Stop the machine and change the upper and lower compound levers to correspond with a setting on the **"Feed thread index plate."** Start the machine and notice the change in the rate of feed. Notice that the lead screw is not turning. It turns when the **"feed thread lever"** is moved to engage it with the gear box and is used only when **"chasing"** threads.

Lining up the centers. After becoming generally acquainted with the levers for operating the lathe, the next thing to do is to check the alignment of the centers. To do this, move the tailstock center up close to the headstock center and after clamping the tailstock casting to the bed, turn the tailstock spindle hand wheel until the two centers almost touch each other. Observe any discrepancy in the alignment of the center points. If the tailstock center is out of line, either to the right or left, it may be adjusted as follows:

Procedure

1) Loosen the tailstock clamp bolts and with a wrench turn the set-over screw, on the operator's side of the tailstock casting, so that the two machine centers will coincide.

2) Tighten the clamp bolts and check the alignment, repeating the operation of adjusting the tailstock on the slide until the centers are aligned within the required degree of accuracy.

3) As a further check move the tailstock back and place a 1" × 10" test bar between the centers, after having cleaned the center holes of the bar thoroughly.

4) Install an indicator in the tool post, adjusting it so that the plunger pin bears correctly on the test bar. Set the indicator at zero and move the carriage back and forth noting any deflection of the needle. If the indicator needle shows any variation, adjust the tailstock to give a zero-zero reading from one end of the bar to the other.

It must be remembered that the shanks of the machine centers, as well as the sockets into which they fit, must be thoroughly cleaned and free from nicks.

Cutting tools and holders. The tools used for cutting on the lathe are generally made of high speed steel. This steel is an alloy of tungsten, carbon, and either vanadium or molybdenum and can be used for cutting steels at very high rates of speed.

Sometimes cutting tools made of chromium, cobalt, and tungsten are used. This cutting tool, known as **"Stellite,"** is considerably harder than high speed steel but is very brittle; for this reason it must be well supported.

Tungsten carbide or carboloy is harder than any of the cutting tools with the exception of the diamond. This material is pressed and sintered into shape and then brazed to a steel shank or holder. It is highly recommended for certain kinds of hard, tough materials, and when the cut is long and continuous.

In speaking of the angles of a cutting tool the terms **rake** and **clearance** are often confused. The term **rake** pertains to the angle which the top side of the lathe cutting tool makes with the horizontal at the cutting edge. The angle that this top surface makes in a plane parallel with the length of the tool bit is called **back rake.** The angle that this top surface makes in a plane perpendicular to the length of the tool bit is called **side rake.** Back rake angles vary with the kind of material being cut, the tough cutting steels requiring less back rake than the mild cutting steels. The recommended back rake angle for tough cutting steels is 8°, for very free cutting steels, 16-1/2°. The side rake angle varies in the same manner; that is, 12° for tough cutting steels and up to 22° for free cutting steels.

Clearance is the term applied to grinding away the front and leading side of the tool bit. These angles are very important because they determine the amount of **"bite"** which the bit can take. Insufficient clearance causes hard cutting action, increasing the friction, rapid heating of the tool bit, and finally, burning of the cutting edge of the tool. Excessive clearance weakens the cutting edge, causes **"digging in"**

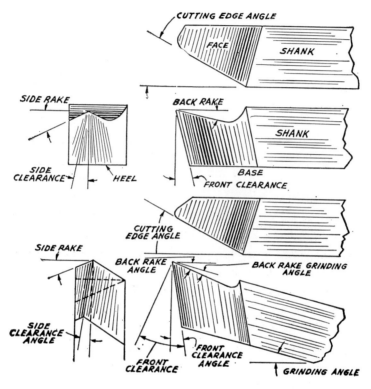

FIG. 5–3. Tool bits showing rake and clearance angles.

of the tool, and produces **"chatter."** The front clearance angle should be about 8°, whereas the side clearance angle should be 10° for tough cutting steels and up to 12° for free cutting steels.

The following diagrams are forms of tool bits commonly used for lathe work. The **angles** of rake and clearance should be ground to suit the type of material upon which they are to be used:

Fig. 5–4 A shows a right-hand (R.H.) turning tool, commonly used for general turning purposes when the carriage is fed toward the headstock.

The left-hand (L.H.) turning tool, Fig. 5–4 B, is used for general turning and finishing purposes when the carriage is fed toward the tailstock.

Fig. 5–4 C shows a R.H. facing and corner tool used for making square shoulders on the work when the carriage is fed toward the headstock. Where the shoulder must have a filleted corner, the point of the cutting tool is ground to produce the correct radius.

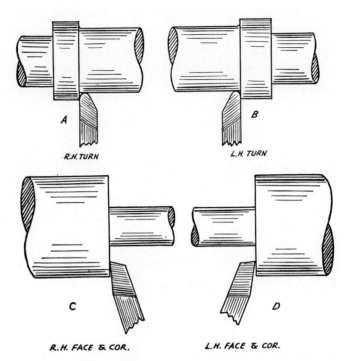

FIG. 5–4.   A, Right hand turning tool.   B, Left hand turning tool.   C, Right hand facing and corner tool. D, Left hand facing and corner tool.

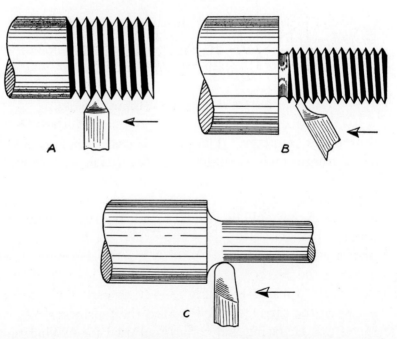

FIG. 5–5.   A, 60° threading tool bit.   B, Shoulder threading tool bit. C, Round nose turning tool R.H.

A L.H. facing and corner tool, Fig. 5–4 D, is used for making square shoulders on the work when the carriage is fed toward the tailstock.

For chasing threads on an unshouldered piece of work, the threading bit shown in Fig. 5–5 A is used. This tool is for American National Form threads, having a flat on

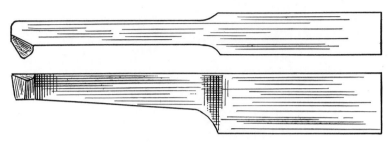

FIG. 5–6. Forged boring tool.

the point equal to one-eighth of the pitch and an included angle of 60°. Except for coarse threads, the flat need not be ground on the point.

Fig. 5–5 B shows a R.H. 60-degree threading tool used for cutting screw threads up against a shoulder. Generally, work of this nature is necked at the shoulder to permit withdrawing the tool bit and reversing the carriage so that the tool will not dig into the shoulder.

The round nose, R.H., cutting tool, Fig. 5–5 C, is suitable for rough or general purpose turning. By giving the tool

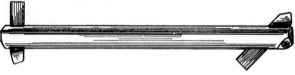

FIG. 5–7. Boring bit inserts and bar.

more back rake and no side rake it can be used for either right- or left-hand turning purposes.

Boring tools are either of the forged type or bit type, and having a cutting head ground like a L.H. turning tool. This tool has a back and side rake of 20° and a side clearance of about 10°. The front clearance depends on the diameter of the hole to be bored, but should be sufficient to keep the tool from rubbing on the surface of the hole. Fig. 5–6 shows a forged boring tool and Fig. 5–7 shows the bit type held by means of a boring bar.

The internal threading tool, Fig. 5–8, is a special boring tool ground the same as an external thread cutting tool. Like the boring bit or tool, it should have sufficient front clearance to keep it from rubbing on the surface of the hole or thread.

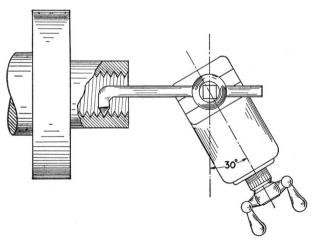

FIG. 5–8. Internal threading tool.

"Cutting-off," or "parting" tools are those which are specially shaped and ground for the purpose of cutting off a piece of stock. As shown in Fig. 5–9, this tool has no back or side rake. It does have front and side clearance. The clearance on each side is ground so that the tool will be wider at the top front edge than at the back end.

FIG. 5–9. Cutting-off tool.

FIG. 5–10 A. R.H. forged tool holder.

FIG. 5–10 B. Straight forged tool holder.

FIG. 5–10 C. L.H. forged tool holder.

Tool holders. Tool bits made of high speed steel, stellite, or tungsten carbide, must be held securely and rigidly if the work is to be done efficiently. To that end, patented, forged holders are made which not only simplify the job set-up but also contribute to the economy of the cutting tool. Figs. 5–10 A, B, and C show three of these patented forged tool bit holders. To differentiate between a left-hand tool holder and right-hand tool holder, hold the head in your hand and observe in which direction the shank points; if it points to the left, it is left-hand; if it points to the right it is right-hand.

Boring bars for bit inserts are held in the tool post of the lathe by means of a special forged holder. This holder is superior to the one piece forged boring tool in that once the position of the bar is set, the tool bit can be taken out and sharpened and can be reset without disturbing the set up. This proves to be very advantageous when counterboring or chasing threads. The holder shown in Fig. 5–11 can be used

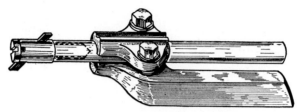

FIG. 5–11.   Boring bar holder.

for bars using the bit insert or for round forged bars of two different sizes. It can also be used for bars which use either straight or angular bits, and does not require extra equipment.

Fig. 5–12 shows a light duty boring bar holder which may be used for either boring or turning. For boring, bar tools varying by eighths of an inch from 1/8″ to 3/8″, can be held. The offset head permits holding square tool bits for right- or left-hand turning purposes.

FIG. 5–12.   Light duty boring bar holder.   FIG. 5–13.   Parting and side tool holder.

Blade type parting tools are held by forged tool holders similar to that used for tool bits. Fig. 5–13 shows a type of holder which may be used for either parting tools or side cutting tools. The blade is held in place by means of a cam which is operated by a wrench and which permits the blade to be adjusted or removed for grinding without disturbing the setting of the holder.

Grinding the tool bit. Success in operating a lathe is dependent on two important factors: the efficiency of the work set-up, and the exactness with which the cutting tool is prepared for the work. In the preceding material, tool shapes and uses were discussed; consider now, the actual operation of grinding a tool bit. *Note.* The tool bit should not be held in the tool holder for grinding.

In the first place, select a grinder with a coarse grain abrasive wheel on one side for roughing out the tool bit, and on the other side a fine grain abrasive wheel for finishing. Such a tool grinder is illustrated in Fig. 5–14. The wheel on the right is used for roughing out the tool and the one on the left for finishing. Note the protecting glass guard in place on the right wheel. These guards should be used, or goggles must be worn, whenever the tool is ground.

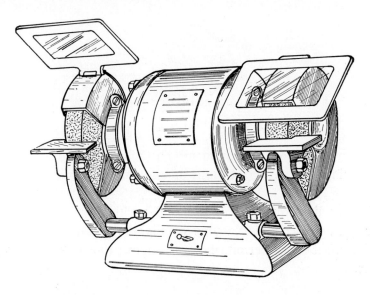

FIG. 5–14.   Tool grinder.

Fig. 5–15 shows two views of how the tool bit is located against the grinding wheel. View *A* shows how the front and side clearances are ground after the tool has been roughed out. It should be moved from right to left so that its contour will be one con-

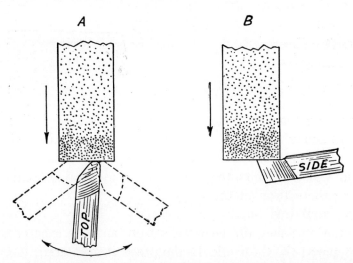

FIG. 5–15.   A, Grinding front and side clearance.   B, Grinding back and side rake.

tinuous clean cut from one side of the tool to the other. **Caution:** Be careful not to draw the temper of the tool or burn it. View *B* shows how the final cutting edge should be put on by holding the leading face lightly against the grinding wheel and moving it back and forth. Before placing the tool bit in the tool holder, it should be touched up with an oilstone to clean up the cutting edge.

Setting the tool. For ordinary turning purposes the tool bit should be placed in the holder so that it will not project further than twice its thickness. Fig. 5–16 shows

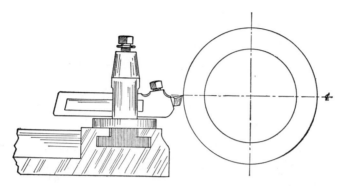

Fig. 5–16. Cutting tool set on centerline of work.

how the tool holder and tool bit should be placed in the tool post. In adjusting the tool to the work, set the point of the tool exactly on center for ordinary work. In cutting cast iron and **"free cutting"** steel the point of the tool should be set slightly above center. This adjustment can be made by moving the crescent-shaped wedge of the tool post either in or out on the tool post ring. Besides setting the point of the tool on center, the tool holder should be set perpendicularly with respect to the axis of the work. Heavy cuts should be taken toward the headstock, and the tool holder should be set in a direction away from that of the carriage travel as shown in Fig. 5–17. This practice keeps the cutting tool from digging in and possibly spoiling the work.

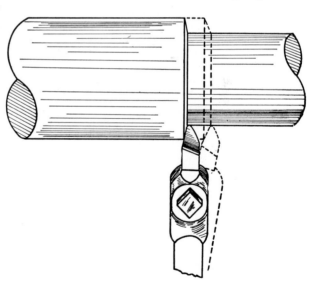

Fig. 5–17. Setting the tool holder with axis of work.

Cutting speed. Relative to lathe work, the cutting speed is the number of feet per minute, measured on the circumference of the work, that will pass a given point. In other words it is the total length of the chip taken off by the tool bit in one minute and is expressed by the letters FPM.

To determine the FPM of a piece of work, multiply the work diameter in inches by 3.1416 by its given RPM and divide by 12; that is,

$$\text{FPM} = (D \times 3.1416 \times \text{RPM}) \div 12$$

The governing factors here are the work diameter and the RPM of the work. The diameter of the work is always specified, but the RPM is dependent on the kind of material to be machined. By experiment it has been found that each kind of steel machines best when the lathe is set to give a definite FPM. The following table gives the recommended speeds in feet per minute for the more common metals.

The following formula for the RPM is derived from the one given for the FPM and is close enough for all practical purposes.

$$RPM = (CS \times 4) \div D$$

Where,

CS = the cutting speed in feet per minute,

D = the diameter of the work in inches.

Until the lathe operator becomes well enough acquainted with the machining characteristics of the various metals, this formula should be used as a starting point for all spindle speeds.

MATERIAL	SAE NO.	FPM
Chrome Vanadium	6145	50–60
Nickel Chromium	3250	50–60
High Speed	71660	50–60
Cast Iron	. . . .	55–65
High Carbon Tool Steel	1095	60–70
Chromium Steel	5140	75–85
Cold Rolled Steel	1010	100–110
Machine Steel	1015	100–110
Wrought Iron	. . . .	100–110
Bronze	. . . .	200–250
Copper	. . . .	200–250
Aluminum	. . . .	200–250

EXERCISES

Example 1.

Suppose it is required to turn a piece of SAE 5140 steel, 1.5″ in diameter.

Solution.

Use formula RPM = $(CS \times 4) \div D$.

The cutting speed for SAE 5140 is 75–85 FPM

Therefore,

RPM = $(80 \times 4) \div 1.5 = 320 \div 1.5 = 215$ approximately

Answer Set the spindle speed as nearly as possible for 215 RPM

Example 2.

Find the RPM at which a piece of cast iron 2″ in diameter should be machined.

Solution.

RPM = $(CS \times 4) \div D$

RPM = $(60 \times 4) \div 2 = 240 \div 2 = 120$

Answer 120 RPM

Example 3.

At what RPM should a piece of aluminum stock 3.5″ in diameter be turned?

Solution.

$$RPM = (CS \times 4) \div D$$
$$RPM = (225 \times 4) \div 3.5$$
$$= 900 \div 3.5 = 257 \text{ approximately}$$

Answer Approximately 257 RPM

Example 4.

A bronze bushing 1.25″ in diameter is to be bored. Find desired RPM.

Solution.

$$RPM = (CS \times 4) \div D$$
$$RPM = (225 \times 4) \div 1.25$$
$$= 225 \times 4 \div 5/4$$
$$= 225 \times 4 \times 4/5$$
$$= 45 \times 16$$
$$= 720$$

Answer 720 RPM

PROBLEMS

FIND the RPM at which the following work should be turned:
1. High speed steel 2.25″ in diameter.
2. Cold rolled steel 3.5″ in diameter.
3. SAE 6145 stock 1.75″ in diameter.
4. SAE 1015 stock 2.5″ in diameter.
5. Aluminum 5.5″ in diameter.
6. SAE 3250 stock 1.5″ in diameter.
7. Wrought iron stock 3.0″ in diameter.
8. SAE 1095 stock 2.75″ in diameter.
9. Cast iron stock 6.5″ in diameter.
10. Copper stock 3.25″ in diameter.

Feed. Obviously, the feed of the cutting tool is dependent on many variable factors, such as the condition, shape, and method of supporting the cutting tool; the kind, shape, and support of the work; the depth of cut, and the condition of the lathe. In other words each new job presents its own peculiar problem relative to feeds and speeds. One job may be of ordinary bar stock which can be supported readily and machined; the next job may be an odd-shaped forging which will necessitate getting under the scale to preserve the edge of the cutting tool; the next job may be an iron casting that may require special effort to set up and will require different cutting tools.

In any event, after the machine has been set for the correct number of RPM, give the cutting tool as much feed and depth of cut as the machine and work will stand. If the chips are not coming off blue, except on a finishing cut, the machine is not working up to capacity.

Roughing cuts are taken to reduce the work to approximate size in the least time possible. These cuts require heavy feeds and a well supported cutting tool. Naturally the depth of cut must be taken into consideration when selecting the feed. In the case of castings it is important to take a depth of cut sufficient to allow the cutting tool to get under the hard scale, otherwise the tool will be dulled quickly. The tool bit used for this kind of metal should have a back rake of 5°, a side rake of 10° to 12°, a front clearance of 8° and a side clearance of about 10°.

REVIEW QUESTIONS

1. Describe the procedure of lining up the centers on the lathe.
2. What is meant by rake and clearance in regard to a cutting tool?
3. Name several alloys commonly used in lathe cutting tools.
4. How is the "hand" of a lathe tool determined with respect to right and left?
5. Name ten common lathe tools?
6. What are the chief advantages of tool bits over forged tools?
7. What is a parting tool used for?
8. Describe the operations of grinding a tool bit.
9. What are the important points to be observed in setting the tool on a lathe?
10. Why should the tool holder be set in a direction away from the headstock when taking heavy cuts?
11. How is the point of the tool set with respect to the centerline of the work?
12. What is meant by cutting speed?
13. What does FPM mean?
14. Why is it necessary to get "under the scale" when machining a casting?

Chapter 6

LATHE WORK

Centering ... Center drilling ... Facing ... Turning ... Filing ... Shoulders ... Chuck and mandrel work ... Draw bar and collets ... Originating and finishing the hole ... Boring ... Counterboring ... Undercutting ... Steady rest work ... Knurling ... Tapers — External ... Taper attachment ... Internal tapers ... Checking tapers ... Threading ... Do's and don'ts for the lathe

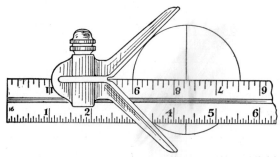

FIG. 6–1. Locating the center with center head and blade.

Centering. Work to be turned between centers requires that the ends be drilled with suitable holes for the center points to enter. The position of these holes may be located in the approximate center of the work by use of the hermaphrodite caliper, by use of a surface gage, or by use of the center head and blade of a combination square, or by chucking it up in the lathe.

On cylindrical work which is not too large, the center head method can be used as shown in Fig. 6–1. First place the work tangent to the inside faces of the center head and scribe a line, holding the scriber point up close against the blade. Revolve the work about 90° and scribe another line. The intersection of these two lines will be the approximate center of the stock. Repeat this procedure on the opposite end of the work.

To use the hermaphrodite caliper for locating the center of the stock, set the legs to slightly more than the radius of the stock; rub chalk on the end of the work and then with the point of the hooked leg resting against the outer surface use the pointed straight leg and scribe four arcs, as shown in Fig. 6–2, moving the hooked leg around about 90° of the work circumference for each arc. Use the center punch and make an indentation as nearly as possible in the center of these arms. Do the same thing on the other end of the work.

FIG. 6–2. Locating the center with an hermaphrodite caliper.

If the work is of square, rectangular or other regular shape the center can be located by drawing lines from opposite corners. The intersection of the diagonal lines will be the approximate center of the work.

After the work center has been located the center hole can be made by using a combined drill and countersink (center drill). Fig. 6–3 shows this tool and a chart of the sizes commonly used.

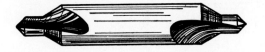

SIZE	BODY DIAM. IN INCHES	DRILL DIAM. IN INCHES	LENGTH
A-1	1/8	3/64	1 1/4
C-2	13/64	1/16	1 7/8
D-1	15/64	5/64	2
E-1	3/10	3/32	2 1/8
E-2	3/10	1/8	2 1/8
F-1	7/16	5/32	2 3/4
F-2	7/16	3/16	2 3/4

FIG. 6–3.　Combined drill and countersink and chart of the sizes commonly used.

Center drilling the work. Probably the most common method of drilling the center holes in the work is by mounting it in a 3-jaw universal or 4-jaw chuck in the lathe. If the work is very long, one end is placed in the chuck and the other end in a steady rest. When the 3-jaw universal chuck is used, the jaws are tightened on the work so that it will run as true as possible; select a R.H. facing tool and install it properly in the tool post; then set the RPM of the spindle for the kind of material to be machined and start the machine. Move the cutting tool to the center of the work and face the end to remove about one-half of the excess stock on the work length. This facing operation should proceed by having the cutting tool feed from the center of the work to the outside, as shown in Fig. 6–4.

To center the work, place a drill chuck of suitable size in the tailstock spindle and in it place the proper center drill. Move the tailstock along the ways until the center drill is about 1″ away from the work. Tighten the tailstock binding screws and "snug up" on the spindle binder lever; then with the headstock spindle revolving at a speed consistent with the size of the work and center drill, turn the tailstock hand wheel feeding the center drill to the work. Feed the drill into the work so that the diameter of the countersunk hole does not exceed one-half of the

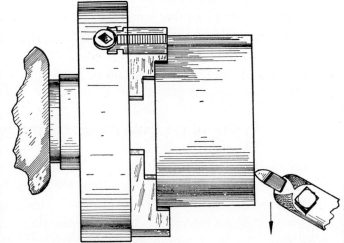

FIG. 6–4.　Facing the end of the work in a 3-jaw chuck.

drill body. To center drill the other end of the work, Fig. 6–5, reverse it in the chuck and proceed as previously outlined.

The centering operation just outlined is for work held by the 3-jaw chuck. The same method applies for the 4-jaw chuck except for the chucking of the work. In this chuck the jaws are moved independently of each other so that the work must be made to run approximately true before the center holes are drilled.

To cause the work to run true, Fig. 6–6, place it in the chuck and adjust the jaws to conform to the concentric circles on the face of the chuck. (See Fig. 6–12.) Adjust the tool holder in the tool post so that the point of the cutting tool can be fed up close to the work at the jaws. With the headstock spindle in neutral, turn the chuck over by hand, meanwhile noting which jaws permit the work to run eccentrically. Loosen the

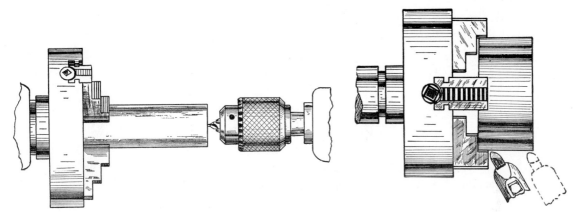

FIG. 6–5. Center drilling the work.   FIG. 6–6.   Truing the stock in a 4-jaw chuck.

jaws which permit the work to run away from the cutting tool and tighten the opposite jaws. Continue this process until the work runs within the required degree of accuracy, then proceed with the centering operation as outlined for the 3-jaw chuck.

Simple turning.

Procedure.

1) After the work has been faced to length and center drilled, remove the chuck from the spindle being careful not to hit the ways with it as it comes off the spindle. Clean the spindle socket thoroughly and after cleaning the shank of the headstock center insert it in the spindle.

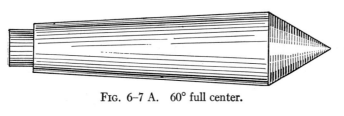

FIG. 6–7 A.   60° full center.

FIG. 6–7 B.   60° half center.

2) Remove the drill chuck from the tailstock by turning the handwheel to pull the spindle in and the shank of the drill chuck up against the knockout pin. Clean this socket thoroughly and after cleaning the shank of the tailstock center — Fig. 6–7 A and B shows the full center and half center — insert it in the tailstock socket.

3) Install a drive plate on the spindle and a lathe dog of correct size on one end of the work. Place the tail of the dog in one of the drive plate slots and the work on the

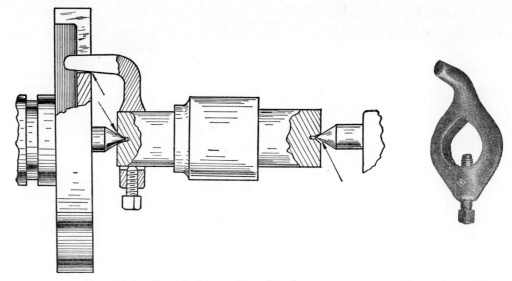

FIG. 6–8 A.   Dog binding on drive plate slot.   FIG. 6–8 B.   Lathe dog.

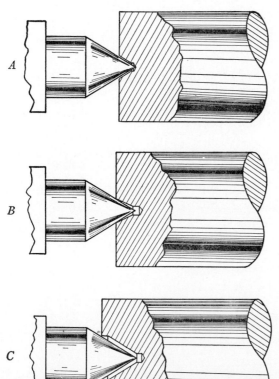

A

B

C

FIG. 6–9.   Faulty centers in work.

A, Drilled hole not deep enough.   **B,** Incorrect angle.
C, Countersunk hole too deep.

headstock center. Then, after moving the tailstock to the approximate location on the ways and lubricating the center, engage it with the work. Be sure that both work centers are perfectly clean, that the tailstock spindle does not stick out too far, that the tail of the dog, Fig. 6–8, is not binding in the drive plate slot; then adjust the tailstock center to permit the work to be rotated freely between the centers, but not loosely.

4) After the work is located properly between the centers, put a sharp right-hand turning tool in a left-hand tool holder in the tool post. Adjust the tool holder for taking a light cut with the point of the cutting tool on center. Adjust the spindle speed for the correct RPM for the material being machined; start the machine and spot the point of the cutting tool on the work.

5) Set the dial on the cross-feed screw at zero and feed the cutting tool in enough to clean up the surface; then engage the feed for moving the carriage toward the headstock and turn a spot about 1/2″ long.

6) Disengage the carriage feed, back the cutting tool out and move the carriage by hand to the dogged end of the work. At this end turn another spot, feeding the cutting tool in to the same depth as for the first spot.

7) Use a micrometer to check the diameter of these two spots to determine whether or not the lathe is cutting taper. If there is any discrepancy in the micrometer readings, adjust the tailstock by setting it over, in the correct direction, an amount equal to one-half the difference between the two diameters.

8) After the machine has been set to turn straight, within the required degree of accuracy, set the point of the cutting tool for taking a roughing cut; that is, about 1/64″ above center. If this cut is quite deep, be sure to set the cutting tool away from the direction of the feed and rough out the entire job.

9) For the finishing cut, the cutting tool should be very sharp. If only one or two pieces have been roughed out, the edge of the cutting tool can be restored by rubbing an oilstone over it. If several pieces have been roughed out the tool bit should be reground. The finishing cut on a lathe should be from .015″ to .025″ deep or .030″ to .050″ on the diameter. Less stock than this will not give the cutting edge a chance to get under the surface and will not produce a uniform shape or a good finish.

10) After the cutting tool has been sharpened and reset, use the cross feed and spot it on the work; move the carriage to the right without disturbing the cross feed screw, caliper the work for size, then feed the cutting tool in a few thousandths short of one-half the amount which the work is oversize.

11) Start the machine, engage the carriage feed, and take a trial cut wide enough to permit the use of the micrometer for checking the work.

12) Stop the machine and check the work for size. After noting by what amount the work is oversize, move the carriage to the right of the work, feed the cutting tool in the necessary distance, start the machine, engage the carriage feed and finish turning the work up to the dog.

13) Disengage the carriage feed, stop the machine and without disturbing the tool setting, remove the work from the machine and move the carriage to the right. Reverse the dog, end for end on the work, protecting the finished surface with a piece of sheet brass or copper placed between the work and the screw on the dog; lubricate the dead center and place the work back in the machine.

14) Start the machine, engage the carriage feed and finish turning the work.

Filing on the lathe is done to produce a good finish or to bring the work down to size but does not replace finishing by turning; it should be resorted to if the job is within one to two thousandths of size and if specifications demand that the work be held closer to size.

When it is necessary to file on the lathe, the following practices should be observed:

Hold the file with the handle conveniently in the palm of one hand with the thumb on the top. Place the thumb of the other hand on top near the end of the file with the fingers curled over the end and gripping the file from underneath.

In the actual filing operation, only light pressure should be applied on the forward

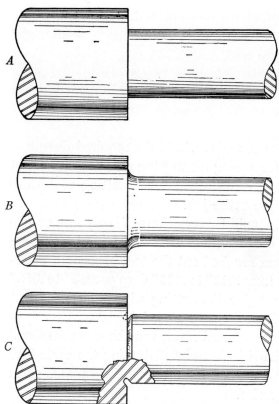

FIG. 6–10.   Three types of shoulders.

A, Square shoulder.   B, Radius shoulder.
C, Undercut shoulder.

stroke, releasing the pressure on the back stroke without lifting the file from the work and taking slow even strokes.

The file should not be held in one place on the work, instead it should be moved diagonally across the work, the stroke alternating from left to right and right to left.

When it is necessary to file close to the chuck or headstock center, do not arch the left arm over the chuck or drive plate. See Fig. 6–12. This practice frequently results in arm injuries and is unnecessary. Instead of filing right-handed, hold the file handle in the left hand and grip the end of the file with the right hand. **"Pinning"** or **"loading"** files, especially new ones, can be overcome by filling the chisel cuts of the file with chalk. The work speed for filing should not exceed twice the turning speed.

Shoulder Work. Work in which the outside diameter steps from one size to another is said to be **"shoulder"** work. These shoulders may have square corners or filleted corners and may have a radius or undercut as shown in Fig. 6–10.

The first step in turning a shoulder should be to lay off the specified distance on the tailstock side. This is generally done by using a rule of suitable size, placing it on the work for the correct length and then scribing a sharp clean line at the end. Chalk applied to the surface of the work in the approximate position will make the line stand out more readily. After the line has been scribed, the cutting tool is used to **"neck"** the work at that point to save time in repeated measurements. In case the shoulder has to be filleted, the necking operation, Fig. 6–11, consists of starting the tool 1/32″ away from the line and feeding it in just far enough to make a pronounced undercut in the work; the balance of the smaller diameters can then readily be roughed out to size.

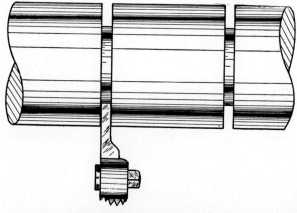

FIG. 6–11.   Necking the work.

For finishing the shoulder, grind the required radius on a finish turning tool and after placing it in the toolholder, adjust it so that both the small diameter and shoulder can be completed at one setting.

For square shoulders, scribe a line on the work as previously described, then using a tool similar to the one used for parting or cutting off, neck the work down at the line to within 1/64″ of the required diameter. Use an outside caliper for checking this diameter, then replace the necking tool with one having a slight radius on the point, and rough out the small diameter to within .005″ to .010″ of size. Oilstone the point of the tool and finish the small diameter to size. Disengage the carriage feed when the tool bit is 1/16″ to 3/32″ away from the shoulder, then complete the turning by feeding the carriage by hand up to the shoulder. At this point set the cross feed dial at zero and feed the tool bit out by hand; check the location of the shoulder and if necessary to face off more stock, feed the tool bit in to the small diameter as noted by the cross feed dial, then re-face the shoulder within the required degree of accuracy.

Fig. 6–12.   Filing on lathe.

Chuck and mandrel work. Uncentered work may be held on the lathe by one of several different kinds of chucks, by a face plate, or on a mandrel. With very few exceptions, all work must be held at some time or other by means of a chuck. These chucks are classified as being **"combination," "universal,"** or **"independent,"** depending on how the jaws can be moved. Another type of chuck known as a **"collet"** chuck is also used.

The **"combination"** chuck is so called because the three jaws may be moved one at a time or in unison. When new, they have a high degree of accuracy, but, because of the many moving parts, they do not retain their accuracy over a very long period of time.

The **"universal"** chuck, Fig. 6–14 A, derives its name from the fact that all jaws are moved at the same time. Like the combination chuck, when new it can be depended upon to center the work with a high degree of accuracy, but after much usage is satisfactory for rough work only. The jaws of this chuck are usually bolted to slides which make it possible to reverse them to grip either from the outside or inside of the work. Small lathes usually employ a chuck of this nature.

Nearly all large lathes are provided with a 4-jaw **"independent"** chuck of very solid construction. Each jaw of this chuck can be adjusted independently of the others which makes it possible to centralize the work just as closely as an indicator can gage it. The jaws can be reversed for gripping the work on the outside or inside and are provided with steps which facilitate holding work of either small or large diameter. As an aid to centralizing the work, the face of the 4-jaw chuck contains a series of concentric circles varying in diameter by 1″ increments. These circles can be seen on the chuck in Fig. 6–14 B. The chucks just described are equipped with a back plate, threaded to fit the lathe spindle nose.

The draw bar and **"collets"** shown in Fig. 6–13 are used as a rapid chucking device for small cylindrical work. The tubular draw bar passes through the back end of the spindle and threads onto the end of the collet, thus pulling the collet into the spindle adaptor and closing it on the work. The collet is kept from turning with the draw bar by means of a pin in the adaptor which fits the keyway in the collet. Bar stock, of a size equal to the largest collet than can be used, may be passed through the draw bar.

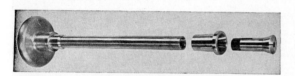

FIG. 6–13.   Draw bar and collets.

Chucking the work. To chuck up work in a 4-jaw chuck, adjust the jaws equally from center according to concentric circles on the face of the chuck and to a diameter that will take the work. Insert the work and tighten each jaw so that when the chuck is revolved by hand the work will run fairly true. Adjust the tool holder so that the tool bit can be located against the work up close to the chuck jaws, as shown in Fig. 6–15 A; then with the lathe spindle in neutral, turn the chuck by hand, observing which jaws permit the work to run away from the cutting tool. Loosen these jaws and tighten the opposite ones. Repeat this process until the work runs true within the limits of the stock to be removed.

Facing the work. Place a right-hand facing tool in the tool holder and set it at an angle of 90° or less with the face of the work but with the point of the tool on center as shown in Fig. 6–15 B. Calculate the spindle speed for the kind of material to be faced and set the machine for this RPM. Determine how much stock must be faced off, feed the cuting tool to the center of the face, and start the machine. Start the cut by moving the carriage so that the cutting tool takes off a chip and engage the cross feed so that the facing operation proceeds from the center of the work to the circumference. If considerable stock must be removed, use a coarse feed and have the point of the tool bit slightly rounded. On the finish cut, oilstone the point of the tool and use a fine feed.

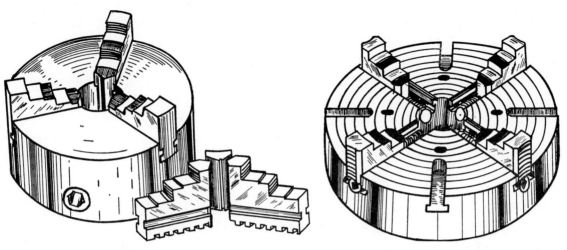

Fig. 6–14.   Chucks.

A, 3 jaw universal chuck.   B, 4 jaw independent.

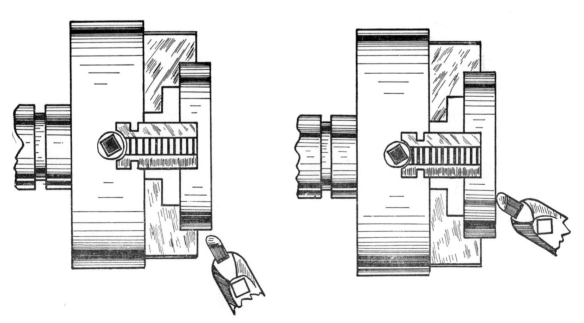

Fig. 6–15 A.   Chucking a job in a 4-jaw chuck.   Fig. 6–15 B.   Facing set up.

Originating and finishing the hole. After the job is faced, if it is necessary to drill, ream, or bore a hole in it the following equipment will be necessary: drill chuck, center drill, one or more drills and a machine reamer. If the hole is to be reamed select a drill 1/64″ less than the size specified for the hole, and a machine reamer which will enlarge the hole to the size required.

If the hole is quite large it may be necessary to use two drills to bring it up to reaming size. The first drill, known as a pilot drill, should be equal to or slightly larger than the web thickness of the final drill size. The first drill to be used can probably be held by the drill chuck located in the tailstock. If the drill has a taper shank it may be possible to sleeve it to fit the tailstock spindle. If this is not possible a drill holder designed especially for the lathe may be used.

Procedure.

1) In starting the hole use a center drill (combination drill and countersink) of suitable size and drill a spot for starting the first drill. Run the tailstock up close to the work and **"snug-up"** on the spindle binder lever to remove any play, and with the headstock spindle set for its fastest RPM, center drill the work, being careful at the start not to force the drill too hard.

2) After the work is center drilled, stop the spindle, loosen the tailstock and move it back on the ways; remove the center drill and insert the first drill in the drill chuck. Reset the spindle speed to what is judged as being best suited for the size of the drill, then move the tailstock and drill up to the work and start the machine. With the tailstock locked in place on the ways feed the drill to the work and after the drill point passes the countersunk hole keep it well lubricated with lard oil or other suitable cutting compound. If the hole is quite long, back the drill out occasionally to free the chips from the flutes.

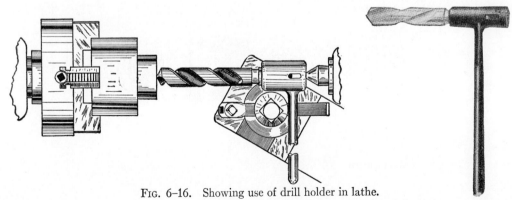

FIG. 6–16. Showing use of drill holder in lathe.

3) After the hole has been roughed out with the first drill take it and the drill chuck out of the tailstock and after cleaning the tailstock center install it in the spindle socket.

4) Clean the shank of the larger drill and the socket of the forged drill holder; place a tool holder in the tool post so that it is parallel with the spindle axis and tighten it in place. Put the point of the drill in the hole in the work and engage the tailstock center with the center hole of the drill holder. Adjust the position of the carriage so that the handle of the drill holder can rest on the tool bit holder and up against the tool post as shown in Fig. 6–16.

5) Set the spindle speed to satisfy the larger drill and with the point of the drill in the hole start the spindle, at the same time starting to feed the drill into the work by means of the tailstock hand wheel. Since the feed of the drill is dependent on the advancement of the tailstock center, be sure to keep it tight against the drill holder and keep the carriage adjusted so that it does not put a side strain on the drill.

6) As the drill breaks through the back of the work, use a slower feed and keep the holder up against the tool post to avoid having it pulled through the hole. After the drill is completely through the hole stop the spindle, then back the tailstock center away and remove the drill and holder.

It is always good practice after a hole has been drilled, if it calls for reaming, to take a cut through it with a boring tool to straighten it up, because the reamer will nearly always follow the hole as it was drilled. Therefore select a boring tool consistent with the diameter and length of the hole and take a light clean-up cut, making sure that enough stock is left for reaming; this can be determined by using an inside caliper or a telescoping gage.

Machine reamers, like drills, have either straight or tapered shanks and can be held by any one of the methods outlined under drilling in the lathe. To ream a large hole, place the reamer in the drill holder, then locate the front end of the reamer in the hole and the tailstock center in the center hole of the drill holder. The handle of the drill holder should then be located against the tool post as for drilling.

To avoid heating the reamer at the cutting edges, reduce the work speed to about half the drilling speed, then start the spindle and at the same time feed the reamer into the work using the tailstock hand wheel. During the reaming operation be sure to keep the reamer well lubricated, keep the tailstock center engaged with the drill holder center, and keep the handle of the drill holder up against the tool post. Do not feed the reamer too fast as it tends to tear the surface of the hole, and might result in work spoilage.

FIG. 6–17. Standard lathe mandrel.

Mandrel work. A mandrel is a shaft or bar, usually of circular cross section, for holding work that has previously been reamed or bored and which must have additional turning done on it. Standard mandrels, Fig. 6–17, have a taper of .003″ to .005″ to facilitate holding the work against the pressure exerted by the cutting tool. The term mandrel should not be confused with **"arbor."** A mandrel always holds the work whereas an arbor always holds the cutter.

Other types of mandrels are the **"gang"** mandrel and the **"expanding"** mandrel. The **"gang"** mandrel, Fig. 6–18, is used for holding several pieces of the same kind such as ring nuts, washers, or similar pieces of work while their outside diameters are being turned.

The "expanding" mandrel consists of a spring hardened steel sleeve, containing a series of narrow slots cut alternately from each end running nearly its length. A tapered pin somewhat longer than the sleeve is provided, which, when pressed into the sleeve, causes it to expand to fill the hole in the work. Fig. 6–19 shows this type of mandrel.

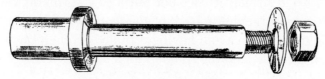

Fig. 6–18.   Gang mandrel.

The mandrel should be started in the work by inserting the small end through the machined face. If a little oil is placed on it the work will slide on much more easily

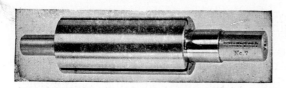

Fig. 6–19.   Expansion mandrel.

and avoid upsetting the hole. After the mandrel has been started in the hole the work should be pressed on tightly by means of a mandrel press, commonly called an **"arbor press,"** to withstand the pressure exerted by the cutting tool.

After the work and mandrel have been properly assembled, place a dog of correct size on the large end of the mandrel and install the unit between the lathe centers as outlined under "Simple turning."

To face work on a mandrel, make the cut from the circumference of the work toward the center. Be careful that the cutting tool does not cut or score the mandrel. Use a square nose tool bit in a straight tool holder and set it at as small an angle as possible with the surface to be faced, or use a facing tool of the proper hand in an offset tool holder. Set it so that if the pressure of the cut causes it to move, it will not dig into the work. Fig. 6–20 shows how this set-up is accomplished for facing the tailstock side of the work.

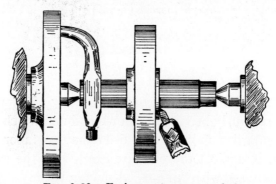

Fig. 6–20.   Facing work on a mandrel.

The outside diameter of work held on a mandrel is turned as previously outlined in simple turning.

Boring. The process of enlarging a hole by means of a single pointed tool, in a manner similar to simple turning, is known as **"boring."** The hole may be one that was previously drilled or it can be one that is cored in a casting.

Cutting tools used for boring are either of the one-piece forged type, Fig. 6–21, or bit type inserts, Fig. 6–22, that are held by a special bar. The forged type of boring tool has a heavy shank to be held by the tool post and a cutting head ground the same as a left-hand turning tool except that the front clearance must be great enough to keep the front of the tool from rubbing on the work as shown in Fig. 6–23. This front clearance is from 10° to 20° depending on the size of the hole. The general shape of the boring tool tip is shown in Fig. 6–24.

FIG. 6–21.   Forged boring tool application.

Boring is one of the few methods by which straight cylindrical holes can be machined. Drilled holes are seldom if ever straight, because of hard and soft spots or **"blow holes"**

FIG. 6–22.   Bit type insert.

in the work, and for this reason can not be depended upon to produce accurately finished work to close limits. If the hole must run true and central with the work, the quick, sure way of doing it is by boring.

Procedure.

1) To bore a hole, select a boring bar or forged tool of a size that will nicely clear the hole and be short enough to prevent springing under cutting action. If a forged boring tool is used make sure that it is sharp and has enough front clearance, and that the leading edge is ground so that it will not dig into the work under a heavy cut. Bit type insert boring tools can be ground without disturbing the boring bar set up. In any event examine the cutting edge to make sure that it is sharp and if it is necessary to grind it, don't forget to stone the cutting edge with an oilstone before engaging it with the work.

2) Set the boring bar or boring tool in the tool post so that it is parallel with the axis of rotation of the work and so that the cutting edge is on center,

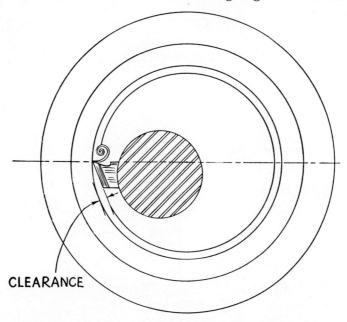

CLEARANCE

FIG. 6–23.   Boring tool engaged with work showing clearance.

3) Set the spindle speed and carriage feed levers in the same positions as for turning, then start the spindle. Move the carriage and cross-feed slide to the correct position for the boring tool and spot the cutting edge in the hole.

4) Set the dial on the cross-feed slide to zero, then engage the carriage feed and take a "clean-up" cut to straighten out the hole. After the tool has fed through the hole, disengage the carriage feed and stop the spindle; then without disturbing the cross feed setting, back the tool out of the hole.

5) To check the hole for size, fit an inside caliper or telescoping gage to it, then check over the caliper points with a micrometer caliper. The telescoping gage is not only easier to use but is also quicker and more positive. To determine how much the hole is undersize subtract the micrometer reading from the required size of the hole.

6) To bore the hole to size, divide the amount of stock to be removed by two, then feed the cutting tool out this amount as graduated on the cross-feed dial.

7) Start the spindle; then, by means of the carriage hand wheel, feed the tool to the work and engage the carriage feed. Permit the tool to enter the work about 1/16 of an

inch, then stop the spindle, disengage the carriage feed and back the tool away from the work.

8) After covering the point of the boring tool with a shop towel, or other protective covering, test the size of the hole with the caliper or with a plug gage corresponding to the finished size of the hole. If the end of the plug gage is in good condition and the cross-feed slide and dial have been handled correctly, the plug gage should be a snug fit in the front end of the hole. If it is, then start the spindle, feed the tool up to the hole and engage the carriage feed and finish boring the hole to size.

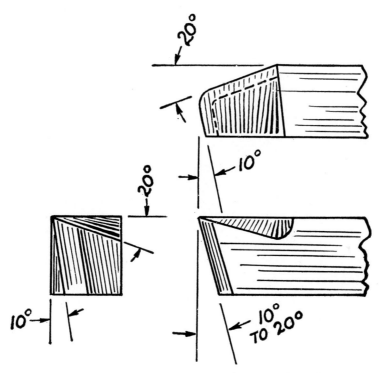

FIG. 6–24. Shape of boring tool tip commonly used.

Where several cuts have to be taken, use a fast feed and rough the hole to within .005″ to .008″ of size; then for finishing, regrind the boring tool or if it is in pretty good shape, touch it up with an oilstone. In the finishing cut, check the hole for **"bell-mouthing."** This is a condition in which the mouth of the hole is larger than other sections and is caused by the pressure of the cut forcing the tool away from the work. It is also caused by taking repeated light cuts for a short distance in an effort to obtain the right size, then throwing the feed in. Naturally when the boring tool comes to the heavier cut, it springs away from the work. When this condition does occur it can be remedied by reversing the carriage feed so that the boring tool takes a cut as it comes back out of the hole.

Counterboring is the process of boring a larger hole on the same axis as a hole previously bored and is accomplished the same as straight boring except that it is done against a shoulder. It may be compared to shoulder work in external turning.

Undercutting a hole is the operation of boring a recess or larger hole at a given distance from the beginning of a hole previously originated. It is done for the purpose of making relief at the end of a counterbored hole or for removing unnecessary stock between internal bearing points. To do undercutting, proceed the same as for boring, but before withdrawing the boring tool from the hole, first set the cross-feed dial at zero to indicate the diameter of the undercut. If the undercut is quite long, set a stop on the ways of the lathe on the headstock side of the carriage to indicate the farthest end of the undercut, then be careful, as the tool is withdrawn, not to run it into the front shoulder.

The shape of the tool used for internal undercutting is similar to the parting tool; that is, it is square nosed with the corners slightly rounded. For long undercuts it can be of regular boring tool shape with a very slight side rake.

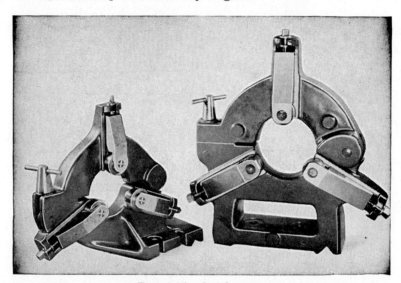

FIG. 6–25. Steady rests.

The location of the inside undercut can be checked with a narrow hook rule having sufficient capacity to measure the location of both shoulders.

Steady rest work. Fig. 6–25 shows two steady rests. This attachment is used to support long slender work in connection with the lathe centers or lathe chucks. It is especially useful when it is necessary to drill, bore, thread or do other internal operations on the end of a long piece of work.

Procedure.

1) To use the steady rest for supporting long slender work, support the work between centers, or use the lathe chuck to hold one end and the tailstock to hold the other end; then turn a section in the center of the work somewhat wider than the width of the steady rest jaws. This spot must be turned perfectly true, otherwise it will put the tailstock center under an unwarranted strain.

2) After the spot is turned, move the carriage to that end of the work on which the first operations are to be performed, and after cleaning the ways of the lathe and the

bottom of the steady rest, place the steady rest in position on the ways, as shown in Fig. 6–26, so that the jaws can be adjusted to the turned spot on the work.

3) Tighten the clamp plate bolt to hold the steady rest to the ways, then adjust the jaws to the work. Adjust the lower jaws first, setting each jaw so that it just contacts the work. Be careful in adjusting the jaws to have the binding nuts **"snugged up"** and if

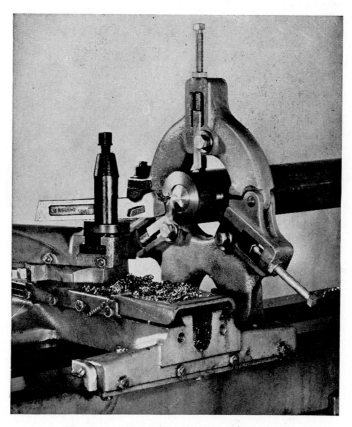

FIG. 6–26. Work supported by steady rest.

the turned spot is to finished size, put pieces of copper or brass between the jaws and the spot to protect it.

4) When the spindle is started keep the steady rest jaws well lubricated with tapping compound or other suitable material.

When it is necessary to drill, bore, thread or do other similar internal operations on the end of a long piece of work, one end can be held by the chuck and the other can be supported by the steady rest as shown in Fig. 6–27.

Occasionally on semi-finished work, it is necessary to do internal operations on one end with the other end supported on the headstock center as shown in Fig. 6–28. To do this, place the steady rest in the approximate position on the ways of the lathe with the upper section hinged back, but do not tighten the clamp plate. Put the drive plate on the spindle leaving it unscrewed about three revolutions. Attach a lathe dog of suitable size to one end of the work, then locate the dogged end of the work in the headstock center permitting the other end to lie on the steady rest. Using a heavy buckskin or canvas lace, tie the dog and work securely to the drive plate and center, then tighten the drive plate on the spindle.

To adjust the steady rest end of the work, first move the steady rest on the ways of the lathe to a position near the free end of the work and clamp it in place; next arrange

FIG. 6–27. Work held by chuck and steady rest.

FIG. 6–28. Work supported by head stock center and steady rest.

a dial indicator and its accessories so that the work can be checked for running true on the surface from the dog to the steady rest. With the indicator in place, adjust the lower jaws of the steady rest to the work so that it runs true, then close the upper half of the steady rest and adjust the top jaw to the work.

Remember the steady rest end of the work may not show any deflection of the indicator needle, yet the work axis may be out of line with the spindle axis. For this reason be certain that the indicator needle shows no variation from the dogged end of the work to the steady rest end.

Knurling. The process of scoring diamond-shaped or straight-lined patterns on the surface of the work is called **"knurling."** It is done for the purpose of providing a surface which will not readily slip when gripped by the fingers or hand, such as the

Fig. 6–29. Standard knurls.

thimble of a micrometer or the handles of plug gages. It is also done for the purpose of increasing the diameter of a shaft to make it a press fit, as is frequently done to armature shafts when rebuilding electric motors.

Fig. 6–30. Illustrations of actual size of knurling.

Fig. 6–29 shows the tools by which knurling is done on the lathe and actual size illustrations of the patterns each tool produces. These rollers, known as **"knurls,"** are held in a special self-centering head in a shank which fits the tool post. The diamond-shaped knurl is crushed on the work when one right- and one left-hand knurl is forced

Fig. 6–31. Tool holder with   Fig. 6–32. Tool holder with
one set of knurls.   three sets of knurls.

against the outside diameter, the lines of one knurl crossing the other to produce the diamond-shaped pattern. In the straight knurl, the lines are formed parallel with the axis of the work.

Fig. 6–31 shows a knurling tool holder provided with one pair of knurls that will produce either a fine, medium, or coarse knurled surface depending on the pitch of the knurls. Fig. 6–32 shows a knurling tool holder with a rotating head containing three sets of knurls and by which any of three grades of knurling may be produced.

Procedure.

1) To do a good job of knurling on the lathe, place the holder in the tool post so that the knurls bear evenly on the work, then tighten the tool post screw securely.

2) Next move the carriage and cross-feed slide so that the knurls will contact the

end of the surface to be scored; set the lathe for coarse feeding and the spindle speed a little slower than that used for turning.

3) Start the spindle and feed the knurls to the work making sure that both rolls are contacting to give the pattern desired. When this fact has been established press the rolls into the work, at the same time applying lard oil or other suitable cutting compound to the work surface.

4) When the diamond pattern is quite pronounced, release the cross-feed pressure slightly and engage the carriage feed. During the roughing cut be sure to keep the work surface well lubricated with the cutting compound.

5) When taking the finishing cut, feed the knurls to the work carefully and make sure that they are tracking in the grooves made by the roughing cut, then force them in to give the type of surface desired.

Handles of plug gages and other similar tools should not be knurled to a sharp diamond point. Such a gripping surface is uncomfortable to the hand and is an unnecessary expenditure of time and power.

Taper and angle work. Mechanically speaking the term **"taper"** may be defined as the gradual and uniform increase or decrease toward one end in the diameter or thickness of a piece of work. It is usually expressed as inches or fractional parts of an inch in a length of one foot. For example, .5 TPF means that the work has five-tenths of an inch taper per foot. It is sometimes expressed as taper per inch or in terms of an angle; however, the standard practice is to express it as TPF (taper per foot).

Nearly all machines that employ revolving spindles depend on a taper of one form or another for holding tools. The reason for this lies in the fact that this method is the quickest and surest for holding tools rigidly and accurately. When the taper shank of tools are kept clean and free from nicks, and the spindle sockets kept in the same condition there is no other method nearly so efficient for holding tools.

There are three general standard taper systems in common use today. They are: the **Morse** taper which has from .600″ to .630″ TPF, and is used as a standard in drill press sockets and taper shank drills; the **Brown & Sharpe** taper which has from .500″ to .5161″ TPF and is used as a standard for milling machine spindle sockets and the shanks of tools to fit these sockets; the **Jarno** taper which has .600″ TPF is used as a standard for headstock and tailstock spindle sockets by many lathe manufacturers.

Taper sizes are specified by a number which represents the specifications both for the socket and shank. In the Jarno taper system the number tells a complete story relative to the specifications; therefore, it is the most simple and convenient to use. The number of the taper indicates the small diameter in tenths of an inch, the large diameter in eighths of an inch and the length of the shank or depth of the socket in halves of an inch.

For example, a No. 8 Jarno taper has a small diameter of 8/10″ or .800″; the large diameter will be 8/8″ or 1.000″ and the length will be 8/2″ or 4.000″. The other taper systems are so complicated that it seems inadvisable to attempt to remember the values corresponding to each number. Therefore, when it is required to make up either a

Morse or Brown & Sharpe taper, be sure to follow the dimensions, as specified in the tables, for the number required.

Tapers can be produced in the lathe by one of the following methods: offsetting the tailstock, setting the compound rest at the taper angle, use of a wide nose forming tool, use of the taper attachment, or by means of a taper reamer.

t = taper per inch
T = taper per foot
L' = length of taper
l' = length gage must advance
L = length of work
D = large diameter
d = small diameter
TSO = tailstock offset
C = cut to be taken by boring tool.

$$t = (D - d) \div L'$$
$$T = 12(D - d) \div L'$$
$$TSO = (t \div 2)L$$
$$C = Tl' \div 24$$

FIG. 6–33.   Offsetting the tailstock.

External tapers. Turning tapers by offsetting the tailstock, Fig. 6–33, becomes necessary when a taper attachment is not available. In this method the length of the job has a definite bearing on the size of the taper; a long job will naturally have less TPF for a given tailstock offset than a short job, but the length of the tapered section of the work itself has nothing to do with the amount of offset.

To determine the amount of offset, divide the taper per inch by 2 and multiply by the length of the work in inches; that is,

$$\textbf{Offset} = (t \div 2)\, \textbf{L.}$$

The taper per inch, t, is equal to the TPF $\div$ 12.

$$t = \textbf{T P F} \div 12.$$

To offset the tailstock the correct amount, several methods are available, but the following method proves to be quite accurate and is easily accomplished. First, with the lathe centers in line install the work between them, then clamp a forged tool holder in the tool post so that it is parallel with the axis of the work and will not interfere with the tailstock. Next, set a planer gage or stack gage blocks for the amount of offset and move the tool post in, using the cross feed, until the gage fits between the post and the tailstock end of the work. Then after having loosened the tailstock and the slide move it toward the tool post by means of the adjusting screws until a piece of thousandth paper or similar thin paper will just slide between the end of the work and the tool post.

EXERCISES

Example 1.

Assume that it is necessary to turn .6 TPF on a piece of work 5″ long.

Solution.

TPI (taper per inch) = .600 ÷ 12 = .050,
the set-over = (.050 ÷ 2) 5 = .025 × 5 = .125
Answer Use a .125″ gage block, parallel, or similar gage to set the tool post relative to the end of the work.

Example 2.

Find the amount of set-over required to turn .8 TPF on a piece of stock 10″ long.

Solution.

Find TPI. TPI = TPF ÷ 12
TPI = .8 ÷ 12 = .0666
Find set-over. Offset = (t ÷ 2)L
= (.0666 ÷ 2) × 10 = .333

Answer .333

PROBLEMS

1. Determine the offset to turn .45 TPF on a piece of work 5.5″ long.
2. How much must the tailstock be set-over to turn .6 TPF on a piece of stock 14″ long?
3. Determine the amount of set-over to turn .325 TPF on a piece of stock 4.25″ long.
4. How much must the tailstock be offset to turn 1.2 TPF on a piece of work 8″ long?

With the tailstock in the correct position tighten the binding nuts securely. The actual turning of the taper is then carried out as a simple turning operation, but be sure to keep the dead center well lubricated to offset the friction due to the cross-bearing of the center in the center hole of the work.

Remember, that where the tailstock is offset in a direction toward the tool post the small end of the taper will be on the tailstock end of the work. If the tailstock is offset in a direction away from the tool post the small end of the taper will be toward the head-stock end of the work.

Taper attachment. This attachment is provided as a lathe accessory so that tapers can be turned with the lathe centers in line, and controls the movement of the cutting tool so that when the carriage feed is engaged, the tool will feed angularly with respect to the spindle and tailstock center axis.

Taper attachments, Fig. 6–34, made by different manufacturers are set by similar methods. Nearly all of them require certain bolts or nuts to be loosened to permit the cross-feed slide to move independently of the cross-feed screw, while other bolts have to be tightened to bind the cross-feed slide to the taper attachment slide block. Provisions are made in the form of hand wheels, cranks, or square ended shafts for moving the taper attachment to a definite position on the scales provided at the end of the plate.

The graduations on the scale usually express taper per foot and the angle corresponding to the taper per foot. Some lathes have a scale at each end of the attachment, one giving taper per foot, the other giving the corresponding taper angle.

FIG. 6-34. Using the taper attachment.

After the taper attachment has been set and the bolts adjusted properly, try it out by turning the carriage hand wheel and observing the action of the cross-feed slide. Due to wear of the moving parts, considerable play may develop which necessitates moving the carriage quite some distance beyond the starting point to have the cross slide engage properly with the taper attachment slide. This play also makes it impossible to use the cross feed for gaging the depth of cut; as a result, the feed screw for the compound rest slide must be used for feeding the cutting tool to the work; for this reason adjust the compound rest slide so that there will be sufficient movement of the screw to complete the taper.

The lathe compound can be used for turning tapers when they are too large to turn by offsetting the tailstock or of such a nature that the taper attachment cannot be used. This method is shown in Fig. 6–35.

To use the compound for turning a taper, if the sketch or print gives it in an angle, set the compound for one-half of the included angle. If the taper is given in terms of TPF, the angle at which the compound is to be set can be calculated by the following formula:

$$\tan A = T \div 24.$$

That is, divide T, the TPF, by 24 and look up the resulting quotient in a table of tangents.

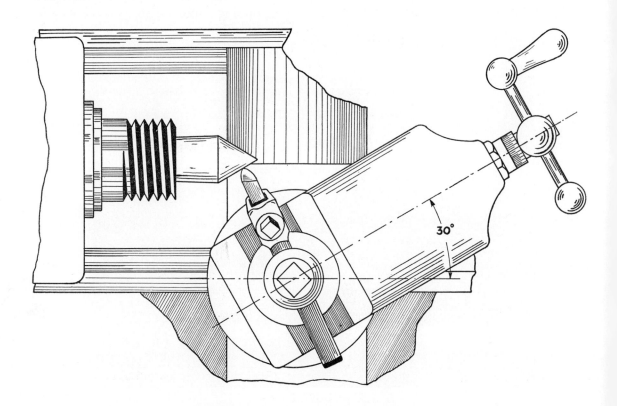

FIG. 6–35.   Using the compound for turning a taper.

Example.

    Suppose that it is necessary to turn 6″ TPF.

Solution.

        The quotient of 6 ÷ 24 is .250; therefore, the tangent of the angle is .250.

        Referring to a table of tangents .250 is approximately equal to 14°2′.

        Answer The compound should be swiveled to 14° out of parallel with the axis of the work.

After the compound has been set, adjust the tool holder in the tool post so that the cutting tool will be perpendicular to the line of travel of the compound lead screw and so the cutting edge will be on the center of the work. The cutting tool is fed to the work by means of the cross-feed screw.

To check a taper of this nature, if a gage or mating part is not available, either a bevel protractor or a sine bar should be set for the included angle and the job set up and checked with a height gage and indicator as outlined in Chapter 17 under "Gages and Inspection."

A wide-nosed cutting tool may be used for cutting tapers of short length, as shown in Fig. 6–36, when other methods are inconvenient to use. The cutting edge of the tool must be set at the desired taper or angle and may be fed to the work by means of the cross-feed slide or by moving the carriage, once the tool is in position.

Internal tapers. Sockets for holding taper shank tools are machined either by use of the taper attachment or by taper reamers.

The work can be held by any of the conventional methods excepting between centers.

When the taper attachment is used the hole is drilled the same as for boring, the drill being no larger than the small diameter of the taper. After

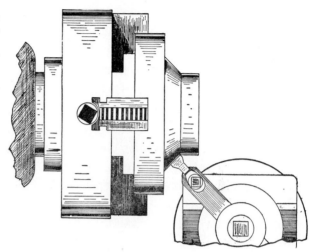

FIG. 6–36. Using a wide nosed tool for taper work.

the hole is drilled the taper attachment is set to produce the required taper, then a boring tool is mounted in the tool post as for simple boring.

Internal tapers formed by reaming are started by first drilling the hole somewhat under the size of the small diameter of the taper; a roughing taper reamer is then arranged with the leading end in the hole and with the shank supported by the tailstock

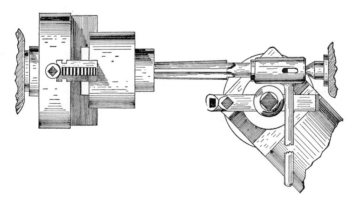

FIG. 6–37. Set up for reaming a taper.

center as illustrated in Fig. 6–37. The reamer is kept from revolving by means of the adjustable tap wrench placed on the square end of the reamer shank, or by means of a drill holder, and fixed as shown.

The reamer for finishing the taper is used in the same manner as the roughing reamer; however, care must be exercised to see that the hole is not reamed oversize.

Checking tapers. The accuracy of tapers is commonly checked by means of either a taper ring gage for external tapers, or by means of a taper plug gage for internal tapers. If the blue print calls for grind, the important thing is to see that the shape of the taper is sufficiently like the gage and has enough stock to make grinding possible. The general procedure for checking an external taper is to secure a ring or **"female"** taper gage of the proper size, and apply a very light coating of Prussian blue to its gaging surface; the gage should then be placed around the work with a slight twisting motion.

If the taper of the work is too steep, as compared to the gage, a blue ring will show at the large end of the taper; if the taper of the work is not steep enough a blue spot will indicate that the gage is bearing at the small end.

Internal tapers may be checked in a manner similar to external tapers by means of a taper plug gage, but, besides checking the shape of the taper, it is also necessary to check the plug depth. To do this, subtract the plug depth from the length of the plug gage; then, with the base of a depth micrometer resting on the end of the plug gage, check to the face of the socket for this distance.

Tapers which are not standard and for which gages are not available can be checked by means of cylindrical plug gages for external tapers, or by standard steel balls for internal tapers, but this involves trigonometric calculations which should be studied from a text book of practical shop mathematics.

Threading. One of the common methods of producing threads in the lathe is by tapping. This procedure calls for drilling a hole of suitable size so that the tap will not have excessive stock to remove in forming the thread, yet will leave sufficient stock to give a thread with the necessary holding power.

The following formula gives the size of drill that will leave enough stock so that the tap can cut approximately a 75% thread:

$$d = D - (.97 \div N)$$

where,

d is the tap drill size,
D is the major diameter of the screw or tap,
N is the number of threads per inch of the screw.

EXERCISES

Example 1.

Suppose that it is necessary to find the tap drill size for a 9/16—12 NC thread.

Solution.

$$\text{Substituting in the formula } d = D - (.97 \div N) \text{ gives}$$
$$d = .5625 - (.97 \div 12)$$
$$= .5625 - .081$$
$$= .4815 \text{ or approximately } 31/64$$

Answer 31/64

Example 2.

Find the tap drill size for a 7/16—10 NS thread.

Solution.

$$d = D - (.97 \div N)$$
$$d = .4375 - (.97 \div 10)$$
$$= .4375 - .097$$
$$= .3405 = \text{approximately } 11/32$$

Answer 11/32

Example 3.

Find the tap drill size for a 7/8—14 NS thread.

Solution.

$$d = .875 - (.97 \div 14)$$
$$= .875 - .0692$$
$$= .8058 = \text{approximately } 13/16$$

Answer 13/16

STARTING TAP

TAP HOLDER

DIE

DIE STOCK

PROBLEMS

Find the tap drill size for each of the following threads:

1. 9/16—8 NS	**5.** 3/4—16 NS
2. 1-1/4—10 NS	**6.** 15/16—8 NS
3. 7/8—12 NS	**7.** 1-1/2—6 NS
4. 1/2—14 NS	**8.** 7/16—20 NS

For tapping in the lathe, special tailstock fixtures are available which hold the tap against the rotating work, permit the tap to advance as the thread is cut, and help to reduce tap breakage to a minimum. If such a fixture is not available, the end of the tap is started in the hole, then turned with a tap wrench on the squared end of the shank of the tap so that as the tap is turned by hand it will be kept straight.

It is very important when tapping to use a good grade of tapping compound and to keep the flutes of the tap free from chips.

Dies can be used for external threading in the lathe in a manner similar to that used for tapping. The die head, using a set of chasers, can be inserted in the tailstock and used to great advantage. The ordinary stock and die can be used by getting the die started on the work; then, with the stock resting on the tool holder, start the lathe spindle at a very slow rate of speed. Before starting the die on the work, however, it should be checked for size against a male thread gage, and if it is found to vary from the required size, it should be adjusted by means of the screw provided for that purpose. After the die has been started on the work and before the lathe spindle is started, be sure to give the section to be threaded a heavy coat of threading compound or lubricant.

Besides using a tap or die, threads may be cut on the lathe by means of a single-pointed threading tool. As a general rule, screw threads with a major diameter of 1/2″ or more are cut by this method.

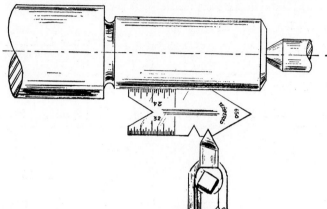

FIG. 6–38   Setting external threading tool to thread and center gage.

External threads are cut by a 60° pointed tool bit in much the same manner as straight cylindrical turning. Internal threads are cut by a 60° pointed boring tool. The cutting tool should be ground and oilstoned to fit accurately the thread template corresponding to the type of thread to be cut. After the cutting tool has been sharpened and placed in the tool holder or post, the point should be set exactly on center and the cutting edges set exactly to the thread and center gage as shown in Figs. 6–38 and 6–39.

To set the threading tool, first swivel the compound to one-half the included angle of the thread, then place the edge of the thread and center gage against the center of the work. With the tool post binding screw snugged up on the cutting tool, or tool holder, use the cross-feed screw and compound rest screw and feed the tool approximately to the gage. Adjust the cutting tool so that one side of the point fits one side of the V-slot of the gage; that is, so one side of the cutting tool at the point excludes all light,

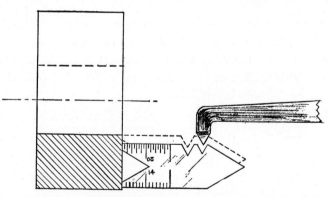

FIG. 6–39   Setting internal threading tool to thread and center gage.

then tighten the tool post binding screw. Be sure to check the setting of the tool bit again to make certain that it did not move during the tightening operation.

Setting up the lathe to cut threads. For standard tool room lathes, the first thing to do is disengage the **"feed rod"** and engage the **"lead screw"** by moving the **"feed thread lever"** provided for this purpose. Then set the **"tumbler"** lever in the slot which corresponds to the number of threads to be cut as indicated by the **"feed thread index plate"** shown in Fig. 6–40. From the feed thread index plate, determine the setting for the **"upper"** and **"lower"** compound levers. These are usually specified by letters as *AC, BD,* and so on. The first letter indicates the position of one lever, usually the lower compound, while the second letter indicates the position of the other lever, the upper compound.

Lathes equipped for cutting threads usually have a lever on the front of the apron for closing the **"split-nut"** or **"half-nuts"** on the lead screw, and most of them are equipped with a chasing dial located on the top right- or front right-hand side of the apron. The purpose of this dial is to allow the operator to unclamp the half-nut at the end of the thread, then return the carriage to the starting point and engage the half-nut on the lead screw so that the threading tool will follow the groove previously cut.

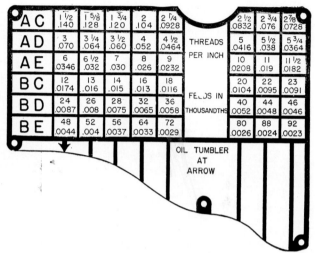

A C	1½ .140	1⅝ .128	1¾ .120	2 .104	2¼ .0928		2½ .0832	2¾ .076	2⅞ .0728
A D	3 .070	3¼ .064	3½ .060	4 .052	4½ .0464	THREADS PER INCH	5 .0416	5½ .038	5¾ .0364
A E	6 .0346	6½ .032	7 .030	8 .026	9 .0232		10 .0208	11 .019	11½ .0182
B C	12 .0174	13 .016	14 .015	16 .013	18 .0116		20 .0104	22 .0095	23 .0091
B D	24 .0087	26 .008	28 .0075	32 .0065	36 .0058	FEEDS IN THOUSANDTHS	40 .0052	44 .0048	46 .0046
B E	48 .0044	52 .004	56 .0037	64 .0033	72 .0029		80 .0026	88 .0024	92 .0023

OIL TUMBLER AT ARROW

FIG. 6–40.   Feed thread index plate.

Before the actual threading operation is started, the operator must decide, from the number of threads required, at what point on the dial to engage the half-nut. For **"chasing"** all even numbers of threads, engage the half-nut at any point on the dial. For odd numbers of threads, engage the half-nut at any quarter-turn of the dial. For half-threads, like 2-1/2 threads per inch, or 3-1/2 threads per inch, the half-nut must be engaged at opposite graduations, that is, No. 1 and No. 3, or No. 1-1/2 and 3-1/2, or No. 2 and No. 4. For quarter-threads, like 2-1/4 or 3-1/4 threads per inch, the half-nut must be engaged at the same point on the dial each time a new cut is started.

Fig. 6–41 shows the half-nut lever and thread chasing dial on the apron of a tool room lathe while Fig. 6–42 shows the same parts on a bench lathe.

Cutting the thread. Neither the automatic cross feed nor carriage feed are engaged when threading on the lathe. These levers should be left in a neutral position. It is important not to disengage the half-nut while the tool is engaged with the work, otherwise a split thread will result.

Procedure.

1) Before the first cut is started, the threading tool should be spotted on the work and the cross feed and compound feed dials set at zero.

2) The single depth should be calculated using the formula suited to the kind of thread to be cut.

3) The threading tool is fed into the work for the first cut, the spindle started and the half-nut closed at the correct graduation on the thread-chasing dial.

4) After the threading tool has progressed for the correct length of the threaded

section, it must be withdrawn from the work very quickly and the carriage reversed at the same time.

5) Return the tool to its original starting point where it is fed in from .003″ to .006″ for the next cut.

6) Before taking the second cut, use a rule or screw pitch gage and check the work to see that the machine is set for cutting the required number of threads per inch.

FIG. 6–41.   Half-nut lever and chasing dial on tool room lathe.

FIG. 6–42.   Half-nut lever and chasing dial on bench lathe.

7) The operations of withdrawing the cutting tool, reversing the carriage, feeding the cutting tool in, using the cross-feed slide, and engaging the half-nut at the correct graduation on the chasing dial is repeated until the thread is within a few thousandths of size. Then the compound is used to feed the cutting tool into the work.

This procedure, to be done correctly, requires considerable practice on the part of the operator. Therefore, before the tool is actually engaged with the work, he should get the **"feel"** of withdrawing the cutting tool and reversing the carriage at the same time and practice engaging the half-nut at the proper graduation on the thread-chasing dial.

In the case of internal threads the cutting tool is disengaged from the thread by turning the cross-feed ball crank handle in a clockwise direction; whereas, for external threading it is turned in a counterclockwise direction.

After the first cut has been taken on the section to be threaded, the surface of the work should be kept well lubricated with a suitable threading compound to preserve the cutting edge of the tool.

Checking threads. Screw threads may be checked by one of the following methods: thread micrometers, ring gage or female thread gage, plug thread gage, or by the **"three wire"** and common micrometer caliper method.

The screw thread micrometer caliper is used for checking the pitch diameter of the screw and is read the same as the common micrometer caliper. The pitch diameter of

American National threads is equal to the Major Diameter minus .6495 divided by the number of threads per inch in the screw; that is,

Pitch Diameter = Major Diameter — Single Depth.

To use the screw thread micrometer caliper: first, select one that is suited to the number of threads being cut; that is, one marked to measure either 8 to 13, 14 to 20, 22 to 30, or 32 to 40 threads per inch; second, calculate, or select from a table of threads, the correct pitch diameter of the screw; and third, with the sides of the V-anvil gripping one thread, fit the conical point of the spindle to the groove opposite the anvil. If the pitch diameter of the thread is of correct size, it will be so indicated on the micrometer.

The ring gage, or **female** thread gage, Fig. 6–66, checks the complete thread with respect to a standard mating part, and readily detects over- and under-size sections of the thread.

The plug thread gage or **"male"** thread gage, Fig. 6–45, is used for the

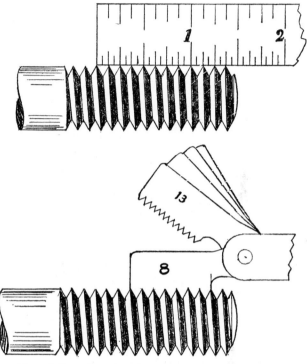

FIG. 6–43.   Checking the number of threads per inch.
A, Using the rule.   B, Using screw pitch gage.

same purpose as the ring thread gage. Both the ring and thread plug gages should be selected for the class of fit which the blue print calls for; that is, a thread specified as 9/16—12 NC-2 means that the major diameter is 9/16″; the screw should have 12

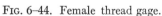

FIG. 6–44. Female thread gage.

FIG. 6–45. Male thread gage.

threads per inch, they should be of the National Coarse type and be Class 2 fit. In other words the class of fit is specified by a number. A loose fit is Class 1; free fit is Class 2; a medium fit is Class 3, and a close fit is Class 4.

Measuring the accuracy of screw threads by means of **"three wires"** and a common micrometer caliper is perhaps one of the most common methods used, especially if **the** thread dimensions must be held to close limits. In this method three wires or cylindrical rods of the same size are selected so that when placed in the thread, they will be tangent to the sides of the V-groove and project out over the top of the thread. Any three wires may be used so long as they fulfill the conditions as stated above, but for best results, the wires should be calculated to contact the thread on the pitch diameter. For all American National threads, the diameter of the wires that will contact the screw on the pitch circle can be found by dividing the constant .57735 by the number of threads per inch, that is, $W = .57735 \div N$. (See Table 10, Appendix.)

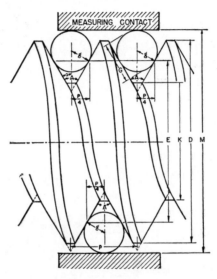

To determine the micrometer reading over the three wires, use the formula:

$$M = D + 3W - (1.5155 \div N).$$

This formula is intended for use in the American National series of threads only.

To determine the micrometer reading over the three wires for a sharp V-thread, use the following formula:

$$M = D + 3W - (1.732 \div N).$$

For the British Whitworth thread use the formula:

$$M = D + 3.1657W - (1.6008 \div N).$$

EXERCISES

Example 1.

Determine the micrometer reading if $N = 8$, $D = 1.5$, and $W = .0722$ for an American National thread.

Solution.

$$
\begin{aligned}
M &= D + 3W - (1.5155 \div N) \\
&= 1.5 + 3 \times .0722 - (1.5155 \div 8) \\
&= 1.5 + .2166 - .18943 \\
&= 1.5272
\end{aligned}
$$

Answer 1.5272

Example 2.

What should the micrometer reading be for a sharp V-thread when using the three wire method if $D = .875$, $W = .05249$ and $N = 12$?

Solution.

$$M = D + 3W - (1.732 \div N)$$
$$= .875 + 3 \times .05249 - (1.732 \div 12)$$
$$= .875 + .15747 - .14433$$
$$= .88814$$

Answer .88814

PROBLEMS

Determine the micrometer reading for checking the following threads using the given data:

1. American National	$D = 4.000$	$W = .115$	$N = 5$
2. Sharp V-thread	$D = .75$	$W = .036$	$N = 18$
3. American National	$D = 2.5$	$W = .115$	$N = 6$
4. American National	$D = 3.25$	$W = .164$	$N = 4$
5. American National	$D = .5$	$W = .028$	$N = 24$
6. Sharp V-thread	$D = 1.25$	$W = .058$	$N = 11\text{-}1/2$
7. Sharp V-thread	$D = 1.75$	$W = .052$	$N = 13$
8. Sharp V-thread	$D = 1.5$	$W = .044$	$N = 14$
9. American National	$D = 3.5$	$W = .175$	$N = 3\text{-}1/2$
10. Sharp V-thread	$D = 2.25$	$W = .096$	$N = 7$

Multiple threads. Screws having two or more separate threads, or starts, as shown in Fig. 6–46, are called **"multiple"** threads. Threads of this type can be cut by one of several methods.

The more common methods are: by setting the compound parallel with the work axis and advancing it a distance equal to the pitch of the screw; by using a drive plate having accurately spaced slots; and by indexing the spindle gear through the necessary fractional part of a revolution to start the second thread.

In using the compound to cut multiple threads, it should be turned so that its lead screw action is parallel with the axis of the work, then cut the first thread completely as for single threads except that the final sizing of the thread is done with the cross slide screw. To cut the next thread, move the compound by means of its feed screw a distance equal to the pitch of the screw to be cut.

To cut multiple threads by means of the face plate, it is necessary to have the slots accurately spaced. To cut a double thread, cut the first thread completely as for single thread cutting; then, without disturbing the cutting tool setting, and without turning the lead screw, remove the work from between the centers and engage the tail of the lathe dog in the slot opposite the one in which it was first engaged; re-engage the tailstock center and cut the next thread as though a single thread were being cut.

The last method for cutting multiple threads. **indexing the spindle,** involves something of a chance. The procedure consists of cutting the first thread as though the screw had one start, or a single thread, then determining the number of teeth in the spindle gear. If this number of teeth is divisible by two, draw a narrow chalk or pencil line across the face of this gear where it is tangent to the intermediate or stud gear; next count one-half the number of teeth in the spindle gear, starting at the chalk line, and draw another line; then disengage the stud gear and turn the spindle until the second chalk line on the spindle gear coincides with the line on the stud gear. This should cause the work to make one-half a revolution and place it in position to cut the second thread.

One manufacturer has marked the spindle gear for 2, 3 and 4 divisions and has a lever arrangement whereby the stud gears can be disengaged from the spindle gear. To cut a double thread on this lathe, after the first thread has been cut, the machine is operated to bring the figure 2 into view in a small hole in the gear guard; the lever is then turned counterclockwise to disengage the stud gear, and the spindle and work revolved by hand to bring the figure 2 into view again, after which the stud gears are again engaged with the spindle gear.

Screws requiring triple or quadruple threads are cut in a similar manner on this lathe.

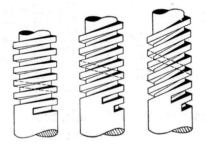

FIG. 6–46.   Sketches of multiple threads.

A, Single thread.   B, Double thread.
C, Triple thread.

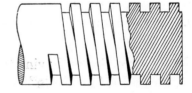

FIG. 6–47.   Square thread.

Left-hand threads. To cut left-hand threads, the cut must be started at the head-stock end of the section to be threaded and the carriage must move toward the tailstock, with a forward motion of the lathe spindle. This is accomplished by reversing the direction of rotation of the lead screw. The threading tool is set the same as for right-hand threads, and should be ground for left-hand threading, but the compound rest should be set at a 30° angle off the axis of the cross-feed screw.

To cut a square thread, Fig. 6–47, the threading tool should be ground similar to a "parting" tool; however, the side clearance of the square threading tool is quite different from that of a parting tool. The leading edge of the square threading tool must have sufficient clearance to prevent rubbing in the thread and possible breakage of the cutting tool and work spoilage. The side clearance angles should be slightly larger than the helix angle of the thread. The reason for this is obvious when the shape of a square thread is compared with the other threads or the slot formed by a parting tool.

To grind a square threading tool, the cutting edge at the front must be held to one-half the pitch of the thread and taper back slightly; that is, about 1° on each side. To determine the angles of the side clearance divide the lead of the thread by the circumference of the pitch circle. This will give the tangent of the helix angle and is expressed in the following formula:

The tangent of the helix angle = Lead ÷ (Pitch diameter × 3.1416)

The pitch diameter of the square thread is equal to the major diameter minus the pitch.

The process of cutting a square thread is the same as that for the American National thread.

When it is necessary to cut threads on a tapered surface, the threading tool should be set perpendicular to the axis of the work. This is especially true when cutting pipe threads.

When cutting an Acme thread, grind the thread tool to fit a 29° Screw Thread gage as shown in Fig. 6–48. This particular thread template can also be used for setting the threading tool to the work.

When placing the dog on the work protect the finished surface with a piece of brass, copper, or similar shim stock and tighten the set screw of lathe dog securely. Once the threading operation has started do not remove the dog until the thread is finished.

Before starting to cut the thread be sure to oil the half-nuts and lead screw. If the work must be removed from between centers during the threading operation, be sure to put the tail of the dog back in the same slot in the drive plate and do not, under any circumstances, disturb the spindle setting while the work is out of the lathe.

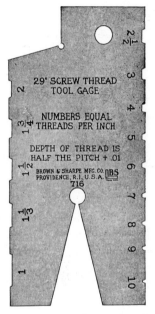

Fig. 6–48.   29° screw thread gage.

After the first cut has been taken on the screw blank, be sure to check the lathe setting for cutting the thread by checking the work with a rule or screw pitch gage.

DO'S AND DON'TS for the Lathe

DO become acquainted with the function of the important parts of a lathe.

DO keep your machine properly lubricated.

DO keep your lathe clean and orderly. A dirty machine is not conducive to good workmanship.

DO thoroughly understand and plan the job before starting to work.

DO be sure that the lathe is properly set up, then proceed deliberately and in an orderly manner.

DO keep the cutting tools sharp. Dull cutting tools require a longer time to do the work, give a poor finish and put the machine under an unwarranted strain.

DO take as heavy a cut as the machine, work, and cutting tool, will permit. A series of light cuts wastes time and makes unnecessary work for the operator.

DO take an interest in your work. Run your machine as though you were in business for yourself.

DO make a habit of oilstoning the edges of cutting tools after they have been ground. It increases the cutter life per grind.

DO learn to shoulder responsibility. It is the fundamental requisite for industrial leadership.

DO keep your mind on your work. A lapse of attention may mean a serious accident.

DON'T ever leave the chuck wrench in the chuck.

DON'T take work measurements in a haphazard manner. Details on a blue print or sketch are dimensioned for a particular purpose. Produce them within the limits specified.

DON'T waste time by working to a finer degree of accuracy than the blue print or sketch calls for.

DON'T offer excuses when you **"scrap"** a job. Accept your responsibility and try to do better the next time.

DON'T push any lever or turn any handle on a lathe unless you know what will happen as a result.

DON'T let the turnings from the work collect around the tool bit. Use a chip paddle to break them or better still grind the tool bit so that it will break up the chip.

DON'T operate the lathe with your shirt sleeves down. Keep them rolled up above the elbow.

DON'T wear loose fitting shop coats or aprons when operating any machine.

DON'T wear long ties or finger rings while operating a machine.

DON'T try to run a machine and engage in conversation at the same time. If you must talk, shut down the machine.

DON'T be afraid to wear goggles when turning work which produces flying chips. Remember you may be able to eat with false teeth and walk with a wooden leg, but you can't see with a glass eye.

DON'T attempt to check the hole when boring, without first covering the boring tool to guard against arm and hand injuries.

DON'T try to file a piece of work in the lathe by arching the left arm over the chuck.

DON'T put your hand or fingers on any revolving work or tool at any time.

DON'T go away and leave your machine running. If you must leave your machine, **"Shut it down."**

DON'T drop chucks, face or drive plates or lay work or tools on the ways of the lathe.

DON'T attempt to operate the lathe with the compound rest hanging out over the compound rest slide.

REVIEW QUESTIONS

1. What is meant by "centering" work to be turned on a lathe?
2. Describe several methods of locating the center of a piece of stock.
3. What is a center drill?
4. Discuss the procedure of center drilling a piece of stock.

5. Describe the steps necessary to true the work in a 4-jaw chuck.
6. What are the steps necessary in simple turning?
7. Discuss several factors to be considered when filing on the lathe.
8. What is meant by shoulder work?
9. What is the difference between an independent chuck and a universal chuck?
10. What is meant by "facing" the work?
11. Discuss the operation of facing a piece of stock held in a chuck.
12. Describe the procedure of drilling and reaming a hole.
13. At about what work speed should reaming be done, as compared with drilling?
14. How does a mandrel differ from an arbor?
15. What is a gang mandrel?
16. Define the term expanding mandrel.
17. Discuss the procedure of mounting work on a mandrel and facing the job to length.
18. What is meant by boring?
19. Describe the cutting tools used for boring.
20. What are some advantages of bit type boring bars as compared to forged boring tools?
21. How is a hole checked for size?
22. What is meant by bell-mouthing?
23. Define the term counterboring.
24. How is undercutting accomplished?
25. Describe a steady rest.
26. When is a steady rest used?
27. How is a steady rest set up?
28. Describe the process of setting up a job supported by headstock center and steady rest.
29. Discuss the procedure of setting up a piece of work held by chuck and steady rest.
30. What is meant by knurling?
31. Describe two types of knurling.
32. Define the term taper.
33. How is taper usually expressed?
34. Name three standard taper systems.
35. When are each of these systems used?
36. Name five methods of producing a taper in the lathe.
37. How is the accuracy of tapers commonly checked?
38. What is meant by tapping?
39. What is a tap drill?
40. How else can threads be cut on a lathe besides using a tap or die?
41. Describe the set-up of a threading tool for an external thread.
42. Describe the set-up of a threading tool for an internal thread.
43. Discuss the set-up of the lathe to "chase" threads.
44. At what point on the dial is the half-nut engaged for chasing various numbers of threads?
45. Discuss the procedure of cutting the thread.
46. Name two methods of checking the number of threads per inch.
47. What is the pitch diameter of a screw?
48. Name several methods of checking screw threads.
49. What does a thread micrometer measure?
50. Discuss several methods of cutting multiple threads.
51. What is a left-hand thread?
52. How are left-hand threads cut?
53. Discuss the thread tool for cutting a square thread.
54. How is the threading tool set for cutting threads on a tapered surface?
55. Why should the set screw on the lathe dog be tightened very securely?

Chapter 7

MILLING MACHINES

INTRODUCTION — Historical note

CLASSIFICATIONS

Types . . . Manufacturing . . . Planer . . . Knee and column . . . Special . . . Knee and column — Vertical, Plain . . . Universal horizontal

ATTACHMENTS

Vises — Plain flanged, Swivel, Universal swivel, Vertical . . . Dividing head . . . Vertical milling attachment — Heavy duty, Light duty . . . Compound vertical milling attachment . . . Rack milling attachment . . . Rotary attachment

CUTTERS

Classification — Formed, Inserted, Saw tooth . . . Plain milling cutters . . . Side milling cutters . . . Interlocking side milling cutters . . . Radius cutters . . . Concave cutters . . . Corner rounding cutters . . . Angular cutters . . . Double angle cutters . . . Tap and reaming fluting cutters

ARBORS

Standard . . . Stub . . . Stub expansion

END MILLS

Two-lipped . . . Shell end mills . . . Face milling cutter . . . Fly cutter . . . T-Slot cutter . . . Woodruff key seater

INTRODUCTION

The pages of history do not disclose who was responsible for inventing the milling machine, but many text books refer to old English and French encyclopediae which contain information relative to milling machines. The year 1772 seems to be the earliest date of a machine which removed metal from the work by means of a multiple toothed, rotary cutter.

The same encyclopediae make mention of the name Vaucanson, a French mechanic, in connection with the rotary cutter which was made shortly before the year 1782. Pictures of this cutter show it to be very similar to our modern burring wheels or rotary files.

The term **"milling,"** as applied to certain kinds of machine tools and operations, is probably based on the action of a multiple toothed wheel on the work, in the same manner as the old **"millstone"** acted on the grain in the early grist mills.

The practice of milling was not widely used, and as a result did not advance very far until the year 1818, at which time Eli Whitney developed a machine that is given credit as being the first "Plain Milling Machine." About the year 1850 milling machines were being widely used for manufacturing parts for firearms; their use proved so successful that an improved machine, known as the "Lincoln Miller," was introduced. Some ten years later, an indexing mechanism and sliding cutter head were added to the milling machine by F. W. Howe. About the year 1861 Joseph R. Brown, a member of the firm of Brown & Sharpe, invented the first universal milling machine. To these inventions were added in quick succession, variable spindle speeds, table speeds, and other valuable features. At the turn of the century, with the invention of typewriters, bicycles, and automobiles, the milling machine grew in importance to take a position alongside the lathe as being an indispensable machine.

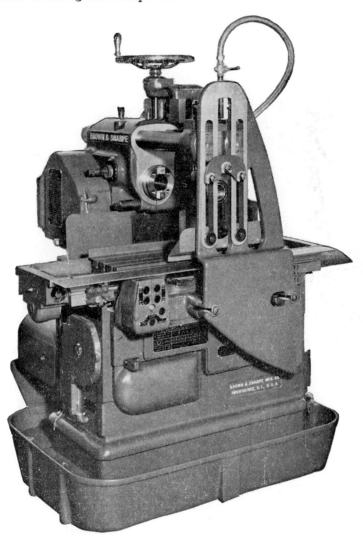

Fig. 7–1. Manufacturing type mill.

MILLING MACHINE CLASSIFICATIONS

Types. Depending on the style of construction, milling machines are generally classified as being of the **"manufacturing"** type, **"planer"** type, **"knee and column"** type, and **"special"** type.

The **"manufacturing"** type shown in Fig. 7–1 is intended for general production purposes. It is built in a variety of styles and sizes and has a fixed table height and vertically adjustable spindle head. Generally these machines are constructed so that the table has only longitudinal movement while a few have limited transverse movement.

This machine is used for large runs of work of a repetitive nature and is fully or semi-automatic in operation.

The **"planer"** type milling machine is used for heavy slab and face milling operations. This machine derives its name from the fact that the table resembles that of a planer and the vertical spindle is supported on a cross head on two upright columns. Some of the larger sizes are equipped with double vertical spindles, and double horizontal spindles.

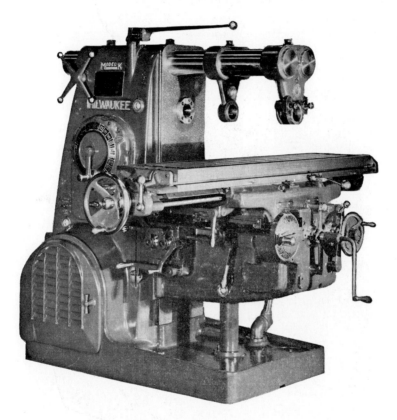

Fig. 7-2. Plain tool room milling machine.

"Special types" of milling machines include "Thread Mills," used for milling various kinds of threads, both external and internal; "Spline Mills," used for cutting single or multiple keyways, tang slots, and the like; and "Gear Millers" used for cutting various kinds of straight tooth gears.

These machines form a part of any special machine section of large tool and machine shops, but since their operation is of a specialized nature, they will not be discussed in this text. It is the intention of this section to discuss only those machines which are commonly used in tool rooms or machine shops and discuss phases of their operation which are of fundamental importance to the beginner.

Knee and column mills. The **"knee and column"** type mill gets its name from the fact that the table is supported by a **"knee-like"** casting which slides up and down on a column. This type of machine is used more frequently in tool and die rooms than any other kind of milling machine. Depending on the position of the spindle and table adjustments, the knee and column mill is classified either as "Vertical" or "Horizontal."

The vertical mill has its spindle in a vertical position with provisions for raising and lowering it. This machine has many of the advantages of other milling machines, but is especially suited to boring and for profile work.

The horizontal knee and column milling machine is used more frequently in tool and machine shops than any other. Depending on the movements of the table it is divided into two classes, "Plain" and "Universal."

The **plain** milling machine, Fig. 7–2, differs from the "Universal" milling machine, Fig. 7–3, in that the table is not capable of being adjusted through as many positions. The table can be raised or lowered (vertical feed), moved in and out from the column, (transverse feed), and can be moved crosswise of the knee (longitudinal feed).

This machine is used principally for classes of work which are easy to set up. It has a wide range of usefulness, particularly in tool rooms which do not have work requiring the use of a universal table.

The **universal horizontal** milling machine, Fig. 7–3, has all the advantages of the plain milling machine, and in addition, the table can be swiveled in a horizontal plane. This adjustment of the table makes it possible to do a much wider range of work such as milling spirals, helices, and cams.

QUESTIONS

1. What is the earliest date of record of any milling machine?
2. How is the name Vaucanson connected with the milling machine?
3. What is meant by the term milling as applied to certain machines?
4. What did Eli Whitney contribute to the development of the milling machine?
5. In what year and for what purpose was the "Lincoln Miller" developed?
6. What did F. W. Howe contribute to the development of the milling machine?
7. When and by whom was the first universal milling machine invented?
8. Into what classifications are milling machines generally divided?
9. What characteristics identify the manufacturing type of mill?
10. What type of mill is used for heavy slab and face milling operations?
11. What are the identifying characteristics of a planer type mill?
12. How can the knee and column type mill be distinguished from the planer type mill?
13. Why are some mills referred to as being horizontal while others are called vertical mills?
14. What is the difference between a plain mill and a universal mill?
15. What is meant by: Vertical feed? Transverse feed? Longitudinal feed?
16. What kinds of milling machines are commonly used in machine shops and tool rooms?
17. For what kinds of work is the universal mill especially adapted?
18. What is the function of each of the following parts of a universal mill?
    a—The column. *b*—The knee. *c*—The saddle. *d*—The table. *e*—The overarms.

FIG. 7–3.   Universal horizontal tool room mill.

A. Handwheel for longitudinal movement of table.
B. Spindle speed selector handle.
C. Spar for locking overarms.
D. Start and stop push buttons.
E. Lever for starting and stopping spindle.
F. Column. Supports knee and table.
G. Spindle.
H. Overarms for supporting the arbor.
I. Work table. Swivels in saddle.
J. Lever for longitudinal power feed of table.
K. Lever for power feed of table traverse.
L. Handwheel for table traverse.
M. Crank for vertical adjustment of knee.
N. Lever for power vertical adjustment of knee.
O. Feed selector handle.
P. Knee. Supports saddle and work table.
Q. Lever for binding knee.
R. Side control for vertical adjustment of knee.
S. Side control for table traverse.
T. High speed feed control lever.
U. Side control feed levers.

ATTACHMENTS

The range of usefulness of milling machines may be greatly increased through the many practical attachments which are available. In some cases these attachments make it possible to change the style of one machine into another, thus cutting down on the **"laying around"** period of the work.

Vises. These commonly used work holding devices are of four common types. They are: the "Plain Flanged," "Swivel Flanged," "Universal Swivel," and "Vertical" vises. These attachments are provided with broad bases having **"keys"** attached for positioning the vise in the table T-slots, and the flanges of the base have slots in the ends, or sides, to provide for bolting it to the table.

Plain flanged vise. This vise is most commonly used for plain milling operations requiring heavy cuts of a slabbing or deep slotting nature. Its rugged low construction keeps the work close to the table thus reducing work vibration to a minimum.

Swivel vise. This vise is designed to make it possible to mill an angular surface in relation to a straight surface without removing the work from the vise. These angular

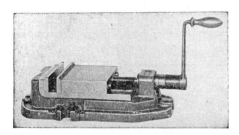

FIG. 7-4.　Plain flanged vise.

FIG. 7-5.　Swivel vise.

surfaces can be cut parallel, or perpendicular, or at some acute angle to the straight surface. The vise proper is fitted to the base and held in place by T-head bolts which operate in a circular T-slot. The flanged base is held to the table the same as the plain flanged vise.

FIG. 7-6.　Universal swivel vise.

FIG. 7-7.　Vertical vise.

Universal swivel vise. This vise, Fig. 7-6, is designed to make it possible to mill angles in relation to each other, and to do a greater number of operations without removing the work from the vise. It is extremely useful to tool and die makers because it is adaptable to the milling of compound angles. It can be set at any angle or series of angles. The flanged base is graduated in a manner similar to the swivel vise; the jack-knife section can be set at any angle from 0° to 90° in a vertical plane. The vise proper swivels on the upper section of the jack-knife which is graduated from 0° to 180°.

Vertical vise. Fig. 7-7 shows a type of vise that is valuable for milling operations which must be performed on the end of the work. It is essentially a plain vise with the jaws in a vertical position; the base is heavily flanged and is provided with keys and slots for clamping it to the work table.

Dividing head. The mechanism shown in Fig. 7–8 is an attachment used in connection with the milling machine for dividing the surface of the work into equally spaced divisions. The principal parts of it are the **case, spindle, worm-wheel, worm, crank, sector arms, and index plates.** The size of the dividing head is governed by the distance from the axis of rotation of the spindle to the base of the mechanism, with the spindle in a horizontal position.

FIG. 7–8. Dividing head and footstock.

The **footstock,** shown with the dividing head, enables work to be held between centers. The work center can be adjusted horizontally for engaging and disengaging it and the work; it can be adjusted vertically, and can be set at an angle to facilitate the handling of tapered work.

Vertical milling attachment. There are many different types of vertical milling attachments which do the same kinds of work; the two considered here are for heavy duty and light duty work. These attachments are used for adapting the horizontal milling machine to a light class of vertical milling work such as drilling, boring, T-slot cutting, and so on.

FIG. 7–9. Vertical milling attachment (Heavy duty).

FIG. 7–10. Vertical milling attachment (Light duty).

The **heavy duty vertical milling attachment,** shown in Fig. 7–9, has a standard spindle which can be set at any angle from a vertical to a horizontal position. It is connected to the milling machine by an adaptor which fits over the spindle nose, and by clamping the frame to the column.

The **light duty vertical milling attachment,** shown in Fig. 7–10, is held in place by the overarms of the milling machine and is driven by means of an adaptor which fits the milling machine spindle. The spindle of the attachment is of a small size and cannot be swiveled.

The **compound vertical milling attachment,** shown in Fig. 7–11, is capable of handling a variety of work. It is so made that its spindle can be operated either off the end or side of the milling machine spindle axis. The driving member of this mechanism is a splined arbor which fits a corresponding splined sleeve of the attachment; the other end of the arbor fits the nose of the milling machine spindle. The attachment is connected to the machine by two split collars which are a part of the main casting, and which fit the milling machine overarms. Another part of the main casting has provisions for clamping it to the milling machine column.

FIG. 7–11.   Compound vertical milling attachment.

The spindle of this attachment can be swiveled from a vertical to a horizontal plane and has a collar graduated for angular readings from 0° to 360°.

FIG. 7–12.   Rack cutting attachment.

FIG. 7–13. Heavy duty rotary attachment.

The **rack milling attachment,** shown in Fig. 7–12, is used for cutting teeth in gear racks and can be used for cutting worm threads when used in connection with the dividing head. This mechanism is connected to the milling machine by clamping it against the column. It contains a hardened steel arbor that is parallel to the longitudinal travel of the milling machine table, and upon which the cutter is mounted.

The **rotary attachment,** Fig. 7–13, is used for circular milling such work as circular T-slots, semi-circular pockets or recesses, or for work requiring circular sections. The circular base immediately below the work plate is graduated to read in degrees, or half-degrees, depending on the size of the attachment, and the worm shaft is equipped with an adjustable dial which gives readings in either two or five minutes of arc.

The attachment shown can be driven either by power or hand feed and can be used for heavy duty face cam milling when properly geared to produce the correct lead of the spiral.

QUESTIONS
Milling Machine Attachments

1. What units are considered as milling attachments?
2. Name four kinds of milling machine vises.
3. What is the difference between a swivel vise and a universal vise?
4. How are vises attached to the mill table?
5. When might a vertical vise be used on a mill?
6. For what kind of work is the universal vise particularly suited?
7. What is the purpose of a dividing head?
8. Name the principal parts of a dividing head.
9. How is the size of a dividing head determined?
10. What is the purpose of the footstock?
11. What three adjustments can be made on the footstock?
12. What is the purpose of the vertical milling attachment?
13. For what work operations is the vertical attachment suited?
14. What is meant by a compound vertical milling attachment?
15. How is the vertical milling attachment connected to the milling machine?
16. What is the purpose of the rack milling attachment?
17. Describe the construction of the rack milling attachment.
18. For what kinds of work is the rotary attachment intended?
19. Describe the graduations of the rotary attachment.
20. How is the rotary attachment used on the milling machine?

CUTTERS

Classification. Milling cutters are classified according to the shape of the teeth, as formed, inserted, or saw-tooth cutters. Included in these three classifications are thousands of different kinds of cutters, each having a particular advantage when used on the class of work for which it was designed. The following discussion of milling cutters is intended to give the student information on the sizes, kinds, and characteristics of the ones commonly used and the purposes for which they are used.

Plain milling cutters. These cutters are of two types, regular or keyway cutters, and slabbing cutters. The keyway cutter is not very wide in comparison to its diameter, and its cutting ability depends on peripheral teeth only. The sides of this cutter are ground slightly concave to reduce the friction between the sides of the slot or keyway and cutter.

This cutter is made in many diameters and widths to accommodate different classes of work. It is used for producing plane surfaces parallel to the axis of rotation and for cutting keyways.

A slabbing cutter is a plain milling cutter that has considerable width in comparison to its diameter. This type of plain milling cutter is used to produce broad, plain surfaces, and sometimes has its teeth notched to break up the chip.

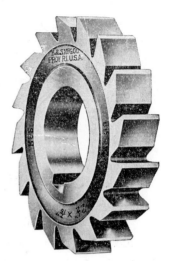

FIG. 7–14. Plain milling cutter.

Plain milling cutters over 3/4″ wide have helical teeth which have a shearing action on the work. This is a desirable feature because it reduces the strain on the cutter and machine, produces a better finish on the work, and requires less power to operate.

FIG. 7–15. Coarse helical tooth slabbing cutter.

FIG. 7–16. Fine helical tooth slabbing cutter.

Plain milling cutters made with comparatively few teeth and having a steep helix angle, are known as **"coarse"** tooth cutters, and are the kind in common use. These cutters have considerably more chip clearance and are particularly efficient on heavy slabbing cuts, because they can remove a maximum amount of material with a minimum power consumption. The common practice today is to make right-hand slabbing cutters with left-hand helical teeth and left-hand cutters with right-hand helical teeth. This arrangement tends to force the cutter into the spindle and to keep it tight on the arbor.

FIG. 7–17. Side milling cutter.

Side milling cutters. These cutters, Fig. 7–17, besides having teeth on the periphery, have cutting edges on the sides which enable the cutter to remove stock when the work is fed into the face of the cutter.

Side milling cutters are very often kept in pairs, as to size, and used for **"straddle milling."** Side milling cutters over 8″ in diameter usually have inserted teeth.

Ordinary side milling cutters do not have sufficient chip clearance between the teeth for deep slot milling; however, side milling cutters, the teeth of which are helical and staggered from side to side similar to the teeth of a wood saw, can be used for milling deep slots and are very efficient. This type of cutter, Fig. 7–18, is known as a **"staggered tooth"** side mill.

Interlocking side milling cutters are those the teeth of which interlock so that they can be placed side by side to mill slots of a standard width. Usually these cutters are of a standard width when new. After they are used for some time the side teeth become dull so that after they are sharpened, the width will be undersize. This is corrected by placing the two halves of the cutter together and checking the thickness to determine how much they are undersize. Whatever this amount is, shims totaling that value are placed between the two halves to bring the width up to size. Fig. 7–19 shows a set of interlocking cutters.

Radius cutters. These cutters have formed teeth which can be sharpened on the face without changing the form of the tooth. They can be resharpened repeatedly until the teeth become so thin that they will not stand the strain of the cutting action.

Concave cutters, Fig. 7–20, are used for milling convex radii, whereas convex cutters, Fig. 7–21, are used for cutting cancave radii.

FIG. 7–18. Staggered tooth cutter.

Corner rounding cutters, Fig. 7–22, A and B differ from concave or convex cutters in that they are used for cutting a radius on the corners or edges of the work. They can be used to cut an arc equal to one-quarter of a circle whereas concave and convex cutters can be used to cut half circles or less.

Angular cutters. These cutters differ from other cutters in that their teeth are neither perpendicular nor parallel to the axis of rotation of the cutter body. Single angle cutters, Fig. 7–23, have the teeth at either 45° or 60°, and are available with teeth on the angular face only, or on the angular face as well as on the long side, so that they will

FIG. 7–19. Interlocking side mill cutters.

FIG. 7–20. Concave cutter.

FIG. 7–21. Convex cutter.

cut both sides of the included angle at the same time. These cutters are used for cutting dovetails, for cutting teeth in ratchets, or for milling the teeth of straight fluted cutters. They may be either right- or left-hand.

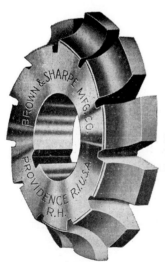

FIG. 7–22-A. Right-hand corner rounding cutter.

FIG. 7–22-B. Left-hand corner rounding cutter.

FIG. 7–23. Single angle side milling cutter.

FIG. 7–24. Double angle cutter.

Double angle cutters, Fig. 7–24, are similar to single angle cutters, except that they have two faces on the outside diameter which are neither parallel nor perpendicular to the axis of rotation of the cutter body. These cutters usually have the teeth on one side at 40°, 48°, or 52° with the vertical centerline, whereas the face angle side has teeth at an angle of from 10° to 15° with the vertical centerline. They are also made with standard included angles of 45°, 60°, and 90°. Double angle cutters are used for cutting spiral teeth in milling cutters, but when so used should have a slight radius on the point of the teeth to produce the required fillet in the gash, thus giving added strength to the teeth of the work.

Tap and reamer fluting cutters are a type of double angle cutter that have the vertex of the angle at the point of the teeth well rounded and are of the formed tooth type. They are generally marked as to size by a number which signifies the diameter and number of flutes of the reamer or tap for which it is intended, and have standard angles. These cutters can be sharpened without changing the profile of the teeth by grinding the face of the teeth radially.

Fig. 7–25. Tap and reamer fluting cutter.

ARBORS

The cutters mentioned above are held by arbors of various kinds. Arbors have a tapered shank to fit the taper of the machine spindle and are held in place by a draw-bar which fits through the back end of the spindle and screws into a threaded hole in the end of the arbor shank.

These arbors are generally of three types: the **standard arbor,** shown in Fig. 7–26; the **stub arbor,** shown in Fig. 7–27, which is the same as the standard except that it is shorter; and the **stub expansion arbor,** Fig. 7–28, which is very short and has the end slotted and tapped to take a special tapered screw for expanding the arbor body to fill the hole in the cutter.

Fig. 7–26-A. Standard milling arbor.

After selecting the arbor to suit the cutter, make sure that it is properly installed in the machine. And, after installing the cutter, see that it is properly supported by the

Fig. 7–26-B. Standard milling arbor with pilot.

arbor yoke or center. If a standard arbor is used to hold a helical cutter, be sure that the cutter is installed so that the work pressure against the cutter teeth tends to push the arbor into the machine spindle rather than away from it.

Standard arbors are made with either right- or left-hand threads at the yoke end. When using these arbors be sure that the cutter is installed so that the work pressure against the teeth has a tendency to tighten the nut on the arbor rather than loosen it.

Before placing the cutter on the arbor be sure that its hubs, and the end of the spacers, are free from

Fig. 7–27. Stub arbor.

dirt and chips. If this is not done and the nut is tightened, the dirt and chips will spring the arbor so that the cutter wear will be uneven, putting a needless strain upon the arbor, yoke bearing, and spindle bearing.

END MILLS

These cutters, Fig. 7–29, besides having teeth on the periphery, have teeth on the end, and are of two types. The **solid end mill** has the cutter body integral with a shank which fits, or can be **"sleeved"** to fit the milling machine spindle. Some of these end mills have straight or specially formed shanks to fit into an adaptor, but the kind commonly used has a tapered shank of either Brown & Sharpe or Morse Standard type.

When the teeth on the periphery are helical, those which have a right-hand cutting action have left-hand helices and those which have a left-hand cutting action have right-hand helices.

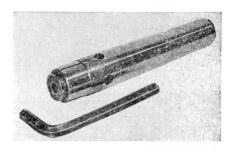

FIG. 7–28.   Stub expansion arbor.

The two-lipped end mill, Fig. 7–30, generally has two straight teeth which meet at the cutting end in much the same manner as a **"flat bottomed"** drill. Like other commonly used end mills, it has a standard taper shank, and can cut with the peripheral teeth

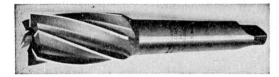

FIG. 7–29-A.   Right-hand helical end mill.

FIG. 7–29-B.   Left-hand helical end mill.

as well as with the end teeth. This end mill is used for deep pocket milling and for taking heavy cuts in solid stock. Generally the depth of cut with this tool is one-half the diameter of the cutter and it operates most satisfactorily at a high speed.

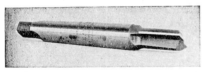

FIG. 7–30.   Two lipped end mill R.H.

Shell end mills. Generally end mills over 2″ in diameter are so made that the cutter head is detachable from a special kind of arbor. This is a distinct advantage from the standpoint of economy because it is cheaper to replace when the cutter head has worn out or the teeth have broken.

The **shell end mill** is held on a special arbor by means of a cap screw, the head of which fits into the counterbored face of the cutter, and screws into the arbor. The arbor is provided with a tongue, or key, that fits a keyway, or slot, in the back face of the cutter head and drives it. The diameter of the cutter is generally from 1-1/4″ to 6″ and the length from 1″ to 2-1/4″.

A **face milling cutter,** Fig. 7–32, is a large disk with cutting blades inserted in such a manner

FIG. 7–31-A.   Shell end mill.   FIG. 7–31-B.   Shell end mill arbor.

that the cutting action takes place on one face and the periphery of the disk. While the name of this cutter would lead one to believe that the face teeth do all the work, actually the peripheral teeth do the stock removing because they lead into and cut the excess stock. The face teeth actually remove the small amount of stock left by the spring of the work or cutter as they brush over the surface machined by the peripheral teeth.

These cutters are held in the machine by a taper shank to which the cutter is bolted, by bolting them directly to the spindle nose, or by means of a special draw-bar fixture which pulls the tapered recessed back face onto the tapered nose of the milling machine spindle. Face milling cutters are used for machining wide, flat surfaces on such work as large castings.

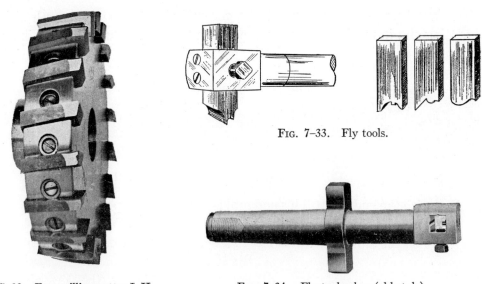

FIG. 7–33.   Fly tools.

FIG. 7–32.   Face milling cutter L.H.

FIG. 7–34.   Fly tool arbor (old style).

The **fly cutter,** shown in Fig. 7–33, is a tool bit, shaped and ground to a special form. While this tool is capable of accurately reproducing its shape in the work, it is not very efficient since it removes only one chip per revolution of the spindle, and cannot be used for very long periods of time without resharpening. It does its best work when a high speed and fine feed are used.

From an economy standpoint, the fly tool is not expensive to make; when an intricate shape must be milled, for which a form cutter is not available, or which does not warrant making up a formed milling cutter, then the fly cutter will save a great deal of time and expense. Fig. 7–34 shows an arbor for holding the fly tool cutter.

T-slot cutters are a form of short end mill used for cutting the wider part of the slots in machine tables, such as mill tables, planer tables, grinder tables, and the like. As generally made, it is a small, staggered tooth side milling cutter with a tapered shank, necked down for a distance of about one inch back of the cutter head.

In machining a T-slot, the narrow top part of the slot is machined first, either by an end mill or a plain milling cutter, then the T-slot cutter is used to cut the wider section at the bottom.

FIG. 7–35. T-slot cutter R.H.

FIG. 7–36 A. Woodruff key seat cutter, callet, and adaptor.

Woodruff key seat cutters. These cutters, Fig. 7–36, are used for cutting the seat for a crescent-shaped key. In cutting an ordinary key seat, plain milling cutters are used and the work on the work table is fed longitudinally past the cutter. When using a Woodruff cutter, the longitudinal feed is not used; after the cutter has been located with respect to the work, the work table is fed vertically into the cutter, so that the key will stick out one-half of its thickness.

FIG. 7–36 B. Woodruff key seat cutter.

The American Standards Association has adopted a numbering system for specifying the size of Woodruff cutters. Under this system, a number containing either three or four digits is used, so that the last two digits give the nominal diameter of the cutter in 8ths of an inch while the preceding digits give the thickness in 32nds of an inch.

Example.

Consider a Woodruff cutter with the size specified as 1008.

Solution.

> The last two digits give the diameter in 8ths of an inch; therefore, this cutter would be 8/8 or 1″ in diameter; the remaining digits give the thickness in 32nds of an inch; therefore, this cutter is 10/32 or 5/16″ thick.

Answer 1″ in diameter, 5/16″ thick.

This method for notating the sizes of Woodruff keyway cutters supersedes the old Whitney and SAE systems. (See Table No. 11, Appendix.)

Woodruff cutters have a straight shank and are generally held by a special adaptor which contains a set screw to lock the cutter in place.

QUESTIONS

Milling Cutters

1. How are milling cutters generally classified?
2. What is meant by a plain milling cutter?
3. How does the slabbing cutter differ from the plain keyway cutter?
4. Why do plain milling cutters over 3/4″ wide have helical teeth?
5. What kinds of cutters are considered as coarse tooth cutters?
6. What are the advantages of coarse tooth cutters?

7. Why do some right-hand cutters have left-hand helices and some left-hand cutters have right-hand helices?

8. What is meant by a side milling cutter?

9. What are straddle milling cutters?

10. Why are the teeth of some side milling cutters staggered?

11. What kind of cutters are known as interlocking cutters?

12. What is the purpose of interlocking cutters?

13. How is the correct width of interlocking cutters maintained?

14. Describe the radius cutter.

15. What is the difference between concave cutters and corner rounding cutters?

16. What can be said about the position of the teeth on angular cutters with respect to the cutter body?

17. At what standard angles are the teeth of single angle cutters?

18. For what kinds of work are single angle cutters generally used?

19. At what standard angles are the teeth of double angle cutters?

20. By sketch, show what is meant by the face angle side of double angle cutters.

21. When are double angle cutters used?

22. How does the tap or reamer fluting cutter differ from a double angle cutter?

23. How is the size of the tap or reamer fluting cutter designated?

24. How are milling cutters commonly held in the milling machine?

25. How are mill arbors generally held in the milling machine?

26. What is the difference between the stub arbor and the stub expansion arbor?

27. What regulations should be followed for installing a standard arbor in the milling machine?

28. Give three important facts relative to placing a milling cutter on the arbor.

29. How should the arbor be supported after the cutter has been properly installed?

30. How does the end mill differ from commonly used milling cutters?

31. How is the common end mill held in the milling machine?

32. What is the purpose of the two-lipped end mill?

33. What determines the depth of cut that can be taken with a two-lipped end mill?

34. Describe the shell end mill.

35. What is the advantage of the shell end mill?

36. Describe the face milling cutter.

37. What fallacy exists relative to the cutting action of this type of cutter?

38. How are face milling cutters held in the milling machine?

39. For what kinds of work operations are face milling cutters intended?

40. What are the advantages of inserted tooth cutters?

41. What is a fly cutter?

42. How is the fly cutter held in the milling machine?

43. For what types of work is the fly cutter used?

44. What is the purpose of a T-slot cutter?

45. How does the T-slot cutter differ from an end mill?

46. How much of the slot does the T-slot cutter form?

47. Describe the Woodruff key seat cutter.

48. Generally speaking, to what depth is the Woodruff cutter fed?

49. How is the size of the Woodruff cutter specified?

50. What size cutter would be specified by the number 809? By the number 1212?

Chapter 8

MILL OPERATIONS

MILLING PRACTICES

*Holding the work — Clamps, Vises, Dividing head . . . How to true up a job in a chuck
. . . Spring collets . . . Between centers . . . Angle plate . . . V-Block . . . Fixtures . . .
Speeds and feeds — Examples, Formula, Feed, Coolant . . . General Suggestions —
Set-up, Selection of cutter, Up-feed, Down-feed*

MILLING SET UP AND OPERATIONS

*Slab milling procedure . . . Gang milling . . . Straddle milling . . . Example . . . Key-
way cutting procedure*

MILLING PRACTICES

Holding the work. Clamps. Work may be held by clamping it to the table providing the milling operation will permit it. When work is held by this method, it is important that the face to be clamped to the table is free from nicks and burrs. The table
and work should be wiped clean. Paper towels or other suitable material should be
placed between the work and the table to avoid slippage. Where the work is exceptionally
large, small pieces of paper should be placed under each corner to act as **"tell tales."**
The reason for this is to test the work to see whether or not it is seated properly on the
table. In any event, the work must be well supported. Long overhanging sections should
be braced properly against the pressure of the clamps to prevent bending or springing
of that section. If this practice is not adhered to and the piece is machined, when the
clamps are loosened, the finished surface will not be accurate.

The work is held to the table by means of strap clamps of various shapes and sizes,
some of which are shown in Fig. 8–1. These clamps are supported at one end by means
of a step block or jack, and held in place by a T-head bolt. These tools are an important
part of milling machine equipment and several sizes of each should be kept on hand
along with an assortment of washers to facilitate setting up the work.

Three important facts which should be borne in mind relative to the use of strap
clamps are: (1) make sure that the clamp is kept parallel to the table; (2) keep the
bolt closer to the work than to the step block so the pressure will be on the work; and
(3) use bolts with sufficient thread on them so that the nut can be run down far enough
to permit it to tighten the clamp on the work. It might also be mentioned here that any
overhanging section of the work that has a clamp bearing on it should be supported
properly from underneath by means of a jack.

Vises. Of all the devices used for holding work on the milling machine, none is used
more frequently than the vise. This attachment can be depended upon for holding the
work accurately, piece after piece, in a good solid manner. The jaws are hardened and
ground in place and may be removed to use specially formed jaws for holding odd shaped
work.

When placing the vise on the milling machine table, it is necessary to align it properly with the centerline of the spindle. The reason for this is because the keys in

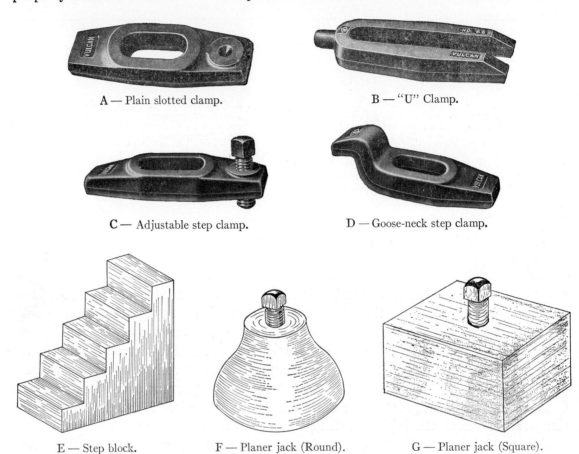

A — Plain slotted clamp.

B — "U" Clamp.

C — Adjustable step clamp.

D — Goose-neck step clamp.

E — Step block.

F — Planer jack (Round).

G — Planer jack (Square).

FIG. 8–1.   Clamping accessories.

the base of the vise and the milling machine table slots develop play or wear, with the result that even though the vise keys are located against the side of the table slot, the vise will not be lined up accurately.

To locate the vise so that the jaws are parallel to the spindle, fix a dial indicator to the arbor and with the indicator plunger bearing on the solid jaw of the vise, Fig. 8–2, move the table back and forth, using the table transverse hand feed; observe any deflection of the indicator needle and adjust the vise to give a zero-zero reading from one end of the solid jaw to the other.

To locate the vise so that the jaws are square with the spindle, Fig. 8–3, place it in that position on the mill table, and use the same pro-

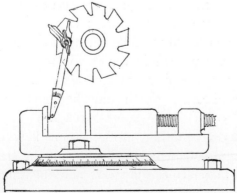

FIG. 8–2.   Aligning vise parallel with spindle axis.

cedure as for setting the vise parallel with the spindle, but move the table back and forth using the longitudinal hand feed.

Dividing head. One of the more common methods for holding work on a dividing head is with a 3- or 4-jaw chuck. The 3-jaw chuck is used where the dimensions of the operation to be performed do not have to be held very close with respect to the center of the work. The reason for this is the fact that the jaws of most 3-jaw chucks operate in unison, so that the operator has no control over the individual jaws; consequently when the scroll gear of the chuck wears, the work cannot be accurately trued.

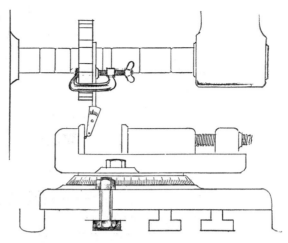

Fig. 8–3. Aligning vise square with spindle axis.

The use of the 4-jaw chuck requires more time to locate the work centrally, but since the jaws are controlled independently, the work can be made to run just as true as the indicator will gage it; this is a distinct advantage over the 3-jaw chuck.

These chucks screw onto the nose of the dividing head spindle, but be sure that the threads of both the chuck and spindle are clean before putting the chuck on.

To true up a job in a chuck on a dividing head, adjust the jaws equally, according to the con-

Fig. 8–4. Dividing head.

centric lines on the face of the chuck; insert the work, then tighten each chuck jaw the same amount on the work; attach a dial indicator, adjusting the indicator for height and reach so that the plunger can conveniently bear on the side of the work. Disengage the dividing head worm and worm wheel and while turning the chuck by hand, observe any deflection of the indicator needle. Stop turning the chuck when the indicator needle shows a maximum deflection; loosen the jaw or jaws immediately opposite the indicator an amount judged to give the necessary correction when the other jaws are tightened. Repeat this procedure of indicating the work and loosening and tightening opposite jaws until the desired accuracy is obtained.

Spring collets. Small work may be held in the dividing head by using a spring collet. To use the spring collet, an adaptor similar to that shown in Fig. 8–5 is inserted in the spindle of the dividing head. A collet of the correct size is selected and placed in the adaptor so that the key pin of the adaptor engages the keyway on the side of collet. The compression cap is then screwed loosely onto the adaptor and the work

FIG. 8–5. Collet adaptor, spring collet, and spanner wrench.

inserted properly so that the cutter, or cutters, will not foul on any part of the holding device; the compression cap is screwed down by means of a spanner wrench so that the collet will grip the work firmly.

FIG. 8–6. Work set up between centers.

Be sure that the adaptor, collet and compression cap are free from dirt and chips before assembling them and do not forget to wipe out the dividing head spindle.

Between centers. Jobs requiring milling operations which must be performed in relation to the axis of rotation are usually done between centers. The work is held by means of a center in the dividing head spindle and the footstock center.

To set the work up between centers, get a clamp or mill dog to fit the work and a work center to fit the dividing head; adjust the dividing head spindle so that it occupies a horizontal position; clean the spindle and work center; insert the work center, then adjust the dividing head and footstock to suit the approximate length of the work. Fasten a driver similar to that shown in Fig. 8–6 to the work center, and attach the clamp dog to one end of the work. Clean the work and machine centers, then locate the end of the work with the dog on it to the dividing head center, so that the tail of the dog fits in the driver; the footstock center is then adjusted to the other end of the work so that it is a running fit and the set screw of the driver is brought up against the tail of the dog to hold the work in position.

Angle plate. Occasionally it is necessary to mill a surface or slot parallel or perpendicular to another face of the work. While this operation might be done by clamping the work to the table, it may be done more conveniently by clamping it to a 90-degree angle plate. For this type of set-up, it is necessary to clamp the angle plate to the table so that it is parallel or perpendicular to the spindle.

A simple method for setting the angle plate parallel to the spindle is that of placing an arbor in the spindle and bringing the face of the angle plate up against it; after loosely clamping the plate in position, back the plate away, insert a piece of paper at each end of the face so that after the plate is fed against

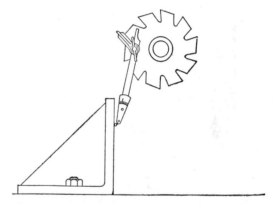

FIG. 8–7. Aligning angle plate parallel with spindle axis, using an Ideal indicator.

the arbor the pieces can be used as test strips to check the position of the angle plate as it is being tightened to the table.

The angle plate may be aligned square with the spindle, Fig. 8–8, by using a dial indicator attached to the arbor; then with the indicator plunger bearing on the face of the plate, observe any deflection of the indicator needle as the table is fed longitudinally. After the necessary corrections have been made, run the indicator across the face of the plate again to make sure that the angle plate did not move during the tightening operation.

Work is held to the angle plate by means of strap clamps or C-clamps, but be sure that they are placed so that they do not interfere with the milling operation.

V-blocks. Cylindrical work that is not centered can be held on the milling

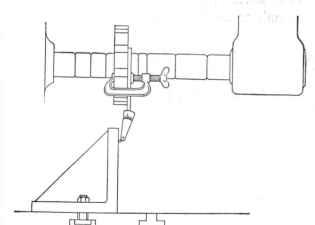

FIG. 8–8. Aligning angle plate square with spindle axis, using an Ideal indicator.

machine by means of a V-block, Fig. 8–9. **Generally, V-blocks** used on milling machines have a flanged base for convenience in **clamping them** to the mill table, and are provided with bridge clamps or other **suitable clamping** devices to hold the work securely in the block.

To align the V-block properly in relation to **the spindle,** clamp it loosely to the table; attach an indicator to the cutter arbor, **indicate** the sides of the block and adjust it to get a zero-zero reading.

FIG. 8–9. Milling a job in a V-block.

FIG. 8–10. Use of a fixture on milling machine.

Fixtures. Milling machines can be **very** conveniently used for work of a repetitive **nature** by the use of special holding **devices** or fixtures. The fixture is clamped to the table and so designed as to hold the **work firmly** while the milling operation is being performed.

In selecting a fixture, or in having one designed, there are certain features which **it** should have if it is to be efficient. First, it should give adequate support to the work to prevent vibration; second, it should hold the work securely; third, it should be so designed as to make it possible for the **operator to locate** the work accurately and quickly and to do as many operations as possible in one setting; and fourth, it should be possible for the operator to check the work without having to remove it from the fixture.

Fixtures which are properly constructed are an important asset to any shop and under modern manufacturing methods have done a great deal to simplify what would ordinarily be a long, tedious job on a shaper, planer, mill, or drill press.

QUESTIONS

Holding Work on the Mill

1. Name seven methods for holding work on the milling machine.

2. Give five important rules for clamping work to the mill table.

3. Why should long, overhanging sections of the work be properly braced when clamps bear on that section?

4. Why is it necessary to keep the strap clamp parallel to the table?

5. Why should the bolt for the strap clamp be placed closer to the work than to the step block?

6. Why is the vise commonly used for holding work on the milling machine?

7. Can the keys in the bottom of the vise be depended upon to align the vise accurately with respect to the mill spindle? Why?

8. Explain how to align the vise jaws square with the mill spindle.

9. Explain how to align the vise jaws parallel with the mill spindle.

10. Give three methods of holding work with the dividing head.

11. When may a 3-jaw chuck be used for holding work on the dividing head?

12. Why is it possible to locate work more accurately with a 4-jaw chuck on the dividing head?

13. Explain how to true up a job in a 4-jaw chuck in connection with the dividing head.

14. Explain how a spring collet may be used in connection with the dividing head for holding work.

15. Why is it necessary to have the adaptor, collet and compression cap clean before placing them in the dividing head?

16. Under what conditions might it be necessary to use the dividing head and footstock centers for holding work?

17. Explain how the work is kept from rotating when it is held between centers on the mill?

18. Under what conditions might an angle plate be used for holding work on the milling machine?

19. Explain a simple method for aligning the face of an angle plate parallel with the spindle.

20. How can the face of an angle plate be squared up with the milling machine spindle?

21. How is the work held to the angle plate?

22. When a V-block is used for holding work on the mill, how is it aligned parallel with the table travel?

23. How is the V-block secured to the mill table?

24. Under what conditions would it be advisable to use fixtures for holding work on the mill?

25. Give four features that a good milling fixture should contain?

26. Of what importance are fixtures in milling operations?

Speeds and feeds. The efficiency of a milling machine is dependent on its ability to remove a given amount of material in the shortest possible time. Therefore, to have the mill operate at peak efficiency it is necessary for the operator to select the proper cutting speeds for the cutter, and feeds for the work.

The amount of metal removed by a cutter from the job depends on the width and depth of cut, whether a coarse or fine feed is used, and the speed of the cutter.

Speed. The speed at which a milling cutter is to run depends on the kind of material used in the cutter and the kind of material to be cut. Speed is expressed in terms of feet per minute (FPM) of a point on the circumference of the cutter. Naturally, the speed at which the point on the circumference is traveling is directly dependent on the revolutions per minute (RPM) of the cutter.

The standard practice in tool, die, and machine shops is to express the diameter (D) of drills, reamers, cutters, and work, in inches. Therefore, to find the cutting speed (CS) or feet per minute (FPM) of a cutter or drill, it is necessary to multiply the RPM $\times \pi \times D$ and then divide by 12.

$$CS \text{ or } FPM = \frac{RPM \times \pi \times D}{12}$$

Consequently, the following formula can be developed to determine the RPM of a cutter, when the cutting speed (CS) of the metal to be machined is known. Note that π or 3.1416 $\div$ 12 is approximately equal to 1/4.

$$RPM = \frac{CS \times 4}{D}$$

EXERCISES

Example 1.

Suppose it is required to determine the RPM of a milling cutter, 3.5" in diameter, to cut a block of SAE 1095 (tool or carbon) steel, using a high speed steel cutter.

Solution.

The RPM can be found by multiplying the cutting speed by 4 and dividing the result by the cutter diameter in inches; applying this procedure to the above example, using the cutting speed for SAE 1095 annealed steel as 70 FPM.

$$RPM = \frac{CS \times 4}{D}$$

CS = cutting speed of the metal = 70
D = diameter of cutter in inches = 3.5

$$RPM = \frac{70 \times 4}{3.5} = \frac{280}{3.5} = 80$$

Answer The spindle speed should be set as nearly as possible for 80 revolutions per minute.

Example 2.

At what RPM should the spindle be set to machine a piece of HSS when a 2" end mill is used?

Solution.

The cutting speed for HSS is 40–50 FPM

Therefore the RPM = $\dfrac{45 \times 4}{2}$ = 45 $\times$ 2 = 90

Answer 90 RPM

Example 3.

How fast should a 4.5" milling cutter be run when machining a piece of cast iron?

Solution.

The cutting speed for cast iron is 80–100 FPM

Therefore the RPM = $\dfrac{90 \times 4}{4.5}$ = 20 $\times$ 4 = 80

Answer **80 RPM**

PROBLEMS

1. Find the RPM necessary for a 6″ side milling cutter for chromium steel.

2. At what speed should a 3″ shell end mill be run for milling machine steel?

3. At what RPM should a pair of straddle mills 5.25″ in diameter be run for milling a piece of tool steel?

4. How fast should an 8.5″ face milling cutter be run for machining a cast iron die base?

5. At what speed should a 4.75″ side milling cutter be run for milling an aluminum casting?

MATERIAL	CUTTING SPEED IN FPM
High Speed and Chromium Steel	40–50
Annealed Tool Steel	60–80
Cast Iron, Cold Rolled and Machine Steels	80–100
Brass	150–200
Bronze, Copper, Aluminum	150–300

These speeds are recommended for use with high speed steel cutters.

Feed. The selection of the proper feed in milling is probably one of the most difficult things for the operator of a milling machine to determine. The reason for this is because there are so many variable factors, that no definite rules can be set up to guide the operator. Factors which affect the selection of the feed are the diameter, proportions, number of teeth and speed of the cutter, the rigidity of the work and cutter set-up, the amount of excess stock to be removed, and the kind of finish required on the work.

In common practice, it is customary to load up the cutter with as much feed as it will stand, being consistent, of course, with the amount of stock to be removed and the condition and proportions of the cutter. Some jobs have considerable material to be removed but the work set-up will not permit a heavy feed. These same jobs may require cutters of small diameter or the spacing between the teeth may be very shallow. In either case a heavy feed and deep cut are impossible because of the lack of chip clearance. Therefore, the milling machine operator should first of all set the cutter at the correct speed for the kind of material to be machined; and secondly, load up the cutter with as much feed as it will stand, being consistent with the factors as outlined above.

When two or more cuts are required to remove the excess stock it is customary to take a series of heavy roughing cuts and for the last cut leave from 1/64″ to 1/32″ of stock. This amount of stock permits the cutter to get under the stock, thereby holding the cutter down rather than causing it to spring away from the work, resulting in a better finish than if less stock is left. When taking this finishing cut it is not advisable to throw out the feed and let the cutter run idle on the work. This practice causes an undercut in the work, due to the run out of the cutter, spring of the arbor, or spindle play which destroys the finish of the work. This mark needs to have only a fractional part of a thousandth of an inch of depth to be very plainly visible. When taking a finishing cut, increase the speed of the cutter and set the table feed to give the required surface quality.

Coolant. The use of the coolant or cutting lubricant does a great deal to preserve the edge of the cutter and helps to give a better finish to the work. When possible, a coolant should always be used in milling wrought iron or steel. The coolants commonly used are soda water or lard oil. Oil refineries make special lubricants which serve the purpose as well as lard oil or soda water.

Do not use a coolant on cast iron. This material does not offer as much resistance to the cutter as steel does, and because of its porous nature readily dissipates the heat, so that the cutter does not have much of a tendency to heat up.

General suggestions. When placing vises, dividing head, fixtures, and the like on the mill table, make sure that the contacting surfaces are clean and free from nicks and burrs.

Set the work up as rigidly as possible to permit as many operations as possible to be done with the one set-up. Keep the table adjusted as close to the machine column as the work will permit.

In selecting a cutter to do a given job make sure that it is sharp, that the spacing between the teeth is wide and deep enough to give plenty chip clearance, and select the smallest possible diameter of cutter being consistent with the work.

Before placing the cutter on the arbor be sure that the arbor spacers and cutter are clean. Place the cutter on the arbor so that the work pressure against the teeth tends to tighten the arbor nut. If the cutter has helical teeth, place the cutter so that the work pressure tends to force the arbor toward the machine spindle. Place the outboard bearing as close to the cutter as possible to give the arbor maximum rigidity.

Concerning the direction of rotation of the cutter and the feed of the work, two methods are commonly used; the **upfeed** and the **climb-**

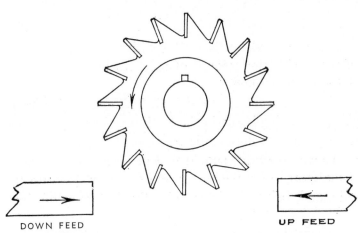

DOWN FEED   UP FEED

FIG. 8–11. Illustration of two methods of feed.

or **downfeed,** as illustrated in Fig. 8–11. These terms pertain to the action of the cutter on the work rather than to the actual feeding direction of the table.

The **upfeed** method is the method commonly used. With this method the work leads into the cutting edges of the cutter and in the case of forgings or castings enables the cutter to get under the hard scale.

The **climbfeed** method, while not used very often, possesses certain advantages over the upfeed method in that the cutter will not be crowded to one side and make a crooked cut. This is especially true when milling slots or grooves, or when cutting off stock using a slitting saw. Be careful in using the downfeed method, to have the cutter running in the correct direction and to keep the table gibs tight, otherwise the action of the cutter will pull the work in, which might spoil either the cutter, or work, or both. Be careful also that the cutter is running in the correct direction, not backwards; if the cutter is run backwards into the work the cutting edges of the teeth will be burned or broken off.

Do not use cutters that are not sharp. Dull cutters require a longer time to remove a given amount of material, give a poor finish, and put an added strain on the arbor and spindle bearings. Continued use of a cutter after it becomes dull means that added time must be spent in sharpening it and much more of the tooth stock must be removed, thereby shortening the cutter life.

QUESTIONS

Speed and Feed

1. Upon what principle does the efficiency of a milling machine depend?
2. Why are the proper speeds and feeds essential in the efficient operation of a milling machine?
3. Upon what factors does the metal removing ability of a milling cutter depend?
4. What factors govern the speed of a milling cutter?
5. What does the abbreviation FPM mean?
6. State the formula for finding the speed of a milling cutter.
7. What does the abbreviation RPM mean?
8. State the formula for calculating the RPM of a milling cutter.
9. Give the cutting speeds for commonly used metals.
10. Why cannot any definite rules be set up for calculating the feed of the work in milling?
11. What factors affect the selection of the feed in doing a definite job on the mill?
12. What common practice is followed in setting the feed for a definite job in the mill?
13. How much stock should be left for a finishing cut in milling?
14. Why is it necessary to leave a definite amount of stock for a finishing cut?
15. What is the result if the feed is disengaged and the cutter is permitted to run idle on the work?
16. What feed and speed changes should be made in the set-up when taking a finishing cut? Why?
17. Of what value is a coolant in the milling operation?
18. What coolants are commonly used?
19. Why is a coolant not used on cast iron?
20. What care should be exercised when placing vises, dividing head, and the like on the mill table?
21. What factors should be considered when setting up the work on the mill?
22. Give three rules for selecting a milling cutter to do a given job on the mill.
23. State four important factors which should be considered when installing a cutter on the arbor.
24. Show by sketch two methods of feeding the work relative to the direction of rotation of the cutter.
25. What are the advantages of the common feeding method?
26. What are the advantages of the downfeed method?
27. What care must be exercised when the downfeed method is used?
28. Give four results of use of a dull cutter.

Slab milling. This operation, Fig. 8–12, consists of milling a broad surface by means of a plain milling cutter, the length of which is greater than the diameter and is probably one of the simplest operations done on the mill.

Procedure.

1) To do this operation, first study the requirements of the job; determine from the sketch or blue print exactly what is to be done. Collect all the tools necessary to do the job. If the tools are kept in a tool crib, try to secure all the tools necessary in one trip so that too much time will not be consumed.

FIG. 8–12. A slab milling operation.

2) If the work is to be held in a vise, clean the bottom surface of the vise and the machine table top thoroughly; install the vise on the table so that the work will be located as near to the machine column as possible and set up the work so that it will be held rigidly. The cutter selected should be wide enough to cover the surface to be milled and should be of helical, coarse tooth construction. It should be installed on the arbor correctly, and should be properly supported by the outboard bearing.

3) After the work and cutter have been installed calculate the cutter speed, (RPM $= CS \times 4 \div D$), and set the machine as nearly as possible for this speed.

4) Set the table feed for what is judged to be correct for the type of cutter, kind of metal from which the work is made, the amount of stock to be removed, and the rigidity of the work set up. If the mill is equipped to use a coolant or cutting lubricant, do not forget to use it; it will save the cutter and give a better finish to the work.

Gang milling. When two or more cutters are ganged up on the arbor, or when two or more pieces of work are ganged up on the milling machine table it is known as "gang" milling. This kind of milling requires care; both in the selection of cutters, and in the work set up, and is usually restricted to work of a repetitive nature.

Fig. 8–13 shows a type of job which readily lends itself to be ganged up for milling the radius on each end. These pieces are loaded on a gang mandrel and placed in a vise as shown in Fig. 8–14. If the mandrel is permitted to extend beyond the ends of the work it can be rested on the top ends of the vise jaws to act as a locator so that the radius of each piece will be milled approximately in correct relation to the hole.

Straddle milling. This is the operation of milling two opposite sides of a piece of work at the same time. It is usually done by placing two side mills, spaced at the correct distance apart, on the mill arbor. Side mills used for straddle milling purposes should be kept in pairs and their outside diameters sharpened to the same size.

When new, these side mills generally have their hubs equal in length to the thickness of the cutter. Repeated sharpening of the side teeth, however, causes the thickness of the cutter to become less than the length of the hubs, with the result that when setting a job up for straddle milling, say a 2″ dimension, if a 2″ spacer were to be placed between the hubs, the work would be oversize by an amount equal the distance between the side cutting edges when the hubs are placed together.

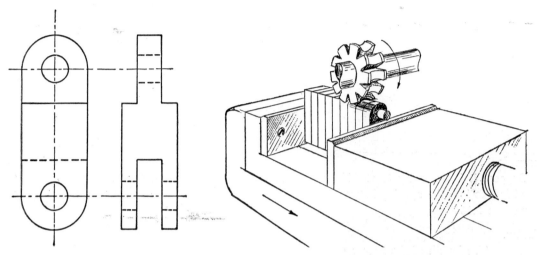

FIG. 8–13. Link.   FIG. 8–14. Links ganged up for milling.

To set the cutters the required distance apart, place them together, hub to hub, as shown in Fig. 8–15, then use a thickness gage or other suitable gage and determine the distance between the adjacent sides of the cutter. This distance subtracted from the finished size of the work will give the total length of the spacers to be placed on the arbor between the cutter hubs.

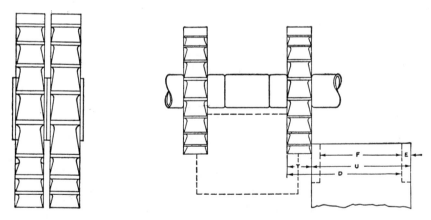

FIG. 8–15. Showing the opening between FIG. 8–16. Centralizing the work for straddle milling.
the cutting sides of straddle mills.

Fig. 8–16 illustrates a method of centralizing the work for straddle milling. After the cutters have been properly installed and the work set up on the machine, move the work table out so that the side of the work toward the machine column can be spotted by the outside face of the outer cutter; raise the table by means of the elevating screw, start the machine, and while holding a piece of paper between the cutter face and the work, feed the table in slowly until the friction between the cutter and the work pulls the paper out. Lower the table and set the dial on the traverse feed screw at zero.

Let D = the distance to move the table to centralize the work; F = the finished size of the work; U = the unfinished size of the work; E = one-half the excess stock, and T = the thickness of the outer cutter.

Then:

$$E = (U - F) \div 2$$

and

$$D = (U + T) - E$$

EXERCISES

Example 1.

Suppose it is necessary to straddle mill a 1.875″ dimension, using a cutter 1/2″ thick. When placed hub to hub the opening between the adjacent sides of the cutters is .056″. Unfinished size of the work is 2.165″.

Solution.

The length of the spacer = 1.875 — .056 = 1.819
$$E = (U - F) \div 2 = (2.165 - 1.875) \div 2 = .290 \div 2 = .145$$
$$D = (U + T) - E = (2.165 + .5) - .145 = 2.665 - .145 = 2.520$$
Answer 2.520″

Example 2.

How should a piece of work be centralized for straddle milling a 2.062″ dimension, if the unfinished size is 2-3/8″ and the distance between the inside cutting edges is .022″ when the cutters are placed hub to hub? The thickness of each cutter is 5/8″.

Solution.

$$E = (2.375 - 2.062) \div 2 = .313 \div 2 = .1565$$
$$D = (2.375 + .625) - .1565 = 3.000 - .1565 = 2.8435$$

After the outside face of the outside cutter has been spotted on the work, move the table longitudinally to clear the cutter, then feed the table in 2.8435″.

Answer 2.8435″

PROBLEMS

Calculate for each of the following the distance to move the table in:

1. U = 1.375″:	F = 1.25″:	T = .5″
2. U = 1.000″:	F = .920″:	T = .5″
3. U = 1.00″:	F = .875″:	T = .625″
4. U = .750″:	F = .625″:	T = .532″
5. U = 1.875″:	F = 1.655″:	T = .745″

Keyway cutting. Seats for standard square keys are usually cut by means of standard plain milling cutters. The work may be held between centers, in a V-block, or by a vise. In any case, the work must be lined up so that the keyway will be parallel with the centerline of the shaft and should be rigidly supported, especially if the shaft or work is quite long. After the work has been set up correctly and the cutter properly mounted, assuming that a plain milling cutter is being used and that the diameter of the shaft is not too large, position the shaft so that it can be spotted on the side by the cutter; start the machine, and while holding a piece of paper between the cutter and the shaft, feed the table slowly toward the cutter until friction between the two pulls the paper out as shown in Fig. 8–17.

To locate the cutter centrally, lower the table; then with the dial on the traverse feed screw set at zero, move the work toward the cutter a distance equal to one-half the diameter of the work plus one-half the thickness of the cutter.

If the work diameter is too large for the plain milling cutter to be spotted on the side, another method of centralizing the cutter is to locate it approximately over the center of the work; use a combination or solid square placed alternately on each side of the work and measure the distance from the cutter face to the blade of the square; then move the table so that the right and left faces of the cutter are equidistant from the right and left sides of the work.

After the cutter has been centralized over the work in the correct location, start the machine and spot the cutter on the work, using the vertical feed until the spot on the shaft is just equal to the width of the cutter. Set the dial on

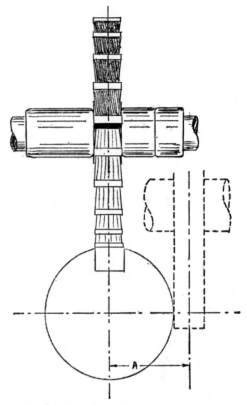

Fig. 8–17. Centralizing a cutter for slot milling.

the vertical feed shaft to zero, and feed the table up a distance equal to one-half of the width of the keyway then feed the table longitudinally to give the keyway the proper length.

For keyways closed at each end, end mills of the correct diameter are used, and are centralized by spotting the periphery of the cutter on the shaft. If a vertical milling attachment is used, lower the table to clear the cutter, then move the work sideways into the cutter a distance equal to the radius of the work plus the radius of the end mill. If the end mill is placed directly in the milling machine spindle, after its periphery has spotted on the

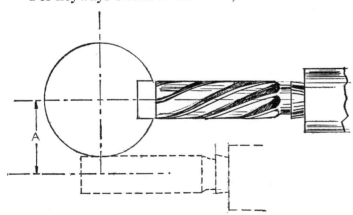

Fig. 8–18. Centralizing an end mill for slot milling.

work, back the table out, and raise it a distance equal to the radius of the end mill plus the radius of the work.

Woodruff key seat cutters are centralized in the work by spotting the end face of the cutter on the side of the work, using a piece of paper as previously outlined. The work table is then lowered to clear the cutter, and fed in a distance equal to the radius of the work plus one-half the thickness of the cutter. Next, place the work under the cutter, using the longitudinal table feed, so that the key seat will be in the correct location; start the machine, and feed the work vertically until the cutter makes a spot on the work equal to the width of the cutter. Set the vertical feed dial at zero, then feed the work up a distance equal to the correct depth of the cutter, which is found by consulting a Woodruff key and cutter chart. Generally speaking, the cutter must be fed deep enough so that the key will stick out of the shaft a distance equal to one-half of its thickness, measured on the side of the key. See Chapter XIX for table of key sizes and corresponding depths.

QUESTIONS

Milling Set-ups and Operations

1. What is meant by slab milling?
2. What factors should be considered prior to setting up the job?
3. Why should the work and cutter be located as close to the machine column as possible?
4. What is the difference between gang milling and straddle milling?
5. For what kind of work is gang milling generally used?
6. How is straddle milling accomplished?
7. How are the cutters used in straddle milling spaced for milling the desired dimension?
8. If a 1.375" dimension were to be straddle milled, would it be all right to put spacers of that size between the hubs of the cutters? Why?
9. Explain a method for centralizing the work in straddle milling.
10. How may work be held for keyway cutting?
11. Explain a method for centralizing a shaft that is to have a keyway cut in it.
12. Generally speaking, to what depth must the cutter be fed in milling a seat for a square key?
13. Is the depth of the seat for a square key measured from the top of the shaft or the side of the keyway?
14. If the depth of the key seat were measured from the top of the shaft, what would be the result?
15. How are square key seats, closed at the ends, milled?

Chapter 9

DIVIDING HEAD WORK

DIVIDING HEAD

Kinds — Milwaukee, Brown & Sharpe ... Classifications — Rapid, Plain, Angular, Graduating, Differential ... Helical and Spiral Milling ... Definitions — Helix, Spiral ... Examples of helical milling — Solutions, Procedures ... Spiral Milling — Solutions Procedures

Dividing head. The dividing head is a device used to divide the surface of the work accurately into equally spaced divisions; i.e., in work such as cutting teeth in gears, reamers, and the like. There are two types commonly used, one having a ratio of 5 to 1, the other a ratio of 40 to 1. This means that to get one complete revolution of the spindle, the hand crank or index crank must make either 5 revolutions or 40 revolutions depending on the kind of dividing head used.

FIG. 9–1. Cut-away dividing head. Ratio 5 to 1.

The Milwaukee Milling Machine Company makes a dividing head with a 5 to 1 ratio, the principal parts of which are: spindle, spindle gear, drive pinion, crank, sector arms, and index plates. Fig. 9–1 shows a cutaway view of this dividing head. The spindle gear and pinion are of the hypoid bevel gear type.

The sector arms are adjustable so that they may be set to include any portion of a circle which coincides with the index plate used. The index plates are circular steel plates having groups of holes accurately located and of a size such that the pin on the end of the plunger contained in the crank will conveniently fit. These holes are arranged in circles making it possible to index any number of divisions from 2 to 50 with the exception of 31, 37, 41, 43, and 47; in addition to these, many numbers above 50 can be indexed. Two special index plates are available which make it possible to index all numbers in sequence from 2 to 100 and nearly all numbers that are divisible by 5 up to 500.

The Brown & Sharpe Manufacturing Company and Cincinnati Milling Machine Company each make a dividing head with a ratio of 40 to 1, the principal parts of which are: the case, spindle, worm wheel, worm, crank, sector arms, and index plates. The worm wheel has 40 teeth and is driven by the worm which has one tooth or a single thread. The crank is attached to the end of the worm shaft so that when it is turned 40 times the spindle will make one revolution.

The dividing head made by Brown & Sharpe comes equipped with 4 index plates. One of these plates, known as the "Rapid Index Plate," contains 24 equally spaced holes and is attached to the nose of the dividing head spindle. The other three index plates, known as "Standard Plates," can be attached individually to the worm shaft sleeve. Each plate contains a series of holes arranged in concentric circles, which make it possible to get a wide variety of fractional parts of a turn of a crank. The numbers of holes contained in each of these circles are:

Plate No. 1—15, 16, 17, 18, 19, 20.
Plate No. 2—21, 23, 27, 29, 31, 33.
Plate No. 3—37, 39, 41, 43, 47, 49.

The dividing head made by the Cincinnati Milling Machine Company is equipped with one standard plate having a different series of holes on each side. The number of holes in each circle is as follows:

First side—24, 25, 28, 30, 34, 37, 38, 39, 41, 42, 43.

Second side—46, 47, 49, 51, 53, 54, 57, 58, 59, 62, 66. This plate may be replaced by one of three special plates drilled on both sides, each side having 11 circles and containing the numbers of holes shown in the table Fig. 9–2.

SIDE	A	B	C	D	E	F
	30	36	34	32	26	28
	48	67	46	44	42	38
	69	81	79	77	73	71
HOLES	91	97	93	89	87	83
IN	99	111	109	107	103	101
EACH	117	127	123	121	119	113
CIRCLE	129	141	139	137	133	131
	147	157	153	151	149	143
	171	169	167	163	161	159
	177	183	181	179	175	173
	189	199	197	193	191	187

FIG. 9–2.   Table of special index plates.

On the "Wide Range Divider" made by the Cincinnati Company, divisions from 2 to 400,000 may be indexed directly. This device consists of dual sector arms, cranks and index plates. The small crank operates the spindle by means of a gear reduction having a ratio of 400 to 1, while the large crank operates the spindle in a 40 to 1 ratio.

Classifications of indexing. The different kinds of indexing for which the dividing head can be used are classified as **rapid, plain, differential, angular and graduating.**

Rapid indexing. Rapid indexing is accomplished by means of the rapid index plate located on the nose of the spindle. On the Brown & Sharpe dividing head, this plate contains 24 equally spaced holes that make it possible to index directly any number of divisions which is a factor of 24. These numbers of divisions are 2, 3, 4, 6, 8, 12, and 24.

On the Cincinnati dividing head this plate has 3 circles having 24, 30, and 36 holes. These plates make possible the following numbers of divisions by rapid indexing:

24-hole circle — 2, 3, 4, 6, 8, 12, 24;

30-hole circle — 2, 3, 5, 6, 10, 15, 30;

36-hole circle — 2, 3, 4, 6, 9, 12, 18, 36.

To do rapid indexing, it is necessary to disengage the worm from the worm wheel. This is accomplished by turning a small knurled hand wheel on the side opposite the crank, through one-half a revolution operating the eccentric in which the worm shaft is mounted. The spindle and rapid index plate may then be turned directly by hand.

EXERCISES

Example 1.

Suppose that it is necessary to index 8 divisions.

Solution.

First disengage the worm from the worm wheel; then, on the Brown & Sharpe dividing head, locate the figure 8 stamped on the edge of the plate opposite one of the holes; insert the plunger D into this hole and after taking the first cut and backing the work away from the cutter, back the plunger out of the index plate, turn the spindle by hand and bring the next hole marked 8 around and engage the pin with it. Continue this process until a complete revolution has been made by the spindle.

In case the edge of the index plate is not numbered, the indexing may be carried out by using the formula $\dfrac{24}{N}$, where N is the number of holes per division.

$$\frac{24}{N} = \frac{24}{8} = 3$$

Answer Engage the pin in any hole, then for each division turn the spindle through three holes, not counting the first one.

Example 2.

Using a Brown & Sharpe dividing head, what indexing is necessary to cut on a shaft 6 equally spaced splines?

Solution.

Using rapid indexing the formula is $\dfrac{24}{N}$.

Therefore $\dfrac{24}{N} = \dfrac{24}{6} = 4.$

Answer 4 holes in the rapid index plate.

Example 3.

Using a Cincinnati dividing head, calculate the indexing for 10 equally spaced divisions by rapid indexing.

Solution.

Since the 30-hole circle is the only one in the rapid index plate that will contain 10 an even number of times, the formula is $\dfrac{30}{N}$.

Therefore $\dfrac{30}{N} = \dfrac{30}{10} = 3.$

Answer 3 holes in the 30-hole circle.

PROBLEMS

Using the Brown & Sharpe dividing head, calculate the rapid indexing for each of the following:

1. 2 divisions		**4.** 8 divisions	
2. 3 divisions		**5.** 12 divisions	
3. 4 divisions		**6.** 24 divisions	

Using the Cincinnati dividing head, calculate the rapid indexing for each of the following:

1. 8 divisions		**3.** 9 divisions	
2. 5 divisions		**4.** 30 divisions	

Plain indexing. Plain indexing is performed with the aid of one of the three index plates furnished with the dividing head, while the worm is engaged with the worm wheel. This kind of indexing is used for precision work. The formula is $\dfrac{40}{N}$ where N is the number of divisions required. If N is a number that can be divided into 40 an even number of times, the answer will be the complete revolutions of the crank. For example suppose that it is required to index 10 divisions, then $\dfrac{40}{N} = \dfrac{40}{10} = 4$ revolutions of the crank.

If N is a number such that it is contained into 40 a whole number of times and a fractional part of a time, the whole number will be the complete revolutions of the crank, and the fractional part of a time will be the fractional part of a revolution. For example, suppose it is necessary to index for 36 divisions, then

$$\frac{40}{N} = \frac{40}{36} = 1\frac{4}{36} = 1\frac{1}{9} \text{ Revolution}$$

To make the 1/9 of a revolution it is necessary to set the index crank in a circle having a number of holes which is a multiple of 9. In this instance either the 18- or

27-hole circle can be used, but the 18-hole circle is in plate No. 1, while the 27-hole circle is in plate No. 2. If plate No. 1 is on the dividing head, adjust the crank pin to fit into the 18-hole circle; to get the sector arm setting, change 1/9 to 18ths; that is $1/9 \times 2/2 = 2/18$, or set the sector arms for 2 holes in the 18-hole circle. If plate No. 2 is on the dividing head set the crank for the 27-hole circle, than change 1/9 to 27ths; that is $1/9 \times 3/3 = 3/27$, or set the sector arms for 3 holes in the 27-hole circle. Therefore, for each division, turn the crank one revolution and either 2 holes in the 18-hole circle, or 3 holes in the 27-hole circle.

If N is a number larger than 40, write it under 40 and reduce the resulting fraction to its lowest terms. Select an index plate such that one of its circles will contain the denominator of the fraction an even number of times, then change the fraction to this denomination.

EXERCISES

Example 1.

Required to index 70 divisions.

Solution.

$$\frac{40}{N} = \frac{40}{70} = \frac{4}{7} \text{ of a revolution of the crank for each division.}$$

Plates No. 2 and No. 3 each contain circles of holes capable of handling $\frac{4}{7}$ of a revolution. Plate No. 2 contains the 21-hole circle, so changing $\frac{4}{7}$ to 21sts $= \frac{4}{7} \times \frac{3}{3} = \frac{12}{21}$.

Therefore, set the sector arms for 12 holes in the 21-hole circle.

Plate No. 3 contains the 49-hole circle, so changing $\frac{4}{7}$ to 49ths $= \frac{4}{7} \times \frac{7}{7} = \frac{28}{49}$.

Answer Set the sector arms for 28 holes in the 49-hole circle.

Example 2.

Using a Brown & Sharpe dividing head, calculate the indexing necessary to cut 32 teeth in a spur gear.

Solution.

32 divisions can be cut by plain indexing.

Therefore $\dfrac{40}{N} = \dfrac{40}{32} = 1\dfrac{8}{32}$ or $1\dfrac{1}{4}$.

$\frac{1}{4}$ of a revolution can be made by using plate No. **1.**

In this plate either the **16-** or 20-hole circle is a multiple of 4, so change $\frac{1}{4}$ to 16ths; $\frac{1}{4} = \frac{4}{16}$; that is, 4 holes in the 16-hole circle. Set the index crank for the 16-hole circle and set the sector arms for 4 holes (not counting the first hole) in the 16-hole circle.

The *complete answer* is 1 revolution and 4 holes in the 16-hole circle.

Using the 20-hole circle, change $\frac{1}{4}$ to 20ths; $\frac{1}{4} = \frac{5}{20}$; that is, 5 holes in the 20-hole circle. The complete answer is 1 revolution and 5 holes in the 20-hole circle.

Example 3.

What indexing is necessary to cut 52 teeth in a gear on a Cincinnati dividing head?

Solution.

$$\frac{40}{52} = \frac{10}{13}$$

On the first side of the standard index plate, a circle contains 39 holes; this is a multiple of **13.** Change $\frac{10}{13}$ to 39ths; $\frac{10}{13} = \frac{30}{39}$ or 30 holes in the 39-hole circle.

Answer For each division turn the crank through 30 holes in the 39-hole circle.

PROBLEMS

Using the Cincinnati dividing head and the standard index plate calculate the indexing for each of the following:

1. 41 divisions   3. 88 divisions
2. 18 divisions   4. 31 divisions

What indexing would be necessary to cut the following, using a Brown & Sharpe dividing head?

5. 17 divisions   8. 120 divisions
6. 28 divisions   9. 33 divisions
7. 60 divisions   10. 45 divisions

Differential indexing. Any number of divisions up to approximately 2000, which, when written under 40 cannot be reduced to a factor of one of the numbers of holes contained in the index plate, may be done by differential indexing.

This type of indexing is accomplished through the use of a geared differential connecting the index plate with the spindle, having the worm engaged with the worm wheel. The formula for this type of indexing is

$$(n - N)\, 40/n$$

where N is the required number of divisions to be indexed;

n is a selected number within the range of plain indexing and approximately equal to N;

$40/n$ reduced to its lowest terms is the ratio of the number of holes to expand the sector arms to the number of holes in the index plate circle. The product of $(n - N)$ and $40/n$ is the gear ratio. The standard gears furnished with the B&S dividing head are: two 24's, and one each of 28, 32, 40, 44, 48, 56, 64, 72, 86, and 100. Special gears are: one each of 46, 47, 52, 58, 68, 70, 76, and 84.

Example.

To illustrate the use of this formula, suppose that it is necessary to index 96 divisions.

Solution.

First test the number to determine whether plain or differential indexing will be required. This is done by writing 96 under 40 and reducing the fraction to its lowest terms, to determine whether or not the denominator is a factor of one of the numbers of holes in one of the index plates.

Since $\frac{40}{96}$ reduces to $\frac{5}{12}$ and since 12 is not a factor of any of the sets of holes it is obviously a differential indexing problem.

Therefore selecting 98 as the value for n the formula reads, $(98 - 96)\, \dfrac{40}{98}$

Reducing $\frac{40}{98}$ to its lowest terms gives $\frac{20}{49}$ or 20 holes in the 49-hole circle; the gear ratio is equal to

$$(98 - 96) \times \tfrac{40}{98} \quad \text{or} \quad 2 \times \tfrac{40}{98} \quad \text{or} \quad 2 \times \tfrac{20}{49} = \tfrac{40}{49}$$

This gear ratio can be arranged into compound gears to suit the standard gears furnished with the Brown & Sharpe dividing head as follows:

$$\tfrac{40}{49} = \tfrac{5}{7} \times \tfrac{8}{7} \qquad \tfrac{5}{7} \times \tfrac{8}{8} = \tfrac{40}{56} \qquad \tfrac{8}{7} \times \tfrac{4}{4} = \tfrac{32}{28}.$$

Therefore, the gear compound is $\frac{40}{56} \times \frac{32}{28}$. Observe that when a number in the denominator position is raised to suit a standard gear, a number in the numerator position **must** be multiplied by this same value to maintain the proper ratio.

The gear compound is arranged on the dividing head as follows:

$A = 40 =$ gear on spindle $B = 32 =$ first gear on stud
$C = 56 =$ second gear on stud $D = 28 =$ gear on worm

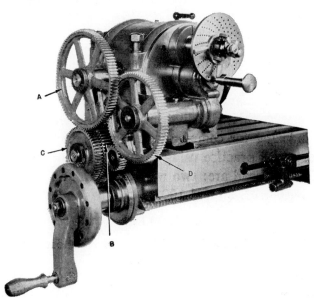

FIG. 9–3.　Compound gears arranged on dividing head.

To have the gear differential make up the difference between the required number of divisions N, and the selected number of divisions n, it is necessary to have the index plate rotate in the correct direction relative to the crank.

If $(n - N)$ is *positive* the index plate must rotate in the same direction as the crank is turned. If $(n - N)$ is *negative* the index plate must rotate in a direction opposite to that of the crank.

When the gearing is simple and $(n - N)$ positive, use one idler gear.

When the gearing is simple and $(n - N)$ negative, use two idler gears.

When the gearing is compound and $(n - N)$ positive, use no idler gears.

When the gearing is compound and $(n - N)$ negative, use two idler gears.

Therefore, the compound gears of the preceding illustration require the use of no idler gears, so that the index plate will rotate in the same direction as the crank, thus making up the difference between the required number of divisions, 96, and the selected number of divisions, 98.

Example.

Calculate the indexing for cutting 323 divisions.

Solution.

Formula is $(n - N) \dfrac{40}{n}$. Let $n = 320$.

Substituting the correct values, we obtain: $(320 - 323)\frac{40}{320}$. $\frac{40}{320} = \frac{1}{8}$; raise $\frac{1}{8}$ to terms of indexing; thus, $\frac{1}{8} \times \frac{2}{2} = \frac{2}{16}$ or 2 holes in the 16-hole circle. Continue as follows to find the gear ratio; $(320 - 323)\frac{1}{8} = 3 \times \frac{1}{8} = \frac{3}{8}$.

Raising $\frac{3}{8}$ to standard gears, $\frac{3}{8} \times \frac{8}{8} = \frac{24}{64}$.

Place the 24-tooth gear on the spindle and the 64-tooth gear on the worm shaft. Since the gearing is simple and $(n - N)$ is negative, two idler gears are necessary so that the index plate will travel in the proper direction relative to the crank. The complete answer is:

$$\frac{2 \text{ holes}}{16 \text{ hole circle}} \qquad \text{Gears} = \frac{A}{D} = \frac{24}{64} \text{ with 2 idler gears.}$$

It is absolutely necessary when doing differential indexing to have the index plate locking pin disengaged from the plate, otherwise it will be sheared off.

Most milling machine manufacturers can, and do, furnish indexing charts that are intended for use with their dividing heads. These charts eliminate the necessity of calculating the indexing for commonly used numbers of divisions. If possible get copies of these charts and practice using them. The standard gears furnished with a Brown & Sharpe dividing head are: two with 24 teeth and one each of the following: 28, 32, 40, 44, 48, 56, 64, 72, 86 and 100.

PROBLEMS

Using the Brown & Sharpe dividing head with the above standard gears and the differential indexing formula, calculate the indexing for the following:

1. 177 divisions	**6.** 818 divisions
2. 83 divisions	**7.** 914 divisions
3. 77 divisions	**8.** 1300 divisions
4. 61 divisions	**9.** 1623 divisions
5. 263 divisions	**10.** 1124 divisions

Angular indexing. This kind of indexing is done about the same as plain indexing, the exception being that the work must be indexed through an angle rather than a certain number of divisions.

One revolution of the index crank equals 1/40th of a revolution of the spindle. $1/40 \times 360° = 9$ degrees, or 540 minutes, or 32,400 seconds of arc on the 40 to 1 ratio dividing head.

Since one revolution of the crank causes the spindle to rotate through 9°, then to rotate the spindle through any other number of degrees would require as many turns of the crank as the number 9 is contained in the required angle. For example, suppose it is required to index an angle of 27°. The number of revolutions of the crank required to index this angle is $27 \div 9$ or 3. In other words, to determine the number of revolutions of the crank necessary to index a given angle, divide the given angle in degrees by 9; or the given angle, changed to minutes, by 540; or the given angle changed to seconds, by 32,400.

The following examples are intended to acquaint the student with the more simple forms of angular indexing. More complicated types can be handled by means of a rather complicated mathematical procedure known as **"continued fractions,"** which is beyond the scope of an elementary text.

Example 1.

Required to index an angle of 17°24'.

Solution.

Change 17°24' to minutes as follows:

17°24' = (17 × 60) + 24 = 1020 + 24 = 1044'. One turn of the crank equals 540'; therefore, to index 1044' the crank will have to be turned as many times as 540 is contained in 1044.

$$1044 \div 540 = 1\frac{504}{540} \text{ or } 1\frac{14}{15} \text{ rev.}$$

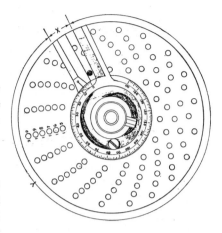

FIG. 9–4. Sector arms set for 14 holes in 15 hole circle.

Since one of the standard index plates contains a 15-hole circle, the complete answer will be one revolution of the crank and 14 holes in the 15-hole circle. Set the sector arms for 14 holes in the 15-hole circle with the left arm up against the index pin, which should be placed in any convenient hole of the 15-hole circle; then turn the index crank once, and on through to the right arm.

Fractional parts of a turn which are very nearly equal to a whole turn such as 14/15, 30/33, etc., require the sector arms to be set as shown in Fig. 9–4, and the crank turned through arc *Y* instead of *X*. That is, the crank must be turned through an arc outside of the sector arms instead of inside.

Example 2.

Required to index an angle 72°15'38".

Solution.

Change 72°15'38" to seconds as follows:

$$\{[(72 \times 60) + 15]60\} + 38 = \{[4320 + 15]60\} + 38 = \{4335 \times 60\} + 38 =$$

$$260,100 + 38 = 260,138''$$

One turn of the crank equals 32,400 seconds; therefore, to index 260,138 seconds the crank will have to be turned as many times as 32,400 is contained in 260,138.

$$260,138 \div 32,400 = 8.02895 \text{ or approximately } 8.0290 \text{ revolutions of the crank.}$$

The whole number is the complete number of revolutions of the crank. The fractional part, .0290, is found, by consulting angular indexing charts in handbooks, to be very close to .0303 which is given as one hole in the 33-hole circle.

The *complete answer* is

8 revolutions and one hole in the 33-hole circle.

While this does not give precisely the required angle, it is close enough for all practical purposes, the error being equal to (.03030 − .02895) × 32,400 = 43.74". Remember this is the error in an angle of 72°15'38", which is less than the guaranteed accuracy of standard dividing heads.

PROBLEMS

Calculate the indexing for the following angles:

1. 7°
2. 11°35'
3. 14°57'30"

4. 15°
5. 17°11'38"
6. 23°45'

7. 37°
8. 19°50'
9. 54°42'28"

Graduating. This kind of work is performed in much the same manner as plain indexing with the exception that it is required to move the milling machine table a specified distance through the medium of the dividing head. The dividing head spindle is geared to the lead screw on the mill table. When even gears are used to connect the spindle with the lead screw, one revolution of the index crank will move the mill table one-fortieth of the lead of the lead screw.

For example, if the mill table has a lead screw with 4 threads per inch, the lead will be .250″, and 1/40 of this is .00625″. One revolution of the index crank, under these conditions, moves the table .00625″. From this relationship the formula

$$R = D \div .00625$$

is developed,

where D is the distance the table must be moved for each graduation,

and R is the number of revolutions of the index crank.

Example 1.

Required to cut graduations with .010″ spaces.

Solution.

Using the formula $R = D \div .00625$

$R = .010 \div .00625 = 1\frac{375}{625} = 1\frac{3}{5}$ revolutions of the crank. Three-fifths of a revolution can be made by using either the 15-hole circle or the 20-hole circle.

If the 15-hole circle is used, change $\frac{3}{5}$ to 15ths; $\frac{3}{5} \times \frac{3}{3} = \frac{9}{15}$. Set the sector arms for **9 holes** in the 15-hole circle.

If the 20-hole circle is used, change $\frac{3}{5}$ to 20ths; $\frac{3}{5} \times \frac{4}{4} = \frac{12}{20}$. Set the sector arms for **12 holes** in the 20-hole circle.

The *complete answer* is 1 revolution of the crank and 9 holes in the 15-hole circle or 1 revolution and 12 holes in the 20-hole circle.

Example 2.

Required to cut graduations .03162″ apart.

Solution.

.03162 ÷ .00625 = 5.0592 revolutions of the crank. Five is the complete number of revolutions of the crank.

By referring to the chart, "Longitudinal Graduating," furnished with the Brown & Sharpe dividing head, the nearest decimal fraction to .0592 is .059215 which equals 18 holes in the 19-hole circle. The error per graduation is equal to $(.059215 \times .00625) - (.0592 \times .00625) =$ .00037009 − .00037000 = .00000009″.

The *complete answer* is 5 revolutions of the crank and 18 holes in the 19-hole circle. Error equals + .00000009″ per graduation.

If it is desired to cut graduations in vernier plates or flat rules and scales, the work should be clamped directly to the table, lengthwise of the table. The cutting tool is usually a fly cutter ground to a sharp V-point and placed in the fly tool arbor in the spindle, so that it will cut the line as the table is traversed.

It should be remembered in graduating that the crank must always be turned in the same direction in order to prevent backlash between the index crank and the table feed screw.

PROBLEMS

Calculate the indexing necessary to cut graduations of the following sizes:

1. .0195"
2. .0255"
3. .0447"
4. .07325"
5. .0964"

6. .1385"
7. .2452"
8. .3498"
9. .4607"
10. .00832"

QUESTIONS
Dividing Head

1. What is meant by the ratio of a dividing head?

2. What is the purpose of the sector arms?

3. How is it possible to judge when a definite fractional part of a revolution has been made?

4. What numbers of divisions can be obtained by use of the index plate furnished with the 5 to 1 dividing head?

5. What numbers of holes are contained in each circle of each plate furnished with the Brown & Sharpe dividing head?

6. What is meant by rapid indexing?

7. What numbers of divisions can be done by rapid indexing on the Cincinnati dividing head? The Brown & Sharpe dividing head?

8. What is the formula for rapid indexing on the Brown & Sharpe dividing head?

9. What is meant by plain indexing?

10. What is the formula for plain indexing using the 40 to 1 dividing head?

11. What numbers of divisions can be done by plain indexing when a 40 to 1 dividing head is used?

12. What is meant by differential indexing?

13. What is the formula for differential indexing?

14. How is it possible to determine whether a given number of divisions is plain or differential indexing?

15. Explain the purposes of an idler gear?

16. Explain how compound gears are placed on the dividing head using the letters AC/BD.

17. What is the effect on the set-up if $(n—N)$ is positive? If $(n—N)$ is negative?

18. State the rules for use of idler gears in differential indexing.

19. By sketch trace the action from the crank back to the index plate in differential indexing when simple gears are used.

20. By sketch trace the action from the crank back to the index plate when compound gears are used.

21. Consult a handbook or manufacturer's chart for indexing tables. Does this chart give complete information regarding plain and differential indexing? Can you use it?

22. What is angular indexing?

23. Explain how an angle of one degree can be indexed.

24. Illustrate how to change an angle given in degrees and minutes into minutes.

25. Change into seconds an angle given in degrees, minutes and seconds.

26. State the formula for angular indexing.

27. What is meant by graduating with respect to dividing head work?

28. How is the dividing head set up for graduating?

29. Explain why one revolution of the crank on a 40 to 1 dividing head will move the table .00625".

30. State the formula used for graduating.

31. What care should be exercised in turning the crank while graduating?

HELICAL AND SPIRAL MILLING

Definitions. (**helix,** singular; **helices,** plural). The path of a point moving at a fixed rate of advance on the surface of a cylinder, such as the threads on a machine screw or bolt, is an example of a helix.

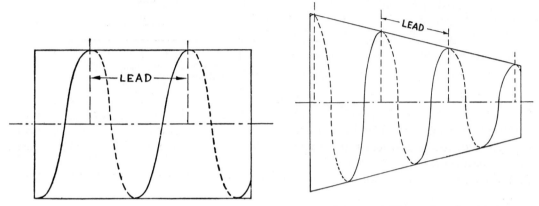

FIG. 9–5. Illustration of a helix.   FIG. 9–6. Illustration of a spiral.

Spiral. The path of a point moving at a fixed rate of advance on the surface of a cone or flat plane, such as the threads of a wood screw or pipe tap, is an example of a spiral on a cone. A watch spring is an example of a spiral with reference to a plane.

The **lead** of a helix or spiral is the distance which it advances in one complete revolution, measured along a line parallel with the axis of rotation, as shown in Figs. 9–5 and 9–6.

Helical milling is the term applied to milling the teeth in helical gears, milling cutters, worms, and the like. The helical path in the work is generated by gearing the dividing head to the mill table lead screw through the index plate, so that when the mill table has moved longitudinally through the distance given as the lead, the work will have made one complete revolution.

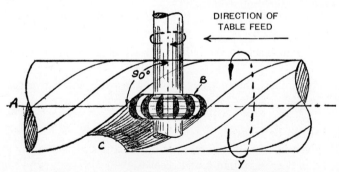

FIG. 9–7. The result of not swiveling the table.

The shape of the helix is dependent on the shape of the cutter used and the magnitude of the helix angle.

The **helix angle** is the angle formed by the intersection of two lines, one being parallel with the helix, the other parallel with the axis of rotation of the work as illustrated in Fig. 9–5. The helix angle must be known so that the table can be swiveled to permit the milling of the slot or groove to the correct width and proper contour of the cutter.

Figs. 9–7 and 9–8 illustrate the necessity for knowing the value of the helix angle.

If the mill table were set at 90° with the arbor axis, and shaft A were moved straight ahead as indicated by the dotted arrow, but at the same time revolved; the cutter B would cut a groove as indicated by C. If the mill table were swiveled to angle H, however, and shaft A were moved straight ahead as indicated by arrow X, Fig. 9–8, and at the same time revolved, the cutter would mill a path as shown by D. It can readily be seen that groove C does not conform to the contour of the cutter, even though it does form a helix and has the required lead. It must be remembered that one of the features required of a helical groove is the conformity to the contour of the cutter used as shown at D. Since this is true, then the table must be turned through an angle such that, when the work advances and at the same time revolves, the path left by the cutter will be identical to the contour of the cutter.

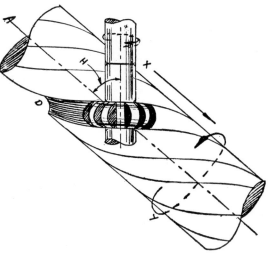

FIG. 9–8. The result of swiveling the table properly.

The helix angle is determined by the required lead and the diameter of the work. It is calculated by use of the following formula:

Tangent of the helix angle $= 3.1416 \times D \div L$

where D is the diameter of the work

and L is the lead of the required helix. (Fig. 9–9.)

Generating the helix. In order to cut a helix, the dividing head must be connected to the mill table lead screw by gears from the worm shaft to the lead screw. Most modern milling machines have a table lead screw with four threads per inch. Some of the older machines have five, some eight threads per inch. In any case it is necessary to connect the dividing head and mill lead screw with gears of a value such that, when the table has traveled longitudinally a distance equal to the required lead, the work or dividing head spindle will have made exactly one revolution. When the dividing head spindle makes one revolution, the worm shaft or index crank must make forty revolutions; and when

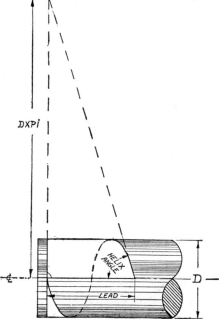

FIG. 9–9. Illustration of the triangle formed by the helix and the lead.

the table has traveled the required lead, the lead screw must revolve N times the required lead, N being equal to the number of threads per inch on the lead screw. The ratio of the gears can be expressed as follows:

$$\frac{\text{Revolutions of the Lead Screw}}{\text{Revolutions of the Index Crank}} = \frac{N \times \text{Required Lead}}{40}$$

If the lead screw is standard with 4 threads per inch, the formula can be simplified as follows:

$$\frac{\text{Revolutions of the Lead Screw}}{\text{Revolutions of the Index Crank}} = \frac{\text{Required Lead}}{10}$$

Example.

Consider the following.   Suppose it is necessary to mill 8 helical flutes on a cutter 3.25″ in diameter, with a lead of 35″.

Solution.

STEP No. 1.   Set the dividing head to index 8 divisions.

$$\text{Revolutions of the crank} = \frac{40}{N} = \frac{40}{8} = 5 \text{ in any circle.}$$

STEP No. 2.   Calculate the helix angle.
Tangent of helix angle $= (D \times 3.1416) \div L$.
$(3.25 \times 3.1416) \div 35 = 0.29172$.
The angle whose tangent is $0.29172 = 16°$ (nearest degree).

STEP No. 3.   Calculate the gear ratio.

$$\frac{\text{Required lead}}{10} = \frac{35}{10} = \frac{7}{2}$$

STEP No. 4.   Since $\frac{7}{2}$ cannot be raised into simple gears, arrange it as a compound, thus: $\frac{1}{1} \times \frac{7}{2}$; raise this to standard gears as follows:

$$\frac{1 \times 7}{1 \times 2} = \frac{(1 \times 2) \times 7}{1 \times (2 \times 2)} = \frac{2 \times 7}{1 \times 4} = \frac{2 \times (7 \times 8)}{1 \times (4 \times 8)} = \frac{2 \times 56}{1 \times 32} = \frac{(2 \times 24) \times 56}{(1 \times 24) \times 32} = \frac{48 \times 56}{24 \times 32}$$

The complete information necessary to set up this piece of work is as follows:
Turn the crank five complete revolutions in any circle;
Swivel the Universal mill table 16°;
48-tooth gear on worm; 24-tooth gear on stud (first gear);
56-tooth gear on stud (second gear); 32-tooth gear on lead screw.

Dividing heads and milling machines usually are furnished with a chart of commonly used leads, the gears necessary to cut these leads, and the proper placement on the machine. Frequently, however, leads are required which are not listed on the chart. When an occasion like this arises, reference can be made to standard "Hand Books" which contain such information. The following problem is placed in the text for the benefit of those who might care to follow it through in an effort to learn how the values contained in the "Tables of Leads" can be calculated.

Example.

Find the helix angle and change gears necessary to cut a lead of 3.429″ on a shaft 1.5″ in diameter. The mill table lead screw has 4 threads per inch.

Solution.

STEP No. 1.   The tangent of the helix angle $= (D \times 3.1416) \div L$.
$1.5 \times 3.1416 \div 3.429 = 53° 57' 27''$ (nearest degree is 54°).

STEP No. 2.   The gear ratio = Required lead $\div 10 = \dfrac{3429}{10000}$.

This gear ratio is too large to factor into standard gears; therefore it is necessary to find a fraction approximately equal to the gear ratio which can be factored into compound gears. This new fraction is found by a method known as "Continued Fractions," which can be studied in more detail in "Practical Shop Mathematics," Vol. II, by Wolfe and Phelps.

STEP No. 3.   Find the successive quotients. These are the quotients found by continually dividing the smaller of the two numbers which make up the gear ratio into the larger as follows: The gear ratio equals $\dfrac{3429}{10000}$.

3429	10000	2	
3142	6858	1	
287	3142	10	
272	2870	1	
15	272	18	SUCCESSIVE
14	270	7	QUOTIENTS
1	2	2	
	2		
	0		

STEP No. 4.   Find the convergents by making up a block system as follows:

		2	1	10	1	18	7	2	QUOTIENTS
1	0	1	1	11	12	227	1601	3429	
0	1	2	3	32	35	662	4669	10000	CONVERGENTS
G	L	G	L	G	L	G	L	O	

Note: When the gear ratio is a **proper** fraction the block system is started out as follows:

1	0
0	1
G	L

When the gear ratio is an improper fraction the block system is started in this way:

1	n
0	1

$(n = \text{1st quotient})$

STEP No. 5. In selecting a fraction or convergent which factors, it will be noted that the convergents to the right of $\frac{12}{35}$ are too large for standard gears; whereas, the farther to the left of $\frac{12}{35}$ that a convergent is selected, the greater the error becomes.

Gear ratio $= \dfrac{12}{35} = \dfrac{3 \times 4}{5 \times 7}$. Multiplying both numerator and denominator

through by 8, we obtain $\dfrac{24 \times 32}{40 \times 56}$.

Arrange the gears on the machine as follows:
24-tooth gear on worm.   40-tooth gear first on stud.
32-tooth gear second on stud.   56-tooth gear on lead screw.

STEP No. 6. The amount of error is calculated as follows:
$$\frac{12 \times 1 \times 40}{35 \times 4 \times 1} = 3.42857. \quad \text{(The lead which the gears will cut.)}$$
$3.42900 - 3.42857 = 0.00043.$ (The error in the total lead.)

Referring to the table of leads furnished by Brown & Sharpe, the gears for this lead are given in the ratio 12 to 35. The amount of error is so small that for all practical purposes it can be ignored.

PROBLEMS

1. If the teeth have a lead of 43.875″, calculate the indexing, helix angle and change gears necessary to cut 48 teeth in a helical gear whose outside diameter is 4.5″. The mill table lead screw has 4 threads per inch.

2. Calculate the indexing, helix angle and change gears necessary to cut 8 teeth in a reamer having an outside diameter of .875″. The lead of the teeth is 72.5″ and the mill table lead screw has 4 threads per inch.

3. What lead would be cut by the change gears $\dfrac{72 \times 48}{44 \times 64}$ if the lead of the machine is 10″?

4. Calculate the change gears necessary to cut a lead of 17.365″.

5. Using standard gears furnished with the Brown & Sharpe dividing head build compound gears to satisfy a gear ratio of 20/11. Determine the lead which these gears will cut if the lead screw has 4 threads per inch.

Cutters. In milling a helix, cutters of various forms are used. These cutters are selected according to the form or shape of the helix, and are usually of the double angle type; that is, instead of a straight sided cutter, the sides of the teeth come together to make a double angle. If a straight sided cutter were used in machining a helix such as is found on drills, reamers, and cutters, an extreme form or shape would be developed, which, insofar as cutting properties are concerned, would be useless.

The included angle on a double angle cutter may have any reasonable value, depending on the desired angle on the helix. The face angle of such cutters, however, are usually from 10° to 20° as shown in Fig. 9–10. Notice that these angles are measured from the sides of the teeth to the vertical axis of the cutter.

In setting up a milling machine for cutting a helix, a definite method of procedure should be followed for obtaining the best results, as follows:

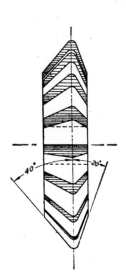

FIG. 9–10. Double angle cutter. FIG. 9–11. Spotting the cutter on the work.

Procedure.

1) After the dividing head and footstock are in place on the table, set the dividing head for the correct number of divisions to be indexed and withdraw the locating pin from the index plate.

2) Select the proper gears for producing the desired lead and mount them on the machine in the correct locations. After they are mounted, try out the set-up to make sure that the table and the dividing head operate freely.

3) Loosen the table clamping bolts in the saddle and swivel the table to the correct helix angle. Do not tighten the table at this time.

4) Place the work between centers and adjust the table so that the footstock end of the work is directly under the axis of the cutter arbor.

5) Move the table saddle in close to the machine column and place the cutter on the arbor so that it comes approximately central over the end of the work. Tighten the cutter securely on the arbor.

6) Swivel the table back to zero and spot the cutter on the highest point of the work.

7) Remove the work from between the centers and raise the table an amount equal to the depth of the cut.

8) Place a rule or thin parallel on the face angle side of the cutter and adjust the table either in or out, so that the side of the rule against the face angle side of the cutter splits the foot-stock center. (**Caution**—Do not elevate or lower the table in making this adjustment.)

9) Mount the work between centers and swivel the table to the correct helix angle. Tighten the table securely.

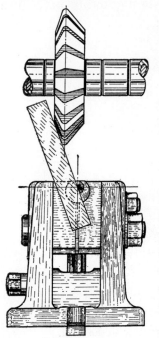

FIG. 9–12. Centralizing the cutter.

10) As a last precaution see that everything is working freely. Start the machine and take a trial cut. Check the work for the correct location of the cut and make any alterations that might be necessary.

The above procedure is for cutting helices which have one face on the centerline, and is the same whether it be a right-hand or left-hand helix. However, it is necessary to swivel the table in the proper direction. Should it be required to mill a right-hand helical reamer, it is necessary to select a right-hand double angle cutter and swivel the table back on the right-hand side. (Operator facing the milling machine.) If it is required to mill a left-hand helical reamer, select a left-hand double angle cutter and swivel the table back on the left-hand side. To have the dividing spindle rotate in the proper direction for cutting a left-hand helix, it is necessary to add an idler gear to the train of gears connecting the table with the dividing head. The above rules are for swiveling the table of the milling machine, when the dividing head is located on the left-hand side of the table. If the dividing head is located on the right-hand side of the table, reverse the swiveling angle of the table.

To determine how much the cutter must be set ahead of, or back of center, take the radius of the work blank and multiply it by the **sine** of the rake or hook angle, as illustrated in Figs. 9–13 and 9–14.

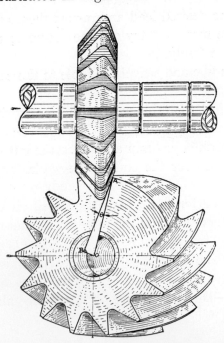

FIG. 9–13. Rake tooth cutter.

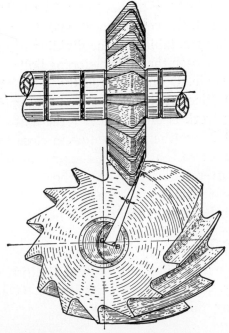

FIG. 9–14. Hook tooth cutter.

Example 1.

Suppose it is required to mill a helix with a 10-degree hook tooth on a blank 3.5″ in diameter.

Solution.

> The radius of the work blank is 3.5 divided by 2 or 1.75″.
> From trigonometric tables the sine of 10° is found to be .17365.
> Then multiply 1.75 by .17365, obtaining .3038″ or approximately 5/16″.
>> *Answer* The cutter must be set 5/16″ back of center.

Example 2.

How much must the milling cutter be set ahead of center to mill a tooth having 7-degree rake on a blank 1.750″ in diameter?

Solution.

> The radius of the work blank is 1.750 ÷ 2 = .875.
> From the trigonometric tables the sine of 7° is .12187.
> Multiplying this value, .12187, by .875 = .1066 or 7/64″.
>> *Answer* The cutter must be set 7/64″ ahead of center.

PROBLEMS

In each of the following problems calculate the distance which the cutter must be set ahead of or back of center if A equals the angle of the hook or rake, and D equals the diameter of the work blank.

1. $A = 4$	$D =$	2.625
2. $A = 8$	$D =$	3.093
3. $A = 10$	$D =$	3.9375
4. $A = 5$	$D =$	.8125
5. $A = 14$	$D =$	2.6875

Spiral milling. The milling of **"cams"** is probably the most common kind of spiral milling. These cams may be of the face, edge, or barrel variety, and from a simple heart shaped cam to a cam containing many "lobes." Most cams are machined on milling machines of special design that operate from the profile of a small master cam. However, when a cam of special shape is needed for which there is no master, it can be machined on a horizontal or vertical mill.

The **"lobe"** of a cam is that part which contains rise or drop, and is bounded by a change of radii.

The **"lead"** of a spiral in a flat plane is the amount of rise or fall in a complete circle or 360°.

The **"amount of rise or fall"** is found by subtracting the short radius of a lobe from the long radius of that lobe.

To determine the lead of a spiral, multiply the amount of rise or fall by a fraction, the numerator of which is 360° and the denominator of which is the angle of the rise or fall.

The method of procedure in spiral milling calculations is the same as for helical milling, with the exception that instead of finding the helix angle, the required lead must be found. The rest of the procedure is identical.

Example.

In the lobe of an edge cam the short radius is .74025, the long radius is 1.0805 and the angle of the rise or fall is 22° 30′. Calculate the required lead and change gears necessary to mill this lobe.

Solution.

STEP No. 1. The amount of rise or fall equals $1.0805 - .74025 = .34025$.
The required lead equals $(360° ÷ 22.5°) × .34025 = 5.444$.

STEP No. 2. The gear ratio is equal to the Required lead $÷ 10 = \dfrac{5.444}{10} = \dfrac{5444}{10000}$.

STEP No. 3. Find the successive quotients:

5444	10000	1
4556	5444	1
888	4556	5
812	4440	7
76	116	1
40	76	1
36	40	1
36	36	9
	4	

The remainder, 4, is the GCD of the fraction $\dfrac{5444}{10000}$.

STEP No. 4. Find the convergents:

		1	1	5	7	1	1	1	9	
1	0	1	1	6	43	49	92	141	1361	× 4 = 5444
0	1	1	2	11	79	90	169	259	2500	× 4 = 10000
G	L	G	L	G	L	G	L	G	O	

STEP No. 5. Select the new gear ratio from the block system keeping in mind that the farther to the left of the original it is selected, the greater the error.

Gear ratio $= \dfrac{49}{90}$ $\dfrac{49}{90} = \dfrac{7}{9} × \dfrac{7}{10}$.

Raise $\dfrac{7}{9} × \dfrac{7}{10}$ to standard gears thus:

$$\left(\dfrac{7}{9} × \dfrac{8}{8}\right) × \dfrac{7}{10} = \dfrac{56}{72} × \dfrac{7}{10} = \dfrac{56}{72} × \left(\dfrac{7}{10} × \dfrac{4}{4}\right) = \dfrac{56}{72} × \dfrac{28}{40}$$

STEP No. 6. Calculate the amount of error:

$$\dfrac{49}{90} × \dfrac{1}{4} × \dfrac{40}{1} = \dfrac{49}{9} = 5.4444 = \text{lead the new gear will cut.}\quad 5.4444 - 5.444 =$$

$+.0004$ error in the lead

STEP No. 7. The *complete answer* is:

The required lead = 5.444. Gear ratio = $\dfrac{49}{90}$

Gear on worm = 56   Second gear on stud = 28

First gear on stud = 72   Gear on table screw = 40

Error = + .0004 inches per lead.

PROBLEMS

1. Calculate the change gears necessary to mill the lobe of a face cam if the short radius is 5.625″, the long radius 6.412″, and the angle of the rise or fall is 75°.

2. Calculate the change gears necessary to mill a lobe on a face cam if the short radius is 3.257″, the long radius 4.457″, and the angle of the rise or fall is 144°.

3. What will be the lead of a lobe having a short radius of 4.875″, a long radius of 5.030″ and an angle of rise or fall of 45°?

4. The short radius of a cam lobe is 6.7″, the long radius is 8.136″, and the angle of the rise or fall is 72°. What is the lead of this lobe?

5. What amount of rise or fall would be expressed by the gear ratio $\dfrac{24 \times 28}{72 \times 86}$ if the angle of the rise or fall of the lobe is 30°?

When using the dividing head for differential indexing or for helical or spiral milling, be sure to have the index plate locking pin disengaged and locked back in place.

Determine whether or not the index crank should be turned clockwise or counterclockwise and always turn in that same direction after the job has once been started.

Always try out the set-up to make sure that everything is working freely, and spot the cutter on the work to check the indexing for correct value.

In helical milling, after the cut is completed, always lower the table before backing up to start a new cut and move the table back far enough so that all **"back lash"** will be removed before the new cut is started.

After the dividing head has been used for rapid indexing, make sure that the worm is fully engaged with the worm wheel before using it for any other kind of indexing or for helical or spiral milling.

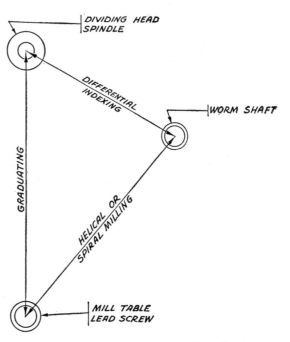

FIG. 9–15. Dividing head gearing triangle.

When using gears on the dividing head make certain that they are placed on the proper shafts, and to suit the type of work for which the dividing head is going to be used.

The preceding sketch, Fig. 9–15, indicates the proper shafting to be geared together when the dividing head is to be used for longitudinal graduating, differential indexing, or helical or spiral milling.

QUESTIONS
Helical and Spiral Milling

1. What is a helix?
2. What is a spiral?
3. Give examples of a helix. A spiral.
4. What is meant by the lead of a helix?
5. What is meant by helical milling?
6. Upon what two factors does the shape of a helix depend?
7. What is meant by the helix angle?
8. Why is the helix angle important in helical milling?
9. State the formula for determining the helix angle.
10. Explain how a helix is generated on a milling machine.
11. How is the gear ratio determined in helical milling?
12. After the gears have been determined for milling a helix, what position do they occupy on the machine?
13. What kinds of cutters are used for milling a helix?
14. What would be the result of using a side milling cutter for milling a helix?
15. What is the value of the face angle of cutters used for helical milling?
16. Explain how the cutter is positioned in helical milling.
17. In what direction should the table be swiveled for milling a right-hand helix? A left-hand helix?
18. What is meant by a rake tooth cutter? A hook tooth cutter?
19. State the formula for calculating the amount of offset of the cutter for milling a rake or hook tooth.
20. Name three forms of cams.
21. What is meant by the lobe of a cam?
22. What is meant by the lead of a spiral in a flat plane?
23. How is the amount of rise or fall of a lobe of a cam determined?
24. How is the lead of a spiral determined?
25. When should the index plate locking pin be disengaged on the dividing head?
26. What care should be exercised in using the dividing head after doing rapid indexing?
27. Illustrate the dividing head gearing triangle.

Chapter 10

VERTICAL MILL

VERTICAL MILLING MACHINE
Work operations . . . Boring . . . Procedures

MILLING SUGGESTIONS
Set-up . . . Selection of cutters . . . Selections of speeds and feeds

SAFETY
Common precautions . . . Do's and Don'ts

VERTICAL MILLING MACHINE

In this machine, Fig. 10–1, the spindle occupies a vertical position relative to the table and can be raised or lowered. The table has the same movements as a plain

A. Rapid feed lever
B. Hand wheel for table traverse movement
C. Crank for vertical adjustment of knee
D. Feed change lever
E. Lever for power adjustment of knee
F. Table longitudinal movement hand wheel
G. Work table
H. Lever for power traverse of table
I. Lever for power longitudinal movement of table
J. Spindle start and stop lever
K. Hand wheel for vertical movement of spindle
L. Stops for regulating depth of spindle down travel
M. Spindle housing binder lever

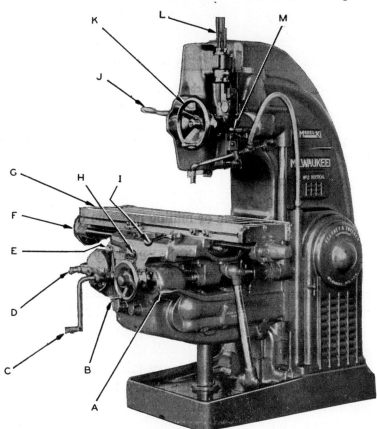

FIG. 10–1. Tool room vertical mill.

milling machine, but has a distinct advantage over other milling machines because of the ease with which the cutter can be applied to certain classes of work. It is especially suitable for doing a wide variety of end or face milling operations, including die sinking, **"template"** milling, and boring.

Work operations. The vertical milling machine is especially suited to the boring

of holes, or to circular milling operations in connection with the circular milling table shown in Fig. 10–2. These rotary table attachments are of two types: one provided with a hand feed, the other for power feed when connected to the lead screw on the table. Some are furnished with a hand wheel and graduated dial which make possible the milling of flat, circular, or angular work. The hand wheel is provided with an adjustable graduated dial or collar which makes it possible to mill within 2 minutes of arc. As an accessory to these tables, an indexing unit is available with three separate index plates, which permits the operator to do accurate indexing similar to that done on a dividing head.

The rotary table is provided with T-slots that are generally of the same size as those in the mill table. These T-slots intersect in the center of the top plate at a hole which accommodates

FIG. 10–2.   Circular milling attachment with index plate.

arbors or standard test plugs to facilitate locating and clamping the work.

When equipped for power drive, these tables have two adjustable trip dogs located in T-slots on the periphery of the table, which can be located in any position around the table, or removed for continuous milling operations. The power feed can be engaged or disengaged at the discretion of the operator, which makes it possible to operate the rotary table or milling machine table independently or in connection with each other.

The rate of feed at which the periphery of the rotary table operates is the same as that selected on the milling machine feed dial for the table. When the rapid traverse is used, the rate at the periphery of the table is the same as that provided for the plain, universal, or vertical milling machine tables.

The power driven rotary table can be used for a wide variety of circular work ranging from that of a very simple nature to complex face cams and scrolls.

In locating work on the rotary table, it can be placed on a plug fitted to the hole in the table. The center of the rotary table can be located on the axis of the milling machine spindle as follows:

Place a plug gage in the center of the table and by means of an indicator located in a drill chuck in the spindle, indicate the plug, making any traverse or longitudinal adjustments of the milling machine table necessary to make the axis of the rotary table coincide with that of the spindle.

The work is then placed on the plug gage, and clamped to the table.

To set the machine to mill the desired radius, if the work is to be machined on the periphery, move the mill table longitudinally a distance equal to the required radius plus the radius of the cutter.

If the radius is in the nature of a circular slot, move the table longitudinally, a distance equal to the required radius and use a cutter, enough undersize, to allow for finishing. By this last method the cutter will be located in the center of the slot.

For milling face cams, the cam blank is located in the center of the rotary table and clamped in place; the **"short lead"** milling attachment is then attached to the end of the mill table, and gears are selected and mounted to produce the correct amount of rise or fall in the first lobe to be milled. If the cam has been **"laid out,"** place a mill wiggler in the drill chuck in the spindle, and adjust the mill table so that the **"layout"** lines of the lobe for which the table is geared coincide with the point of the wiggler.

If more than one lobe is to be milled, separate sets of gears will have to be calculated for the individual lead of each lobe. The cutter used for finishing the cam should be the same size or a trifle larger than the cam roller.

Boring. The boring of holes is accomplished on the vertical milling machine by using a special chuck for holding the boring tool that permits the tool to be moved eccentrically for obtaining the correct size of hole. Fig. 10–3 shows a type of boring chuck commonly used. The boring tool is held in the sliding jaw by means of a set screw. The

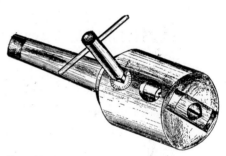

FIG. 10–3. Adjustable boring tool holder.

sliding jaw is moved back and forth by means of a screw surmounted by a dial which is graduated to give movements in thousandths of an inch relative to the radius of the hole being bored.

The work to be bored may be held by any of the conventional methods employed in milling. A common method is to clamp the work to the mill table, supporting it on parallels to provide clearance for the drill and boring tool.

The location of the hole is usually specified in relation to a finished side or surface of the work, which, in jig or fixture work, or piercing dies, is given with very exacting limits. Work of this nature is prepared for boring either by laying out the location of the hole and **"test boring"** or by using **"toolmakers' buttons."**

"Test boring" is the process of boring a hole undersize, to fit a standard plug gage, for the purpose of testing its location.

1) The approximate location of the hole is first laid out using a surface or height gage.

2) The work is then clamped, layout side up, to the table. Place a drill chuck in the milling machine spindle, insert a mill wiggler, Fig. 10–4, and adjust it to run true. This can be accomplished by using a rule or other suitable tool to force it into line.

3) With the wiggler point running true, adjust the milling machine table longitudinally and traversely so that the intersection of the layout lines forming the center for the hole coincides with the wiggler point.

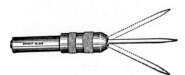

Fig. 10–4.   Mill wiggler.

4) Lock the table against movement and stop the machine; replace the wiggler with a combination drill and countersink, and center drill the work.
5) Remove the combination drill and countersink, replacing it with a drill of a size such that two or three tests may be made before the hole is near the required size, and drill the work.
6) Remove the drill and drill chuck replacing it with a boring chuck; select a boring tool of a size consistent with the diameter and length of the hole, and place it in the boring chuck. Bore the hole to the next size larger than the drill, for a standard plug gage.
7) Insert the gage and by means of a micrometer or other suitable precision measuring tool, check the location of the hole. If it is not in the proper position make the necessary table adjustments and rebore the hole to fit the next larger standard plug gage. When the position of the hole conforms to the dimensions required, bore it to size.

To use toolmakers' buttons, proceed as follows:

1) Drill and tap the approximate position of the hole to take the button screw; fasten the button, not too tightly, with the screw.
2) Using a height gage and indicator or micrometer, adjust the button to suit the given dimensions for the location of the hole, allowing for the radius of the button. Tighten the button in place and recheck it to make sure that it did not move.
3) Clamp the work to the mill table, then place an Ideal or similar indicator in a drill chuck in the mill spindle and indicate the button. To indicate the button adjust the indicator to revolve about the button; turn the machine spindle by hand, and note any deflection of the needle. Adjust the mill table so that there is no variation of the indicator needle from zero at which time the axis of the button will coincide with the axis of the machine spindle.
4) Lock the table against movement and remove the button. The hole left by the button screw can be filled up by putting in a soft machine screw, cutting it off and filing it flat.
5) The work is then ready for drilling and boring.

Holes which have been previously drilled can be located for boring by using an indicator in the same manner as for locating the toolmakers' button.

When several holes have to be bored in relation to each other, Fig. 10–5, their locations can be checked by determining the center distance for any two; to this, add the radius of each of the holes being checked. The result will give the micrometer reading over the plug gages.

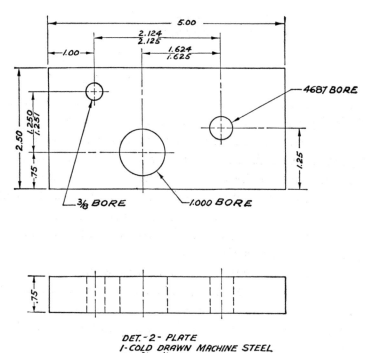

Fig. 10–5. Sketch of typical boring job.

MILLING SUGGESTIONS

Perhaps one of the most important suggestions to the operator of a machine is that he keep it well lubricated. This does not mean that the moving members should be flooded with oil, but rather that the oil reservoirs be checked frequently so as to insure an adequate supply. Modern machines, especially, are so easy to lubricate that there can be no excuse for overlooking this important detail.

A dirty machine or poorly kept tools and attachments are a certain indication of a careless workman. It is much easier to keep the machine clean if it is cleaned as soon as possible after the work is completed. A machine in which dirt and chips are permitted to collect cannot be relied upon to do accurate work. Sooner or later the machine bearings will be severely damaged because of clogged oil lines. Remember that the manufacturer of the machine and accessories is not responsible for the inaccuracies caused by careless maintenance. Good machine tools deserve the best attention that can be paid to them, and a few minutes spent now and then to clean them up or make minor adjustments will pay big dividends in added years of efficient service.

The carelessness of an operator who lays wrenches, hammers, or other tools on the finished surfaces of the work table, knee, or base of the machine, is regrettable. The manufacturer of the machine equips it with racks and shelves to hold the standard tools when they are not in use. Make a resolution to "have a place for everything and keep everything in its place," and see how much more efficient machine operating can be.

The series of operations required in a piece of work involves so many factors, with respect to accuracy and speed, that it is impractical to call the operator's attention to more than a few of them. In the first place, the old axiom, that "speed and accuracy must go hand in hand" is truer today than ever before. The fact that a workman turns out a job in record time is of little consequence unless the limits of accuracy required in the job are maintained. The development of speed and accuracy must come as the result of careful, deliberate planning; not by rushing around at random. Speed comes only as a result of experience and an orderly manner of doing things. On the other hand, accuracy greater than that specified for the part is a waste of time and a hobble to production. Develop the ability to work to close limits when the occasion demands it, and to turn out volume production when tolerances are great enough to permit it.

In obtaining these goals of accuracy and speed, do not attempt to do a job unless the requirements as portrayed in the blue print or sketch are clearly understood. If verbal or written orders are given relative to the work be sure that there is no misunderstanding about them. Do not start the work without being reasonably sure that it can be done as required.

Before starting the job make certain that there is sufficient stock in the proper place to carry it to satisfactory completion. If previous operations have been done on it, or if someone else has started it, be sure to check it so that unnecessary time will not be spent on something that has been already spoiled. Also, there will be no question as to responsibility for errors after the work is completed.

When there is no doubt as to the advisability of going ahead with the job, proceed in an orderly manner similar to that outlined elsewhere in this section. Make every move count. Know what to do and be deliberate. When the work is properly set up, calculate the speed of the cutter and set the machine accordingly, then give the machine as much feed as it will take without stalling, being consistent with the amount of stock to be removed and the kind of finish desired. Do not waste time taking two or three cuts when one cut would do just as well.

SAFETY

Accidents which occur while operating a milling machine are the result of either ignorance or carelessness. The machine requires the human element to make it work and if the operator fails to give it the vigilant attention necessary to avoid accidents then the blame rests entirely on his shoulders. Milling machines can be dangerous. They are driven by motors rated at from 5 to 15 horsepower, and if the operator is inconsiderate enough to get his hand caught between the revolving cutter and the work, the machine won't stop; those 5 to 15 horses are going to keep right on pulling, with the result that fingers, a hand, or even an arm might be lost. These parts of the anatomy are too valuable to risk their loss at any time; for this reason, safety in the operation of a milling machine cannot be urged too strongly upon either the green apprentice or the seasoned journeyman.

The following suggestions are meant to be gentle reminders to prevent very serious accidents and a great amount of spoiled work. They are meant particularly for the milling machine but can be applied to all machines.

DO'S and DON'TS

DO get thoroughly familiar with the STOP lever.

DO make sure that the work is held securely before engaging the cutter with it.

DO make sure that all tools and machine parts are clear of the cutter before starting the machine.

DO keep your hands away from the revolving cutter.

DO handle all cutters carefully to guard against injury to yourself and others.

DO keep the shirt sleeves rolled up above the elbows and wear close fitting shop aprons or coats.

DON'T under any circumstances attempt to operate any machine unless you are thoroughly familiar with it.

DON'T move any lever unless you know exactly what is going to happen when it is moved.

DON'T play around with the lever of any machine.

DON'T attempt to remove chips from the machine with your bare hands or fingers. Use a brush or other suitable implement.

DON'T go away, even for a moment, and leave the machine running.

DON'T try to operate the machine and engage fellow workers in conversation at the same time. Keep your mind on your work and let the other fellow do the same.

DON'T wear rings or long neckties while on the job.

DON'T attempt to oil the machine while it is in operation.

REVIEW QUESTIONS

1. Why are some milling machines called vertical milling machines?
2. What advantage does the vertical milling machine have over other types of mills?
3. For what types of work is the vertical mill especially suited?
4. Can circular sections be generated on the vertical mill? How?
5. Describe the rotary milling attachment and tell how it is operated.
6. Does the fact that the hand wheel has an adjustable, graduated dial increase the usefulness of the rotary milling attachment? How?
7. How is the work attached to the rotary milling attachment?
8. Explain how the power feed of the rotary milling attachment operates.
9. How is the center of the rotary table located on the axis of the machine spindle?
10. How is the vertical mill table adjusted for milling a circular section?

11. If the radius of the work is in the nature of a circular slot, how is the table adjusted to give the proper size?

12. For milling face and edge cams how is the rotary milling attachment used?

13. How can the vertical milling machine be used for boring operations?

14. Explain how the boring tool is adjusted to produce the correct size of the hole.

15. If the location of the hole is given to very exacting limits, how is the work generally prepared?

16. What is meant by test boring?

17. Explain the procedure known as test boring.

18. What are toolmakers' buttons?

19. Explain how toolmakers' buttons are used for locating the position of the hole to be bored.

20. How can the center of a hole that has been previously drilled be located for boring?

21. When several holes must be bored in relation to each other, how is their position checked?

22. Why is it important to keep the milling machine well lubricated?

23. What is the result if the machine is permitted to accumulate dirt and chips?

24. How does the old axiom "Have a place for everything and keep everything in its place" apply to milling machine practices?

25. How can speed and accuracy be developed in operating a milling machine?

26. Speed in doing a job is the result of what?

27. What is the first important thing to be certain of before proceeding with a job?

28. What caution must be exercised in accepting verbal or written orders?

29. If previous operations have been done on a job what caution should be exercised before proceeding with it?

30. What is the most frequent cause of accidents to machine operators?

31. Why is it dangerous to "play around" with the levers of a machine?

32. Why are finger rings, long neckties, and loose fitting articles of apparel safety hazards to machine operators?

Chapter 11

CYLINDRICAL GRINDERS

DEFINITIONS
CLASSIFICATION

External . . . Internal . . . Surface . . . Cutter . . . Tool Grinder . . . Off-hand Grinder . . . Plain Cylindrical Grinders . . . Types of Work . . . Universal Cylinder Grinder . . . Holding the Work . . . Driving the Work . . . Adjusting the Machine . . . Wheel Feed . . . Speed of Work

WORK OPERATIONS

Plain Cylinders . . . Tapers . . . General Comments . . . Mottled, Checked, or Cracked Work . . . Undercuts . . . Plunge-cut . . . Dressing the Wheel . . . Truing . . . Glazing . . . Loading . . . Gaging Cylindrical Work . . . Common Amplifier

SAFETY SUGGESTIONS

Centerless Grinder

DEFINITION

The word **Grinders** is commonly accepted as a general term applied to all forms of grinding machines. Specifically, it is a machine employing an abrasive wheel for the purpose of removing excess stock, at the same time leaving a good finish on the work.

CLASSIFICATION

Grinding machines are classified as follows: **external, internal, surface, cutter, tool grinders,** and **off-hand grinders.** Under each of these headings are to be found many different kinds of grinders made by different manufacturers. It is not the purpose of this chapter to deal with all makes of grinders; instead, it aims to treat only of those things which have been found through experience and practice to be beneficial to students of the machine trades. Anyone interested in learning how to operate a certain given type of grinder, made by some particular manufacturer, should secure descriptive material from the builder relative to that machine and study it thoroughly.

Plain cylindrical grinders. Plain cylindrical grinders, Fig. 11–1, are machines designed to do the most simple types of external grinding. The wheel head is made to operate to and from the work table but cannot be swiveled. The work table holds the work head and footstock, and can be swiveled for slight tapers only. The work head is rigidly attached to the work table and cannot be swiveled. It is located to the left of the operator and is usually made with a self-contained drive to transmit variable speed and motion to the work. The footstock is located on the work table to the right of the operator. The base of the footstock is so made as to facilitate sliding it along the work table to compensate for the length of work.

The work table slide can be traversed on the ways of the bed either by hand or automatic feed. A mechanism for changing the rate of automatic feed is contained in the base.

Types of work. Plain cylindrical grinders can be used for producing plain or stepped, external cylinders, tapers, concave and convex radii and undercuts. By dressing the grinding wheel to the desired shape, form grinding can also be done.

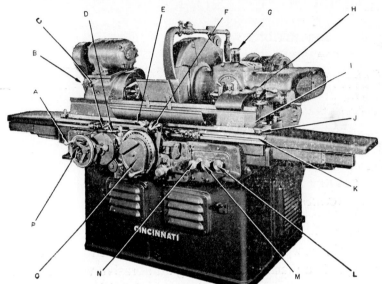

A.   Graduated table traverse hand wheel.
B.   Headstock unit
C.   Table reversing dogs
D.   Table reversing lever
E.   Pick feed device
F.   Hydraulic infeed lever
G.   Visible oil supply to grinding wheel spindle
H.   Footstock unit
I.   Swivel table
J.   Swivel table clamp and adjustment
K.   Sliding table
L.   Table tarry regulating knob
M.   Knob for adjusting rate of table travel
N.   Knob for adjusting table start and stop
O.   Hand wheel for feeding grinding wheel to the work
P.   Starting buttons

Fig. 11–1.   6″ × 18″ Plain cylindrical grinder.

Work is held in this machine on two centers; one in the footstock which is **"dead,"** and one in the work head which can be made either **"live"** or **"dead."** A **"live"** center is one which revolves with the work; a **"dead"** center remains stationary.

Fig. 11–2.   Universal cylindrical grinder.

Universal cylindrical grinder. The Universal cylindrical grinder is capable of doing any external cylindrical work. Fig. 11–2 shows a picture of a commonly used universal cylindrical grinder.

In this machine the wheel head can be swiveled on its base and can be fed to and from the table. The upper work table can be swiveled, and is equipped with scales and adjusting screws for setting the table to produce slight tapers. Steep tapers may be

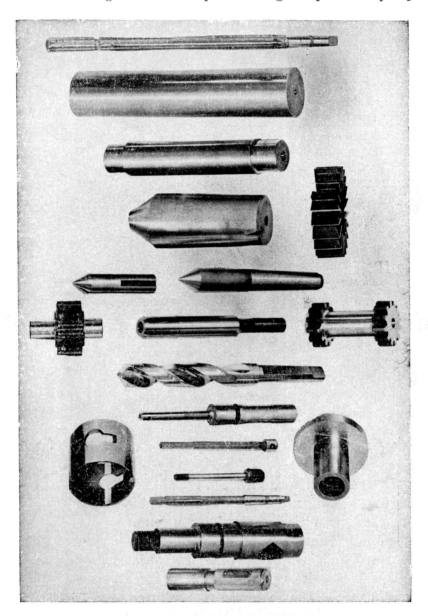

FIG. 11-3. Samples of cylindrical grinding work.

ground by swiveling the work head on its base. The work head is equipped with a self contained driving mechanism with provisions for variable work speeds. The head stock center may be made either live or dead by engaging the work drive plate with the spindle. The lower work table can be traversed on its ways either by hand or power feed and has provisions for controlling the rate of traverse.

Holding the work. In cylindrical grinding, the work is rotated on its axis while held between centers, Fig. 11–4. Whenever possible the work head center should be kept dead. The reason being that the center can be ground in place and because it

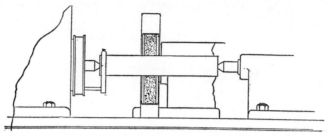

FIG. 11–4. Work between centers driven by dog.

saves wear and tear on the spindle. Long slender work, in addition to being held by the machine centers, is supported by work rests, Figs. 11–5, 11–6, and 11–7. The

FIG. 11–5. Universal back rest.

number of rests used is dependent on the diameter of the work. The usual procedure is to place them at intervals of from six to eight times the work diameter. They support the work from the back and bottom and have provisions for keeping the jaws or *shoes* adjusted to the work.

Driving the work. The work is given its rotary motion by means of a drive plate which revolves about the work head center and is driven by a pulley which is belted up to the motor. The drive plate contains an adjustable arm, to compensate for varying work diameters, into which a pin is screwed. This pin engages the "V" of

the grinding dog, or a sweated bracket which has been previously placed on the end of the work. Through this arrangement the rotary motion of the drive plate is transmitted to the work.

Adjusting the machine. The rotation of the work on its axis must be accomplished smoothly. To do this the work centers must be clean and free from nicks and the machine centers must not be loose, nicked, or irregular in form.

To insure a good finish and accurate sizing of the work, the movement of the table back and forth in front of the grinding wheel, and movement of the wheel slide, must be accomplished without jerk or jar.

The length of the table traverse should be so set as to permit one-third of the wheel face to run off the end of the work. This is necessary to insure uniformity in the work diameter at that point. If the table traverse is set so as to permit the wheel to completely over-run the end of the work, it will cause the job to be undersize at that point. The pressure required to make the wheel cut, even though slight, is released when the wheel leaves the work; therefore, on the return traverse when the wheel contacts the work, it will cause it to be undersize. Most modern machines have provisions for adjusting the length of time of **"table dwell"** at the end of the work. This is necessary to give the grinding wheel a chance to finish the cut and to clear itself on the new cut before the table motion starts again. This action of the machine must be accomplished smoothly or the work will show low and high spots. Therefore, adjust the table dwell properly. The speed of the table traverse depends on the width of the wheel and the kind of finish that is required on the work. It is generally set so that the table will move from two-thirds to three-fourths of the wheel face width for each revolution of the work.

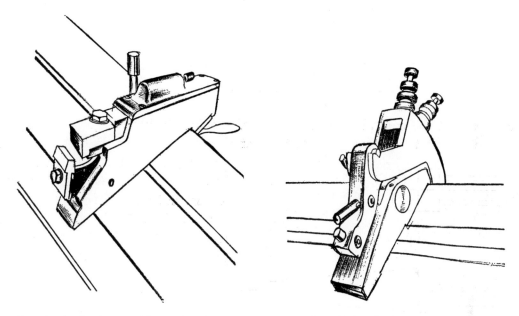

FIG. 11–6. Back rest with wooden shoes.   FIG. 11–7. Spring type back rest.

Wheel feed. Most cylindrical grinders permit feeds from .00025″ to .004″. These feeds may be accomplished either by hand or power. Whenever possible, power feeds should be used rather than hand feeds. This automatic feed permits cuts of from .00025″ to .005″ for each traverse of the table with regularity, thus preserving the life of the machine by keeping the pressure constant between the wheel and work.

Roughing cuts may be from .002″ to .005″ or more for each reversal of the table depending on the amount of stock to be removed, the rigidity of the machine, and the work set up. Generally speaking, for roughing the job, a fast traverse, heavy feed, and slow work speed is used. For finish grinding, a slow traverse, light feed, and high work speed should be used.

Grinding wheels used on cylindrical grinders are generally made of silicate or resinoid bond and employ aluminous oxide abrasive wheels as follows: 46-*J*, 46-*K*, 60-*K*, 60-*L*, 80-*O* and 120-*P*.

Speed of work. Due to the many variable factors in grinding, no set rule can be given since the speed of the work conditions, such as work diameter, kind of metal, and heat treatment, are all important factors and should be taken into consideration. The grinding wheel will wear away very fast if too high a work speed is used, while too slow a work speed causes hard grinding action and glazing of the wheel. Common work speeds are from 30 to 50 surface feet per minute. Very hard steels of a tough nature may have to be ground more slowly than 30 SFPM, while very soft materials may be ground as fast as 100 SFPM.

WORK OPERATIONS

Plain cylinders. The following procedure is a typical analysis of the successive steps in grinding a plain cylinder.

Procedure.

1) Adjust the footstock on the table to accommodate the length of the work.

2) Check the machine centers to see that they are not loose in their sockets and are large enough to fill the work centers.

3) See that the conical point and body of the footstock center is cut away sufficiently to permit the grinding wheel to clear the end of the work. **"One-half-full"** centers, Fig. 11–8, are those which have the conical point and body cut almost in half. **"Three-quarter-full"** centers, Fig. 11–9, are those which have about one-fourth of the conical point and body cut away.

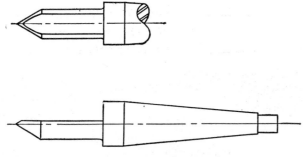

FIG. 11–8. One-half full center.

4) Check the work with a micrometer to determine the amount of grind stock and to detect any tapering of the work. Check the work centers for being clean and true and of sufficient depth.

5) Place a grinding dog of correct size on the end of the work. If the work has threads, keyways, etc., protect them by putting thin pieces of brass, copper, or other soft material between the work and the dog.

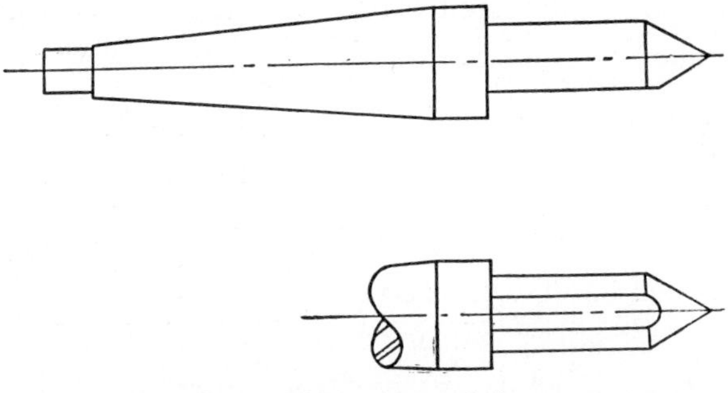

6) Lubricate the machine centers and check the table stops, feed trips, and levers to make certain that they are not engaged. Be sure that the wheel is moved back far enough not to interfere with easy mounting of the work.

7) Place the work in the machine, making sure that the work centers are

FIG. 11–9. Three-quarter full center.

properly engaged and that the drive pin is properly engaged both in the grinder dog and drive plate. If the work is long and slender, mount the steady rests and properly adjust the shoes.

8) Adjust the table traverse for the length of work, making allowances for the over-run of the wheel and for the space occupied by the dog.

9) Start the machine and let it run for one full minute to give it a chance to warm up. During this time permit the coolant to run on the wheel to balance it, especially if the machine has been idle for several hours.

10) For roughing out the job, dress the wheel by passing the diamond across the face of the wheel quite fast.

11) Set the work speed at the correct SFPM, and cautiously feed the grinding wheel to the work by hand until sparks indicate that contact has been made. Take a light trial cut, noting the action of the wheel on the work.

12) Without removing the work from the machine, check it for size and taper. Make any adjustments necessary to insure that the work will be straight.

13) Grind the job to rough size. If several pieces are to be done, set the stop and feed ratchet on the wheel head slide hand wheel. Proceed to rough out the remaining pieces keeping the wheel sharp and clean.

14) To rough out the end that the dog was on, place the dog on the other end of the work and proceed as in the above outline.

15) For finish grinding, dress the wheel by passing the diamond slowly across the wheel face, then set the machine for fast work speed and slow traverse.

16) Mount the piece to be finished and take a trial cut, checking the work frequently for size and taper.

17) Finish the first piece and set the stop on the feed ratchet so that the infeed will produce the required size on the remaining pieces. Have the first piece inspected for size, shape, and surface quality.

If the work has shoulders, keyways and the like in it, some deviation from the above procedure must be made. If work rests are used, the keyways or slots should be filled with lead or other suitable material

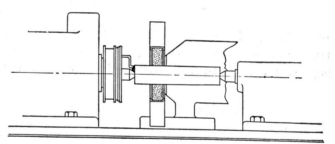

FIG. 11–10. Work with bent driving bracket sweated in place.

to prevent the shoes from catching in the work.

Sometimes it is desired to finish a job in one operation. A job of this nature may be done by sweating a bent bracket on the end of the piece, as shown in Fig. 11–10, to act as a driver. The bracket should have an offset sufficient to allow ample clearance for the over-run of the wheel. This method would have little advantage where a number of pieces of the same kind had to be worked.

Tapers. Taper work, Fig. 11–11, can be done on the cylindrical grinder by one of several methods: the work head, work table, or wheel head may be swiveled or the grinding wheel dressed at an angle. The table is set by using the swivel adjustment located on the right-hand side of the table. Three sets of graduations are generally provided. The scale marked in degrees represents one-half of the taper angle, whereas the scale marked **"taper per foot,"** or "**per cent,**" indicates the whole taper angle.

This scale is not to be relied upon to give accurate tapers; it is intended as an approximate starting point only. To produce accurate tapers, the work must be checked by means of a standard female taper gage, ring gage, or sine bar. If a standard female

FIG. 11–11.   Taper work on cylindrical grinder.

taper gage, Fig. 11–12, is used, three light stripes of Prussian blue should be applied lengthwise of the work about 120° apart. The work is then carefully inserted into the gage with a slight twisting motion. This twisting motion causes the gage to rub the blue

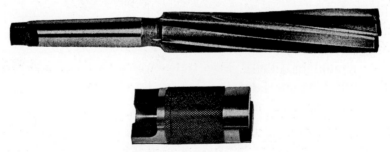

FIG. 11–12.   Female taper gage and work.

off the work wherever the work surface does not conform to the gage, leaving a bright, clean mark to indicate the location of the irregularity. If the taper is too steep, the blue will be rubbed off at or near the large diameter. If the taper is not steep enough, the blue will be rubbed off at or near the small diameter. If neither of these bearing spots appear, but if one or two lines show a complete bearing, it indicates that the work is out-of-round.

To produce steep tapers, either the work head or wheel head is set to the correct taper angle, or the angle may be dressed on the wheel. Generally the base of the work head is graduated in degrees and provided with a vernier to make accurate settings possible. If the wheel is to be dressed at an angle, care must be exercised to see that the diamond is set on the exact center-line of the wheel. If this caution is not observed the wheel will not be dressed to the correct angle.

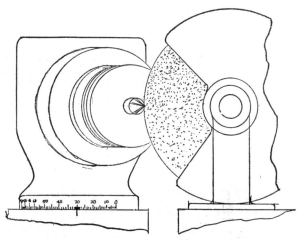

To grind the 60-degree conical point on a machine center, Fig. 11–13, the work head should be swiveled to 30°. After cleaning the taper socket of the work head spindle and the taper shank of the center, place the center in the spindle. Next dress the grinding wheel and take a trial cut, observing how the wheel contacts the work. If the trial cut does not follow the original point, check the point with the flat

FIG. 11–13.   Grinding a 60° machine center.

center gage, Fig. 11–14, or the cone center gage, Fig. 11–15, and make the adjustments necessary to insure accurate results.

The flat center gage is used by locating the conical point in the *Vee* of the gage and observing where the sides of the "V" do not contact the work.

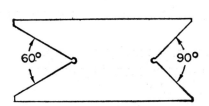

FIG. 11–14.   Flat center gage.

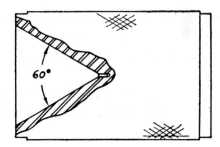

FIG. 11–15.   Cone center gage.

The cone center gage is used in much the same way as the female taper gage. The conical point of the machine center is given three stripes of Prussian blue terminating at the apex of the cone, then the cone gage is carefully placed on it with a slight twisting motion. When the gage is removed the bearing spots will indicate whether or not the center corresponds with the gage.

After the necessary adjustments have been made, proceed with the grinding operation with care. The change in work speed, due to the steep taper, will cause burning of the center point. This may be overcome by taking light cuts, using a slow work speed, a flood of coolant, and working the cut from the point back to the large diameter of the center.

Contour grinding, such as concave or convex radii, Fig. 11–16, or a radius and an angle, may be ground by dressing the wheel to the desired shape. Generally the manufacturer of the machine supplies such a mechanism as extra equipment. Fig. 11–17 shows an attachment used for dressing radii on the wheel.

For dressing a radius on the wheel, the fixture is set so that the point of the diamond falls behind or ahead of the fixture center a distance equal to the required

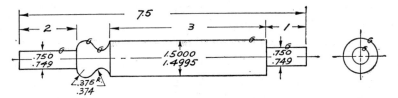

Fig. 11–16.   Job with convex and concave radii.

radius. If the grinding wheel must be dressed concave, the diamond is set ahead of center; if the grinding wheel must be dressed convex, the diamond is set behind center.

When dressing the grinding wheel at an angle or radius it is absolutely necessary that the diamond point and its path of travel be kept on the exact centerline of the wheel, otherwise the wheel will be dressed incorrectly.

General comments. "Out-of-roundness" of the work is a condition in which one side of the work, though radial, will be lower than other sections. This condition may not show up when the work is checked with an ordinary micrometer caliper, but if it is placed in a set of bench test centers, and a dial indicator used, the low side of the work will readily show up. This out-of-roundness may be caused by one of several factors, but two of the most common reasons are nicked or dirty work centers or loose machine centers.

"Mottled," "checked," or **"cracked"** work surfaces may be due to improper work speeds, wheel too hard, or a loaded or glazed wheel. To overcome these conditions try setting the work speed a little faster, keep the grinding wheel

Fig. 11–17.   Radius truing device.

clean and sharp, and keep a good supply of coolant running on the point of contact between the wheel and work. If the wheel is too hard it will still cause the work to burn and crack even though the work speed is correct and a good supply of coolant is used. The remedy then would be to try a wheel with a slightly softer bond.

"Undercuts" in the work are caused by irregular movement of the work table past the grinding wheel. Any interrupted travel of the table permits the grinding wheel to grind longer in one place than another, resulting in a smaller diameter ground at that point. To correct this condition keep the machine well oiled and all operating members working freely.

"**Plunge-cut**" grinding is the term applied to the grinding of a surface without traversing the work table. It is used when grinding a flange or shoulder which is narrower than the width of the wheel face. It is also used to good advantage when grinding a cylindrical surface with multiple diameters. In this instance it keeps the corner of the wheel sharp, thus making a square corner between the shoulder and cylindrical surface, and speeds up the operation of grinding the remainder of the cylinder.

To use plunge-cut grinding for shoulder work, locate the grinding wheel close against the shoulder and feed it in to the required depth; then traverse the table by hand so that the shoulder moves away from the grinding wheel. The wheel should then be dressed, and the table traversed by hand almost up to the shoulder to finish grinding that section.

"**Dressing**" the wheel is the process of removing material from the surface of the wheel for the purpose of restoring its cutting properties. The best results are obtained by setting the diamond and shank as shown in Fig. 11–18. To dress the grinding wheel for fast cutting or roughing out a job, pass the diamond quickly across the face of the wheel taking cuts of about .001″. To dress the grinding wheel for a finishing cut pass the diamond slowly across the face of the wheel, using feeds from .0001″ to .0002″ for soft wheels and from .0003″ to .0005″ for hard wheels.

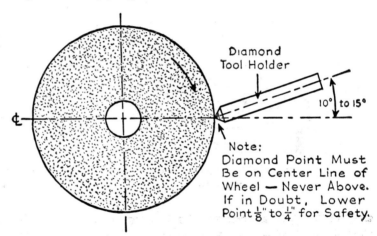

Fig. 11–18.   Correct position of diamond tool.

"**Truing**" is the act of fracturing the surface of a grinding wheel for the purpose of making the periphery run concentric with the wheel spindle axis, to make the sides parallel, or to change the shape of the wheel.

"**Glazing**" of the wheel is a condition in which the abrasive particles in the wheel have become dull and are not released by the bond, causing the cutting surface of the wheel to take on a shiny or glass-like surface. Generally this condition is caused by the wheel being too hard for the material being ground, or the work speed is too slow. If, after the wheel has been dressed and the work speed increased, the condition is not corrected, then it is an indication that the wheel is too hard and it should be changed for a softer one.

"**Loading**" is the term used to express the condition in which the material being ground becomes imbedded in the pores of the grinding wheel. It is caused by the work being too slow, the bond of the wheel too hard, or crowding the wheel into the work. If dressing the wheel does not correct this condition, try taking a lighter cut or increasing the work speed.

Gaging cylindrical work. The micrometer caliper is commonly used for gaging work which comes within its scope. Frequently, however, cylindrical grinding must be done that requires the use of gages calibrated to a finer degree of accuracy than ordinary micrometer calipers are capable of producing. For this purpose gages known as *"Comparators"* or *"Amplifiers"* are used.

The **common amplifier,** Fig. 11–19, is a mechanical instrument employing a lever arrangement in which one thousandth of an inch is amplified ten times. For quick and

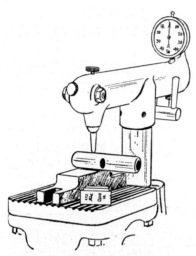

FIG. 11–19. Common 10 to 1 amplifier.

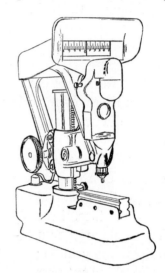

FIG. 11–20. Amplifier calibrated to read .000025 inches.

easy reading, a dial indicator graduated to read in tenths of thousandths is arranged so that an end of one of the lever arms acts upon it. The dial accurately records any deviation of the needle from any required setting.

Another type, Fig. 11–20, which contains a fan shaped dial illuminated electrically, is graduated to read in steps of twenty-five millionths of an inch. The total reading of the dial is ± 0.0005″.

To set either of these instruments, gage blocks can be combined to the size of the required dimension. (See page 259.) After cleaning the rest block of the amplifier, the gage blocks are placed upon it and the contact point and indicator dial adjusted so that the indicator needle will not have to move more than ten graduations to equal the size of the gage blocks, Fig. 11–21. The gage blocks are then removed and the part to be gaged is placed on the rest block and slowly rolled under the contact point. While the part is thus being rolled the indicator needle should be observed for any deflection. If the indicator needle shows a maximum deflection after it gets past zero, Fig. 11–22, the part is oversize by an amount equal to the value of the number of divisions by which the needle passes zero. If the indicator needle does not go to zero, the work is under-size in the amount registered.

SAFETY SUGGESTIONS

1) Before starting the machine check all machine stops and levers to see that they are disengaged, so that when the machine is started it will not be damaged by one moving part colliding with another. When starting the machine, especially after it has stood idle over night, step to one side as the starter button or switch is pushed. This precaution should be taken to insure being clear of the wheel in case it should burst because of the carelessness of a former user.

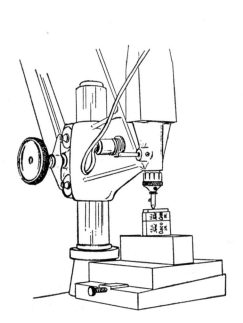

FIG. 11–21. Setting amplifier with gage blocks.

FIG. 11–22. Checking the work on an amplifier.

2) Before engaging the wheel with the work make sure that the work is properly located between the machine centers, and that the drive pin, connecting the drive plate and dog, is correctly adjusted and locked in place.

3) Keep the machine well oiled and keep a good supply of coolant running at the point of contact between the wheel and work.

4) When machining work, especially that which contains keyways, splines, or other surface irregularities, do not put your hand on it while it is in motion.

Do not wear rings while working. Many serious injuries result from this practice.

5) When checking work on a cylindrical grinder without removing it from the machine, it is not necessary to stop the grinding wheel, but be sure that the wheel has been moved far enough away from the work so the checking may be done without injury to yourself.

Centerless grinding. The centerless grinder, Fig. 11–23, was designed for the rapid production of plain external cylinder, external taper, or external profile work, Fig. 11-24. It might be assumed from the foregoing that the centerless grinder is purely a production machine; this is not the case, however. The machine possesses many characteristics that suit it to tool room use. It eliminates the necessity of having to center drill the ends of the work and of taking all the painstaking care incident to this operation.

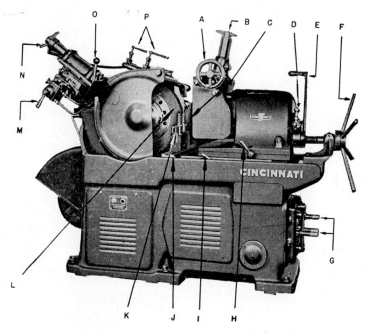

FIG. 11–23.   External centerless grinder.

A. Handwheel for operating regulating wheel truing attachment.
B. Truing attachment for regulating wheel.
C. Regulating wheel.
D. Crank for micrometer adjustment of regulating wheel.
E. Lever for pressure adjustment on regulating wheel.
F. Spar for adjusting regulating wheel and work rest slide.
G. Levers for varying the speed of the regulating wheel.
H. Handle for clamping the regulating wheel slide to the lower work rest slide.
I. Handle for clamping the work rest slide in position.
J. Slide for transverse adjustment of work rest.
K. Work rest.
L. Grinding wheel.
M. Lever for hydraulic control of grinding wheel truing attachment.
N. Truing attachment for grinding wheel.
O. Lever for operating profile attachment.
P. Valve handles for controlling coolant supply to diamond and grinding wheel.

It eliminates the time required to load and unload the work properly between the centers of a cylindrical grinder. Heavier cuts can be taken making it possible to reduce the work to size by taking fewer *passes* of the wheel. The machine is rigidly built and simple to set up and operate; therefore, it does not require the high upkeep cost or the services of a highly skilled mechanic.

From an operator's point of view, the important operating members are the grinding wheel, the regulating wheel, and the work rest. The action of the grinding wheel exerts a pressure on the work, forcing the work down against the work rest and regulating wheel. The regulating wheel, which is actually a rubber bonded abrasive wheel, rotates in a clockwise direction the same as the grinding wheel, Fig. 11–25, causing the work to revolve in a counterclockwise direction and feeds the work through the machine. The grinding wheel operates continuously at about 6000 SFPM whereas the regulating wheel can be operated at from 12 to 300 RPM.

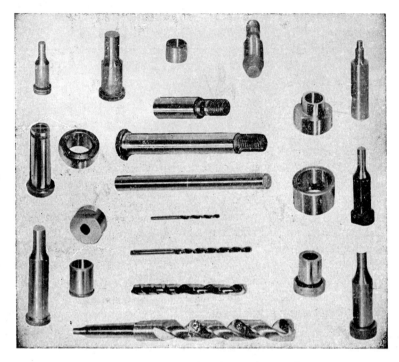

FIG. 11–24. Samples of centerless work.

With this method of grinding, the work does not need to be perfectly cylindrical to start with because the location of the axis of the work, with respect to the centerline of the two wheels, governs the length of time required to grind the work into a cylindrical shape. The higher above the center of the two wheels that the work is placed, the quicker the rounding-up action will be. However, it is possible to have the work located too high, which causes it to be lifted off the work rest.

To get the best rounding action, the work rest should be adjusted so that the center of the work is located one-half the work diameter above the centerline of the two wheels, as shown in Fig. 11–25.

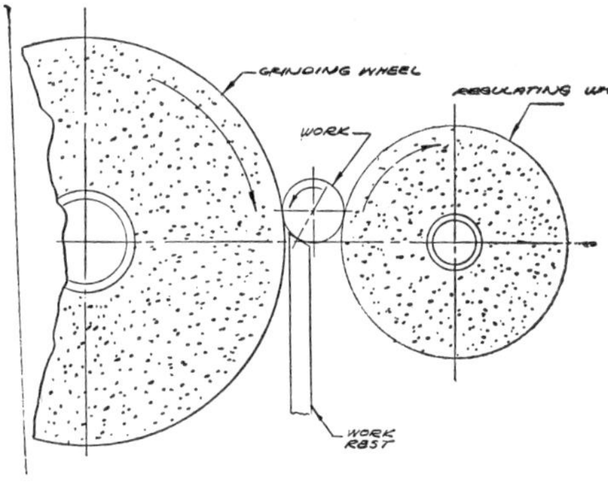

FIG. 11–25. Rotation of grinding wheel, work and regulating wheel.

For grinding plain cylindrical work, where it can be fed completely through the machine, the method of feeding the work is known as **"Through-Feed Grinding."** If the work must be ground to a shoulder or taper, the method of feeding is known as **"In-Feed Grinding."**

For either method of feeding, the rate of feed is governed by the position of the regulating wheel axis with respect to the axis of the grinding wheel and the speed of the regulating wheel. Ordinarily for work that is straight, the regulating wheel should be set from 3° to 4°. If the work is badly warped or bent the angle can be increased to as much as 6°.

REVIEW QUESTIONS

1. Name six classifications of grinders.
2. What types of work can be performed on the plain cylinder grinder?
3. Discuss live and dead centers.
4. Describe several methods of holding the work for cylindrical grinding.
5. How does a grinder dog differ from a lathe dog?
6. How much of the wheel face should be allowed to run past the end of the work? Discuss.
7. What is meant by the term table dwell?
8. What is the range of wheel feed?
9. What is the common range of work speeds in number of surface feet per minute?
10. Discuss the procedure for grinding a plain cylinder.
11. Name several methods of grinding tapers.
12. Discuss the operations of grinding a 60-degree machine center.
13. How is a radius dressed on a wheel?
14. How is out-of-roundness detected on a piece of work?
15. What is meant by plunge-cut grinding?
16. Discuss the process of dressing the wheel for roughing and also for finishing.
17. Define the terms truing, glazing, and loading.
18. What is a common amplifier?
19. How are gage blocks used in setting an amplifier?
20. Discuss common safety precautions in connection with cylindrical grinding.
21. What are some of the advantages of a centerless grinder?
22. Name the important members of a centerless grinder from the operator's point of view.
23. What is meant by through-feed and in-feed grinding?

Chapter 12

INTERNAL GRINDERS

DEFINITION

CLASSIFICATION

Work Rotating Type ... Planetary Type ... Centerless Type

METHODS OF HOLDING WORK

Chucking the Work ... Internal Cylindrical Grinding — Thirteen step analysis ... Internal taper grinding ... Flat Work ... Chuck and Steady Rest ... Center and Steady Rest ... Face Plate and Angle Plate ... Face Plate and V-Block ... Special Fixtures

SAFETY SUGGESTIONS

Internal Centerless ... Cylinder Grinder

DEFINITION

An **internal grinder** is a machine especially designed to facilitate the finishing of holes. This finishing is generally for the purpose of bringing the hole to the correct size and shape and to give it good surface quality.

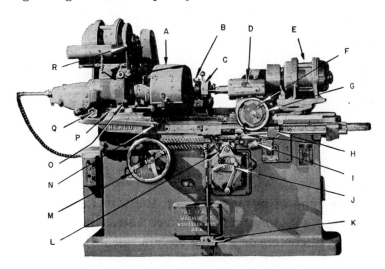

FIG. 12–1. Universal internal grinder.

A. Spindle nose and chuck guard. Lifts up
B. Diamond for truing grinding wheel
C. Grinding wheel guard. Works automatically
D. Grinding wheel spindle head
E. Motor for driving wheel head
F. Fine adjustment for feeding wheel to work
G. Cross slide handwheel for feeding wheel to work
H. Dogs for controlling length of stroke of table and grinding wheel head
I. Knob for adjusting engagement of quick return of wheel head
J. Table speed control lever. Adjusts from 0 to 44 FPM
K. Foot treadle lifts dogs and permits table and wheel head to go to rest
L. Ball lever. Reverses the table in the direction that it is thrown
M. Hand wheel for controlling movement of table
N. Collet lever. Holds or releases work
O. Spindle lock knob. Locks spindle when removing chucks or fixtures
P. Work head base. Graduated for grinding tapers or angles
Q. Knob for swiveling and lining up work head
R. Lever for starting and stopping the work head

CLASSIFICATION

Internal grinders are classified according to three types: **work rotating, planetary,** and **centerless.**

The machines commonly used in tool and die rooms are of the **work rotating type.** In this machine one of two principles is employed with respect to work and wheel movement; that is, the wheel head may be stationary with a reciprocating work table, or the wheel head may reciprocate and the work table remain stationary. Both machines have the wheel head mounted on a slide with provisions for feeding the wheel to the work.

A. Guard. Covers spindle nose and swings upward permitting access to chuck, faceplate, or collet
B. Wheel head or graduated swivel base.
C. Wheel head slide. Moves in and out
D. Fixture for tripping diamond truing device
E. Fine adjustment for upper table swivel
F. Table traverse locking lever
G. Screw for adjusting upper table swivel
H. Knob for engaging wheel head slide power cross feed
I. Hand wheel for operating wheel head slide. It is graduated in 0.0005
J. Pilot wheel for traversing table by hand
K. Crank for setting length of table stroke
L. Change gear handle for changing speed of table traverse
M. Belt tension adjusting lever
N. Screw for positioning table stroke
O. Work head base. Graduated in degrees for cutting steep tapers
P. Lever for starting and stopping the work head

Fig. 12–2. Universal internal grinder.

In the **planetary type** of internal grinder, the wheel spindle is so arranged that besides rotating on its axis it can be made to run eccentrically, thus making it possible to grind holes of varying diameters depending on how much the wheel spindle is made to run eccentric. The work is mounted on a table which has vertical, horizontal, and longitudinal adjustments similar to those of the plain milling machine.

The **centerless grinder** works on a roller chucking principle in which the rollers hold the work and impart the rotary motion to the work. The wheel head has a reciprocating motion and may be fed in and out by hand. This machine is used for work of a repetitive nature, and possesses advantages similar to those of the external centerless.

METHODS OF HOLDING WORK

In the work rotating type grinder, Fig. 12–2, straight cylindrical holes, combination straight and tapered holes, taper holes, blind holes, and holes having irregular shapes may be ground. Work is held on this grinder by one of the following methods:

1) In a 3- or 4-jaw chuck screwed to the work head spindle nose.
2) Clamped to a face plate attached to the spindle.
3) In a spring collet held in the spindle opening by a draw bar.
4) One end of the work held by the 3- or 4-jaw chuck while the other end is supported by a center rest.
5) One end of the work resting on the work head center and tied in place by passing a buckskin thong around the grinder dog and drive plate, the free end being supported by a center rest.
6) The work may be clamped to a 90° angle plate and the assembly clamped to a face plate.
7) The work may be held in a V-block clamped to the face plate.
8) When the work is of an odd shape and there are a great number of pieces, fixtures may be devised and used to cut down on the set-up time.

Chucking the work. All of the foregoing methods are used in general machine tool grinding, but the 4-jaw chuck method is used to a greater extent than the others. This is because the jaws can be moved to accommodate a wide range of work diameters and because the independent action of the jaws permits greater accuracy in lining up the work.

Fig. 12–3 illustrates the method of truing a job in a 4-jaw chuck.

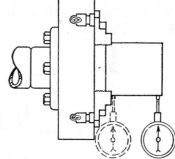

FIG. 12–3. Truing the work in a 4-jaw chuck.

Procedure.

1) The jaws are opened as concentrically as possible and the work put in place, allowing sufficient room for the inside over travel of the wheel.
2) The jaws are then tightened equally on the work with sufficient pressure to hold it but not enough to spring it out of shape.
3) The chuck is then turned over by hand to determine which jaws permit the work to run out. When this is determined loosen the jaw that is moved in too far and tighten the opposite one. When the amount of runout comes within the scope of a dial indicator place the point of the indicator on the work, up as close to the jaws as possible, and continue the operation of loosening one jaw and tightening the opposite one, until the job runs within the required accuracy.
4) Move the indicator to the outer end of the work and while turning the chuck by hand observe the amount of **"runout."**
5) With the indicator showing the low spot, use a soft mallet and bump the work over an amount equal to half the runout at that point. It is good practice to pull back on the indicator plunger while the bumping is being done, otherwise the indicator may be damaged.

6) Repeat this operation of indicating and bumping the outer end of the work until the required accuracy is obtained. As an added precaution be sure to run the indicator back and forth over the length of work to see if it is running parallel.

Internal cylindrical grinding. The following is an analysis of the procedure required to set up the machine to grind a straight cylindrical hole.

Procedure.

1) Check the inside diameter of the hole with a telescoping gage for sufficient grind stock and to determine whether or not the hole is tapered.

2) Mount a 4-jaw chuck firmly on the work head spindle and chuck up the work as outlined. Make sure that the work head is set at zero on its base graduations.

3) Select the proper wheel. The selection of the wheel is based on the diameter of the hole and the kind of material to be ground. Generally speaking the diameter of the wheel should not exceed two-thirds of the diameter of the hole. These wheels are usually of the vitrified bond with a grain size and hardness of 46-*H*; 46-*I*; 46-*J*; 60-*H*; 60-*I*; 60-*J*; 60-*L*; and 120-*P*. The diameters of the wheels are from 1/4" to 2-1/2" and the length 3/8" to 2".

4) Select the largest quill possible, being consistent with the diameter and length of the hole, and mount the grinding wheel. Be sure to protect the ends of the wheel with soft metal washers.

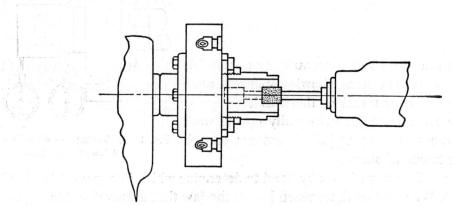

FIG. 12–4.   Setting length of stroke to avoid bell-mouthing.

5) Set the machine for the length of the work making allowances for the overtravel of the wheel. The length of stroke should be such that not more than one-half of the wheel face width is uncovered at the extremities of the stroke to avoid **"bell-mouthing"** of the hole, as shown in Fig. 12–4. **"Bell-mouthing"** is the term used to express a condition in which the ends of the hole flare out to a bell shape.

6) Adjust the table to cut straight. This is done by setting the table graduations on the right hand end to zero.

7) See that all feed and trip levers are disengaged and start the machine, stepping to one side as the starter button is pressed. True and dress the grinding wheel for rough

grinding. Diamond truing and dressing devices are usually a part of the standard equipment which is supplied.

8) Take a trial cut, removing as little stock as possible. See that the wheel guard is adjusted properly to cover the wheel.

9) Check the hole for straight cutting and out of round. Make any necessary table adjustments at this time.

10) With the machine set for cutting straight, rough out the hole to within .001" to .003" of size depending on its length and diameter.

11) Dress the wheel for taking a finishing cut by passing the diamond over the wheel slowly.

12) Finish grinding the hole, checking it frequently for size with a telescoping gage as shown in Fig. 12–5. As the hole approaches its true size, check it with a plug gage, but be careful that the plug does not **"freeze"** in the hole. **"To freeze the plug"** is the term applied to a condition in which the work contracts on the cold plug gage thus causing the gage to stick in the hole. This condition may be overcome either by holding the plug gage in the hand until it heats up slightly, or permitting the work to cool off. Where several pieces of the same kind are to be ground it is good practice to leave the plug gage in the last piece which was ground, thus keeping it ready for gaging the next hole.

FIG. 12–5. Checking the hole with a telescoping gage.

13) After the first piece has been ground to size have it inspected.

Internal taper grinding. Tapered holes can be machined on an internal grinder either by swiveling the work table or the work head. When slight tapers are desired the work table is moved so that the graduations at the right hand end of the table indicate the correct taper per foot. Steep tapers may be machined by swiveling the work head to one-half of the taper angle. The work head base is graduated in degrees and is equipped with a vernier for greater accuracy.

It is obvious that these graduations can not be relied upon for extreme accuracy. For this reason a plug gage having the correct taper per foot must be used to check the work immediately after a trial cut has been taken. The plug gage should be given a very light coat of Prussian blue and be inserted in the hole with a slight twisting motion. Be sure that the hole is free of all dust and grit before inserting the gage. When the gage is extracted, if the two tapers do not correspond, the blue will be rubbed off indicating the point of contact. If the blue is rubbed off at or near the small end of the gage it indicates that the taper of the work is too steep. If the blue is rubbed off at or near the large end of the gage it indicates that the taper of the work is not steep enough. In either case correction should be made by adjusting the compensating screws at the foot stock end of the table.

If the taper to be cut is not standard it may be checked by using the mating part as a gage. It should be used in the same manner as a plug gage.

Flat work. The face plate may be used for holding flat work, Fig. 12–6, which can not be held conveniently in a chuck. The face plate may also be used for holding work which must be clamped either to an angle plate or V-block.

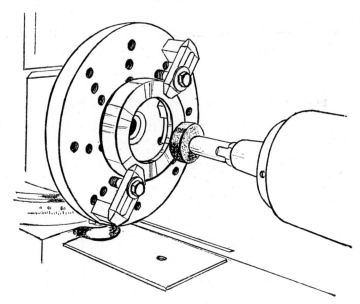

FIG. 12–6.   Face plate set up with flat work.

Procedure.

1) To set up the work on the face plate select two parallels of a size consistent with the size of the work. Use these as rest blocks to raise the bottom of the work away from the face plate so that there will be clearance for the overrun of the wheel.

2) Place the parallels in position on the face plate and locate the work on them. If jacks or adjustable step blocks are not available, use blocks of wood or fiber that will be the same height as the work on the face plate, and set them on either side of the work.

3) Select studs long enough so that when the clamps are put in position there will be enough of the threaded section sticking out to permit running the nut on its entire length. Screw the studs into the face plate across the work from each other, and keep them reasonably close to the work.

4) Put the clamps in position, locating them so that they will not interfere with the grinding operation. Put a washer over each stud and put the nuts on.

5) Adjust the position of the step blocks so that the stud is closer to the work than to the step blocks. This puts the clamping pressure on the work.

6) Before tightening the nuts be sure that the work rest blocks and clamps do not interfere with the grinding operation and that the clamps are parallel with the face plate.

Where a set-up of this kind occurs very frequently, fixtures are provided for holding the face plate while the hole to be ground is being indicated. This saves considerable time and makes it much easier than trying to line up the work after the face plate has been attached to the work head spindle.

If the location of the hole in the work is such that the work is eccentric on the face plate, a counter weight, Fig. 12–11, should be bolted to the face plate to compensate for the centrifugal force of the work and also to prevent unwarranted strain on the spindle.

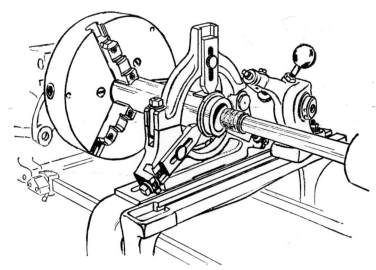

FIG. 12–7. Three jaw chuck and steady rest set up.

Chuck and steady rest. The 3-jaw chuck and steady rest are used to hold a spindle-like piece of work which requires a hole to be ground in one end concentric with the outside diameter. In this set up, Fig. 12–7, the work is **"chucked-up"** within the required degree of accuracy and the steady rest located near the outer end of the work. After the steady rest has been tightened in place, set a test indicator against the outer end of the work, and adjust the steady rest **"shoes"** so that the work runs true within the required degree of accuracy.

Center and steady rest. Sometimes it is necessary to grind a blind hole in the end of a spindle-like piece of work having a center hole in the opposite end. To do this type of job a machine center is placed in the work head spindle and a drive plate attached to the spindle nose in place of the chuck. A grinder dog is attached to the centered end of the work and a steady rest put in place on the work table.

The drive plate is backed off about two turns and the work located on the work head center and steady rest. Use a piece of buckskin lace, passing it around the grinder dog and drive plate, to tie the work securely in place, then tighten the drive plate. Fig. 12–8 shows a picture of this set up.

Face plate and angle plate. The use of an angle plate for holding work on the face plate is shown in Fig. 12–9. The angle plate used in this instance must have all its opposite faces parallel and adjacent sides perpendicular to each other. To set the work up, turn the angle plate on its side and clamp the work against the face of the angle plate with a small C-clamp. Using a height gage and indicator, indicate the side of the hole and adjust it parallel with the sides of the angle plate. Turn the angle plate right side up and put another C-clamp on the work opposite the first one. See that the work is raised

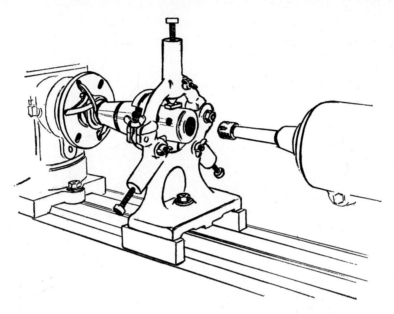

FIG. 12–8.   Center and steady rest set up.

far enough from the base of the angle plate to give clearance for the overrun of the grinding wheel. Locate and clamp the angle plate on the face plate as previously outlined and install a counter weight.

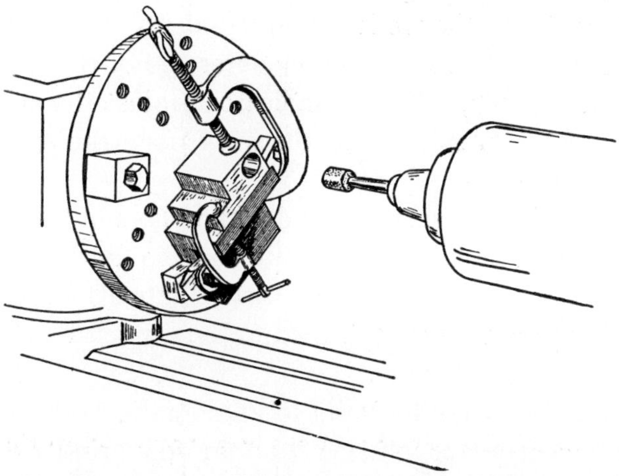

Face plate and V-block. Fig. 12–10 shows a type of job which requires the hole to be ground at 90° with the cylindrical shank. This operation can be done conveniently by holding the work in a V-block and clamping the assembly to a face plate as shown in Fig. 12–11.

To locate the work properly in the V-block, use a 10″ height gage and either an **"Ideal"** or **"Last Word"** indicator to check the work

FIG. 12–9.   Face plate and angle plate set up.

for being central in the block. Use the height gage and indicator to locate the hole perpendicular to the base and tighten the work securely. Be sure to check the position of the hole again to see that it did not move when the piece was tightened. Next mount the V-block assembly on the face plate using clamps and step blocks as outlined in face plate work. Use a counter weight to balance the eccentric weight of the V-block.

Special fixtures. These are used for holding work of a repetitive nature. Fixtures of this type make it possible for the operator of a grinder to locate the work easily, quickly and accurately, and support it properly.

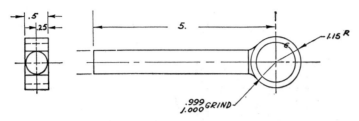

FIG. 12–10. Hole to be ground 90° with cylindrical shank.

Blind holes may be ground on an internal grinder, provided that the bottom of the hole is sufficiently undercut and recessed to allow room for the overrun of the grinding wheel.

Internal form grinding may be done by dressing the wheel to the desired shape.

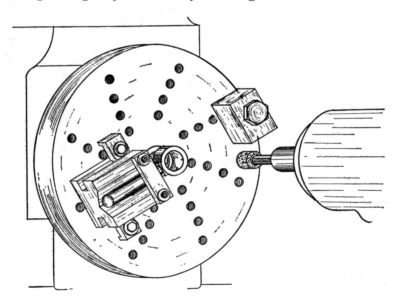

FIG. 12–11. Face plate and V-block set up.

SAFETY SUGGESTIONS

1) When mounting internal grinding wheels, use paper or brass washers between the wheel and spindle and the retaining screw and wheel to equalize the pressure on the wheel.

2) It is dangerous to use wheels larger than 2-1/2″ in diameter for internal grinders. If wheels larger than this must be used consult the foreman.

3) When setting-up a job, or machine attachments, or when making any changes in the set-up, stops, or guards, be sure to shut the machine down.

4) Work set up on a face plate should be clamped properly and securely.

5) If the work must be set up eccentrically on the face plate use counter weights.

6) Many painful hand and finger injuries result from trying to clean out a hole, for the purpose of checking it, while the work head is in operation.

7) Internal grinding machines are equipped with a guard to enclose the wheel while the work is being checked, Fig. 12–12. See that this guard is working properly at all times.

8) When checking work that is too long to permit the proper operation of the wheel guard, **shut the machine down.**

9) Wear goggles when doing facing operations on the internal grinder and keep the wheel sharp. Wear goggles when the internal grinding operation necessitates the use of extra hard wheels or thin rubber wheels.

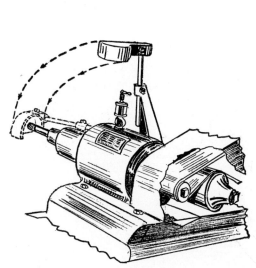

FIG. 12–12. Action of wheel guard on internal grinder.

FIG. 12–13. Internal centerless grinder.

Internal centerless grinder. This machine, Fig. 12–13, is capable of producing straight cylindrical or taper holes, interrupted holes, holes having a shoulder, or blind holes. The work is so held and revolved that the hole will be concentric with the outside diameter.

This machine is adaptable to large runs of repetitive types of bushing work and possesses many of the advantages of the external centerless grinder. The work is supported and revolved by three rollers. One roller, known as the **"regulating"** roll, drives and regulates the speed of the work. See Fig. 12–14. It acts on the work in much the same manner as the regulating wheel of the external centerless grinder, supporting the work on the outside at the point where the wheel contacts the work and preventing the grinding wheel from driving the work too fast. A second roll, known as the pressure roll, is mounted on a swinging bracket and holds the work against the **"supporting"** roll and regulating roll. The supporting roll is located below the work and is adjustable. These rolls move in and out automatically to provide for loading and unloading the work.

In this machine the wheel head moves in and out while the work head remains stationary.

Cylinder grinder. This machine, Fig. 12–15, commonly known as a **"Planetary"** grinder, was designed for grinding holes in work too cumbersome or bulky to be held in the work rotating type of grinder.

The work is held on a work table either by bolting it directly to the table or to a 90° angle plate. The work table is similar to that of the milling machine, being supported by a knee which can be raised or lowered on the machine column. The table reciprocates to and from the column and has provisions for setting the length

FIG. 12–14. Work held in the internal centerless grinder.

and position of the stroke. It can also be moved crosswise with respect to the knee.

The grinding wheel on this machine is so mounted that besides rotating on its own axis, it rotates around the axis of the hole to be ground. The amount of eccentric

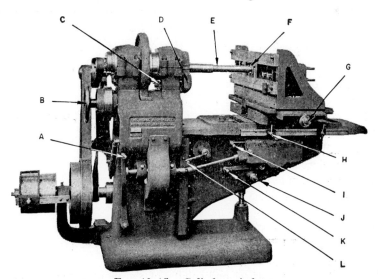

FIG. 12–15. Cylinder grinder.

A. Starting lever
B. Hand wheel for revolving spindle
C. Adjustment for depth of cut in increments of .0005
D. Hole sizing mechanism
E. Grinding wheel quill or arbor
F. Grinding wheel
G. Screw for longitudinal adjustment of table

H. Trip dogs for setting length and position of stroke
I. Speed control lever for table reciprocation
J. Shaft for vertical adjustment of knee
K. Lever for engaging table feed
L. Hand control for moving work to and from the grinding wheel

motion of the wheel spindle is regulated by hand through the medium of a lever conveniently located on the wheel head, as shown in Fig. 12–16.

This type of grinding machine is suited to railroad shops and the aircraft engine industry, since much of the work is too cumbersome to be rotated.

FIG. 12–16.   Wheel head of cylinder grinder.

REVIEW QUESTIONS

1. Name three types of internal grinders. Discuss.
2. Discuss various methods of holding work in an internal grinder.
3. What method is most frequently used?
4. Outline the procedure of truing the work in a 4-jaw chuck.
5. Describe the procedure of setting up the machine for grinding a straight hole.
6. Discuss the use of a tapered plug gage.
7. When is a face plate used?
8. Discuss the procedure of mounting work on a face plate.
9. How and when are counterweights used?
10. When is an angle plate used?
11. How is internal form grinding accomplished?
12. Discuss general safety suggestions for internal grinder operations.
13. What kind of work can be produced on an internal centerless grinder?
14. How is work held on the planetary grinder?
15. Describe the motion of the wheel and spindle of the planetary type grinder.
16. For what types of work is this machine best suited?

Chapter 13

SURFACE GRINDERS

DEFINITION

Rotary Type ... Planer Type ... Vertical Spindle ̄ Rotary — Work Operations ...
Horizontal Planer Type ... Holding the Work ... Operations Witness Marks ...
Grinding Work Parallel ... Grinding Work Square ... Angular Work ... V-Block
Work — Work operations ... Slot Grinding — Work operations ... Radius Grinding
... Surface Grinder Wheels

GENERAL INFORMATION

Safety ... Wheel Selection

SAFETY SUGGESTIONS

DEFINITION

A surface grinder is a machine designed for doing operations similar to those done on a shaper, planer, or milling machine, but is capable of producing these surfaces more accurately both as to size and surface quality.

These machines fall in two general classifications, **rotary type** and **planer type,** depending on the action of the table in operation. These types are divided into groups depending on the position of the spindle and how the grinding wheel acts on the work.

The rotary type is divided as follows:

1. Horizontal spindle using the periphery of the wheel.
2. Vertical spindle using the rim of the wheel.

The planer type is divided into:

1. Horizontal spindle using the rim of the wheel.
2. Vertical spindle using the rim of the wheel.
3. Horizontal spindle using the periphery of the wheel.

All of these machines are adaptable to machine tool work and each machine has its particular advantages, but for the purpose of general tool work this text will limit its scope to the horizontal rotary type of surface grinder shown in Fig. 13–1, the vertical rotary type shown in Fig. 13–3, and the horizontal spindle planer type shown in Fig. 13–5.

The machine shown in Fig. 13–1 uses the periphery of a grinding wheel mounted on a horizontal spindle. The wheel head is similar in construction to the ram of a shaper and operates with a reciprocating motion, having adjustments for setting the position and length of stroke.

The work table is circular in shape and employs a magnetic chuck for holding the work. It is so constructed that it may be tilted for producing either flat, concave, or convex surfaces and has both hand and automatic feed. Flat surfaces are produced only when the work table is set at zero. The work is then placed on the magnetic chuck with the surface to be ground exposed to the grinding wheel and the magnetic chuck switch turned on. The work table is then lowered to permit the grinding wheel to be spotted on the work and the wheel head traversed by hand. After the wheel is

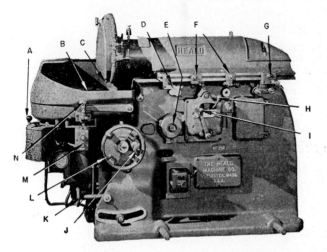

A. Control switch for magnetic chuck
B. Magnetic chuck
C. Grinding wheel
D. Wheel slide safety stops
E. Adjustment for speed of wheel slide
F. Stops for adjusting length of stroke
G. Trip dog for engaging quick return (adjustable)
H. Hand lever for reversing wheel slide
I. Control for adjusting speed of wheel slide and wheel
J. Micrometer adjustment for feeding the work to the wheel
K. Adjustment for setting work chuck for concave or convex surfaces
L. Hand wheel for vertical adjustment of magnetic chuck
M. Electrical controls for starting and stopping the machine
N. Wheel truing and dressing mechanism

FIG. 13–1. Horizontal rotary surface grinder.

spotted on the work, the length and position of stroke is set and a trial cut taken. The work is then checked for size and parallelism and any necessary corrections made, after which the work may be ground to size.

When small pieces are to be ground, they should be grouped close together and blocked or supported on the magnetic chuck with pieces of steel. These steel blocks should be low enough to permit finish grinding of the work. When it is necessary to grind a large number of small cylindrical pieces to length it is good practice to use retaining rings of varying thicknesses, the outside diameters of which are equal to the diameter of the magnetic chuck. These rings are located on the chuck and the pieces of work placed inside, as shown in Fig. 13–2.

Many suitable grinding wheel dressers are available for truing and dressing the wheel on this machine. One type consists of a small silicon carbide abrasive wheel mounted on an axle in a suitable cast iron fixture. This dresser is used by placing it on the magnetic chuck so that the axis of the dressing wheel is at a slight angle to the axis of the grinding wheel. The magnetic force in the chuck is turned on and the rotating grinding wheel brought into contact with the dresser. The grinding wheel is then traversed over the dresser to produce the desired cutting face. The magnetic chuck should be turned on but the table should not be permitted to revolve.

Other types of dressers such as cemented carbide tips and commercial diamonds, fixed in suitable holders, are used in a manner similar to the silicon carbide dresser.

Vertical spindle rotary. This machine, Fig. 13–3, is used for the production of accurate, flat surfaces and when properly handled will remove stock faster than any of the commonly used tool room machines. It uses a cylindrically shaped wheel, either of the solid or segmented type, the rim of which engages the work for stock

FIG. 13–2. Retaining ring in place on chuck.

A. Wheel dresser
B. Feed variator
C. Oil flow indicator
D. Feed dial 1 turn = .100
E. Feed wheel 1 turn = .025
F. Oil filter
G. Feed and head elevating control
H. Chuck speed control
I. Pump control for coolant supply
J. Grinding wheel control (start and stop)
K. Table traverse control
L. Chuck rotation control
M. Switch for magnetic chuck
N. Magnetic chuck (work table)
O. Guards to protect operator
P. Coolant supply valves
Q. Air cooling inlet to motor
R. Air outlet from motor

FIG. 13–3. Vertical rotary surface grinder.

removal purposes. The wheel is held in a special wheel chuck attached to a vertical spindle supported by a vertical column. The wheel head is constructed to permit raising or lowering either by hand or automatic feed.

The work is held in this machine by means of a circular magnetic chuck supported on ways or slides providing a means for moving the work to and from the grinding wheel.

To illustrate the operation of the machine, suppose that it is necessary to grind a number of steel blocks to the same size.

Procedure.

1) The work is placed on the magnetic chuck by beginning at the outer edge of the chuck and assembling it toward the center. After the work is in place turn on the magnetic switch and test each piece to see that it is held securely.

2) Dress the wheel for fast cutting, then move the work table in so that the rim of the wheel will cover the work. The wheel head is then fed down until sparks indicate contact between the wheel and work, after which the coolant valve is opened.

3) The automatic feed is engaged and permitted to operate until the exposed surface of each block is cleaned up.

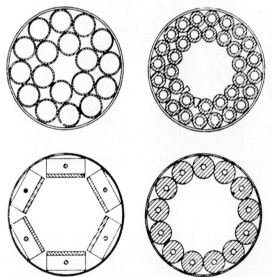

4) The wheel head is then raised, and the work table moved out; the work is removed from the chuck and the chuck cleaned, after which the work is again placed on the chuck with the ground surface down.

5) If the work is to be ground to a decimal dimension, one of the pieces should be ground to the correct size on one corner and be covered with copper sulphate (blue vitriol), or other suitable material. This piece is then placed on the magnetic chuck with the other pieces, and used as a **"sizing"** block.

6) The wheel is again engaged with the work as outlined and the wheel should be fed down until it just scratches the spot on the sizing block, then the feed is disengaged and the wheel head raised from the work.

Fig. 13–4. Locating work on a Blanchard chuck.

This machine, like other grinders, is most efficient when the operator observes certain pertinent facts relative to its operation. Some of these are: (1) the proper loading of the work on the chuck, as shown in Fig. 13–4; (2) the use of the proper grade and grain of wheel and keeping it properly dressed; (3) the selection of the proper work speed and feeds to preserve the cutting qualities of the grinding wheel;

and (4) the keeping of the surface of the magnetic chuck clean and true. To prevent glazing of the wheel the speed of the work chuck should be adjusted properly and the feed of the wheel kept great enough so that the wheel wear will keep new cutting particles in contact with the work.

Horizontal planer type. This machine, Fig. 13–5, characterized by a horizontal spindle, utilizes the periphery of a disk wheel for removal of stock in much the same manner as a milling cutter removes stock from work on a milling machine. It is capable of doing many of the milling machine operations but does them much more accurately.

The wheel head is supported by ways on the column of the machine and is provided with a lead screw and hand wheel for raising and lowering it.

The work table is constructed on much the same principle as a mill table; that is, it is fitted to a saddle so that it can be moved back and forth under the wheel, and the saddle can be moved to or from the column either by hand or power feed.

FIG. 13–5. Horizontal planer type surface grinder.

A. Hand wheel for longitudinal movement of table
B. On and off switch for power to magnetic chuck
C. Grinding wheel
D. Hand wheel for vertical adjustment of grinding wheel head
E. Magnetic chuck
F. Work table
G. Hand wheel for transverse adjustment of table

Holding the work. The table is provided with T-slots making it possible to bolt the work directly to the table, or to bolt a vise or other suitable fixtures for holding the work.

Frequently the table is equipped with a magnetic chuck, Fig. 13–6. This chuck is equipped with a back rail ground in place to act as a guide or rest against which the work is placed.

Besides holding the work directly on the magnetic chuck, fixtures and tools such as 90° angle plates, adjustable angle plates, sine bars, V-blocks, or a vise can be used

FIG. 13–6. Electro-magnetic chuck.

for attaching the work. The entire assembly is held by the magnetic chuck. It must be remembered that the magnetic chuck will only hold pieces of steel or iron. If non-magnetic materials such as brass or copper, are to be ground, they must be held in place by pieces of iron or steel.

Operations witness marks. Frequently the operator of a surface grinder is called upon to grind a piece of work to **"clean-up."** This means that the grinding wheel is to be spotted on the work and only sufficient material removed so that a slight portion of the original surface can still be seen. This is commonly known as leaving **"witness marks."** These marks testify that only a small amount of material has been removed from the job. Sometimes these witness marks are tool marks from former machining, at other times they are nicks inflicted on the piece through careless handling. If the surface of the work has a fairly good finish or is quite regular, it may be given a coat of copper sulfate (blue vitriol) and then ground to clean up. The copper sulfate will fill in the depressions in the work, acting as witness marks after the work is ground.

Grinding work parallel. Few jobs are ever done on the surface grinder which are not required to be ground parallel within rather close limits.

To grind thick work parallel, first see that the work surface of the magnetic chuck is clean and free from nicks and that the back rail is parallel to the table travel. If these conditions are satisfactory, the job can be done by turning the work end for end, putting it as nearly as possible in the same place on the chuck, then without disturbing the wheel setting take a cut across the work.

Thin pieces of work may be ground parallel by taking very light cuts alternately from each side. If this does not correct the tapering, support the work on two small parallels, and use a free cutting wheel. In this case the work must be properly blocked on the chuck to keep it from being thrown off when the grinding wheel comes in contact.

"Blocking" the work on the chuck consists of placing pieces of steel, of a height slightly less than the work, alongside and at the ends of the work for the purpose of holding it in place.

Grinding work square. This operation requires the use of a 90° angle plate, Fig. 13–7, for holding the work in conjunction with the magnetic chuck.

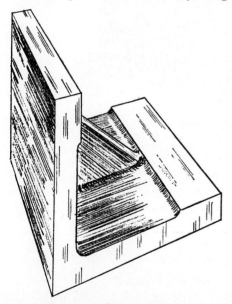

FIG. 13–7.   90° angle plate.

Ninety-degree angle plates used on the surface grinder should be maintained in perfect condition. This consists of keeping all adjacent faces at 90° to each other and all opposite faces parallel. If the plates are not so kept they can not be depended upon for accurate results. For this reason they should be checked with a solid square or try square frequently.

To set the work up for grinding it square.

Procedure.

1) After two sides have been ground parallel, place the surface to be ground in contact with the magnetic chuck, then alongside the work, place a thin parallel or rule.

2) Place the 90-degree angle plate with top edge down on the parallel or rule, and

up against the finished surface of the work, so that one side of the angle plate is clear of the work, then turn on the magnetic chuck.

3) Use a C-clamp of the proper size to clamp the work and angle plate together, but be sure to place the screw end on the inside of the angle plate so as to reduce the overhang and not interfere with the grinding operation, as shown in Fig. 13–8.

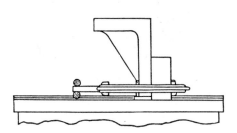

FIG. 13–8. Clamping work to angle plate for squaring.

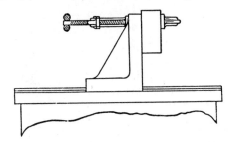

FIG. 13–9. Angle plate with work in position to be ground.

4) Turn off the magnetic chuck and turn the angle plate right side up. If the work has been attached to the angle plate, as outlined, it will be possible to grind in one setting, two sides square with a third side.

To grind the work square.

Procedure.

1) Dress the grinding wheel (see Fig. 13–11) for finish grinding, then raise the wheel head high enough to permit locating the work on the chuck.

2) Place the work on the chuck with the back, lower edge of the angle plate up against the back rail, as shown in Fig. 13–9, then turn on the magnetic chuck.

3) Adjust the work table so that the outer edge of the wheel will contact the work on the inside edge by about 1/8″ and feed the wheel to the work.

4) When sparks indicate contact between the wheel and work, feed the table longitudinally, and at the same time feed the table in, noting the action of the wheel on the work. If the work is considerably out of square, the depth of cut may have to be either decreased or increased depending upon whether the wheel is spotted on the low or high side of the work.

5) In any event grind this surface to clean up, then check it with a solid square to insure that the proper degree of accuracy is being attained; if it is, take another cut so as to remove all witness marks.

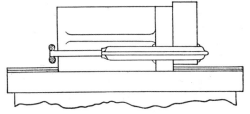

FIG. 13–10. Angle plate set up for squaring end of work.

6) To grind the second side square with the other two sides, turn the angle plate over so that the side which clears the work comes in contact with the magnetic chuck, as shown in Fig. 13–10, and proceed as outlined above.

Angular work. There are two methods of producing angular work on the surface grinder. In one method the grinding wheel is dressed to the required angle while the work is held on the magnetic chuck. In the other method the work is set to the required angle.

The grinding wheel should never be dressed at an angle except as a last resort; not because it is unsafe or impractical but because it destroys much of the grinding wheel life.

FIG. 13–11.   Dressing and truing the wheel.

The grinding wheel may be dressed at an angle by one of several methods. Generally a sine bar, Figs. 13–12, 13–13, is set to the required angle as shown in Fig. 13–14, and a flanged slide for holding a mounted diamond moved up and down the sine bar to shape the wheel. If the grinding wheel is not already dressed to an angle, it will save wear on the diamond if the angle is roughed on the wheel with a piece of silicon carbide, then finished by using the diamond. It is important, however, no matter what method is used, to have the diamond set on the exact vertical center line of the wheel, Fig. 13–15, otherwise the grinding wheel will not be dressed at

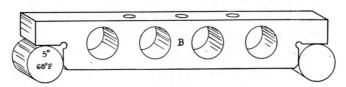

FIG. 13–12.   Johansson 5″ sine bar.

the proper angle. Also make sure that the angle dressed on the wheel is the correct one, not the complement of it. Fig. 13–16 shows a universal wheel dresser which can be used for shaping either angles or radii on the grinding wheel. Standard master angle blocks

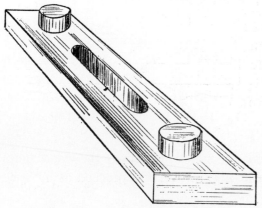

FIG. 13–13.   Taft-Pierce 5″ sine bar.

FIG. 13–14.   Sine bar set up at a given angle.

are available that can be put together much the same as gage blocks to give a wide range of angles. These can be used conveniently for dressing the wheel to the desired angle.

The work may be set at an angle by one of several methods, as follows: setting the magnetic chuck to the desired angle; using a sine bar to locate the work against a standard 90-degree angle plate; setting an adjustable angle plate to the desired angle and locating the work on it; or setting the work in an angular vise.

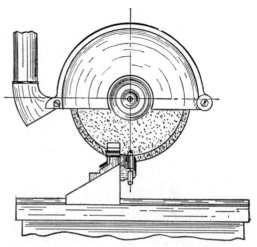

FIG. 13–15. Diamond set on centerline of wheel.

Fig. 13–17 shows the work set on an adjustable angle plate. Fig. 13–18 shows the use of the sine bar for setting the work at an angle against a 90-degree angle plate.

To set some sine bars to the required angle all that is necessary is to set a planer gage, or to stack gage blocks to five, or ten times the sine of the angle depending on the length of the sine bar, then set one end of the sine bar to this height. Others require that the addition of the radius of a plug or thickness

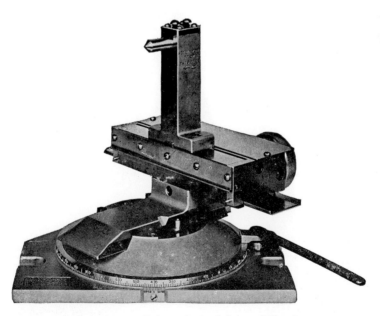

FIG. 13–16. Universal wheel dresser (Vinco).

of the base of the sine bar be added to 5 or 10 times the sine of the angle, depending upon whether a 5″ or 10″ sine bar is used.

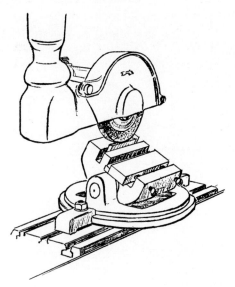

FIG. 13–17. Work set on adjustable chuck plate.

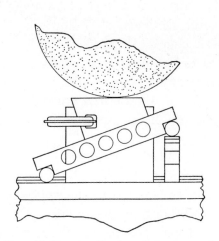

FIG. 13–18. Application of sine bar and angle plate.

EXERCISES

Example 1.

How much must one end of a 5″ sine bar be raised to produce an angle of 25°?

Solution.

sin 25° = .42262

5 × .42262 = 2.11310

Answer 2.1131″

Example 2.

At what height must a planer gage be set, when placed under one end of a 10″ sine bar, to produce an angle of 18°30′?

Solution.

sin 18°30′ = .31730

10 × .31730 = 3.1730

Answer 3.1730″

PROBLEMS

To what height must one end of a 5″ sine bar be elevated to produce the angles given as follows:

1. 45°15′
2. 30°
3. 10°30′
4. 16°
5. 24°20′

6. 36°
7. 8°40′
8. 45°
9. 45°50′
10. 15°45′

V-block work. The V-blocks commonly used on the surface grinder are accurately ground, hardened, steel blocks with a 90-degree *Vee* located exactly in the center. The adjacent faces are 90° to each other and all opposite faces are parallel. As generally made, these blocks are intended for holding cylindrical work. Some of them, however, can be used for holding square or rectangular work while a grinding operation is done.

The following outline gives the successive steps in grinding two opposite flats central and to size, on the cylindrical shaft shown in Fig. 13–19.

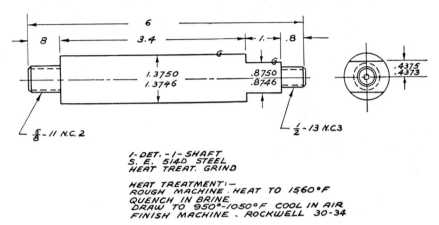

1- DET. -1- SHAFT
S. E. 5140 STEEL
HEAT TREAT. GRIND

HEAT TREATMENT:–
ROUGH MACHINE . HEAT TO 1560°F
QUENCH IN BRINE
DRAW TO 950°-1050°F COOL IN AIR
FINISH MACHINE . ROCKWELL 30-34

FIG. 13–19. Job with two opposite flats to be ground on one end.

Procedure

1) Dress the grinding wheel square, and also for finish grinding.

2) Check the flats for sufficient grinding stock and parallelism.

3) Place the work in the V-block so that the end containing the flats is clear of the *Vee* and in position to be ground.

4) Using a 10″ height gage and an indicator, check the shaft for being central in the *Vee*. This is done by indicating the side of the shaft, than turning the V-block over 180° and indicating the other side to see that the readings are the same.

5) Check the flats for being central, noting which side is high and whether the flat is in a horizontal plane.

6) Locate the V-block on the magnetic chuck with the low side of the flat up and take a light clean-up cut, as in Fig. 13–20.

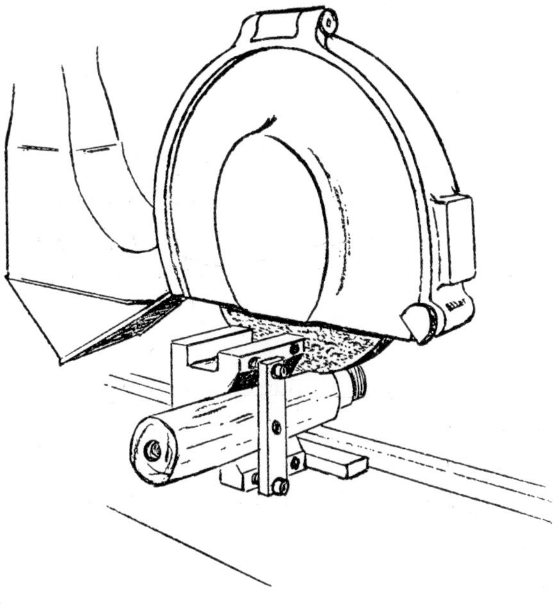

7) Turn the V-block upside down to bring the unground flat into grinding position, and without disturbing the wheel head setting take the same cut from this side.

FIG. 13–20. Job set up for grinding the flats.

8) Check the flats for being parallel and determine by what amount the thickness is oversize.

9) Put the work back in position on the magnetic chuck and take a series of light finishing cuts alternately from each side to bring the work to the correct thickness and to keep it central. To do this, if the grinding wheel head is fed down to take a half-thousandth cut from one side, turn the V-block upside down to bring the underneath side of the flat up, and without disturbing the wheel head setting, take the same cut. This is repeated until the flat is central and to size within the required degree of accuracy.

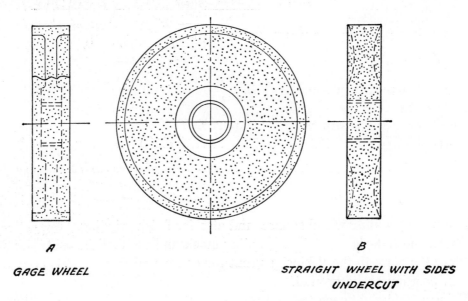

A
GAGE WHEEL

B
STRAIGHT WHEEL WITH SIDES
UNDERCUT

FIG. 13–21.   Shapes of wheels for slot grinding.

Slot grinding. Slots may be ground on the surface grinder by one of several methods depending on the nature of the work. Generally, if the work is of rectangular shape, the grinding operation is done by setting the work directly on the magnetic chuck. If the work is cylindrical in shape it may be held in a V-block or between the centers of a special fixture.

For either set-up, a grinding wheel, shaped as in Fig. 13–21 A and called a "Gage" wheel, or a plane grinding wheel with the sides undercut, Fig. 13–21 B, is used. The wheels are generally of the vitrified bond with a grain size of 60 and a bond hardness of M.

To grind a slot central in a shaft by **holding** it in a V-block.

Procedure

1) Place the shaft in the block with the slot up, clamp it loosely and determine the amount of grind stock.

2) Turn the V-block on its side and indicate the shaft for being central as outlined in step 4 of **"V-block work."** At the same time indicate the slot for being central

and for tapering, then tighten the clamps on the work. After the shaft has been tightly clamped, check the slot again to make sure that it did not move.

3) Dress the periphery of the grinding wheel square and for finish grinding. Use a piece of silicon carbide and undercut the back face of the wheel so that a rim of about 1/16″ to 3/32″ will bear on the side of the slot.

4) Place the V-block on the magnetic chuck against the back rail with the slot to be ground exposed to the grinding wheel, Fig. 13–22. Centralize the grinding wheel in the slot and feed the wheel head down until sparks indicate contact with the bottom of the slot.

5) Grind the bottom of the slot to give the required depth, then feed the work out until the back face of the grinding wheel contacts the side of the slot. It is good practice at this stage to hold a blunt pointed stick against the center of the wheel spindle to keep the end play in one direction during the grinding of the sides of the slot to avoid bell mouthing.

6) Take a clean-up cut on the side of the slot, leaving witness marks. Turn

FIG. 13–22. V-block and job set up for slot grinding.

the V-block 180° in a horizontal plane, placing it against the back rail and without disturbing the **"in"** and **"out"** setting of the table take the same cut on the unground side of the slot. When taking this same cut, traverse the table cautiously, and as the wheel approaches the slot, feed the work slowly so as not to chip the sides of the wheel or knock it off balance.

7) After the same cut has been taken from both sides check the slot for size and for being central.

8) Set the V-block in place on the magnetic chuck against the back rail and, by use of the micrometer table feed knob, feed the table out to within 1-1/2 to 2 thousandths inches of the amount of grind stock left on that side. While the table is being fed out, the work should be traversing under the wheel.

9) Turn the V-block 180° in a horizontal plane and take the same cut on the work.

10) Check the work for size and by repeating the process of turning the V-block from side to side gradually finish the slot to size. Be sure to keep the side of the wheel undercut properly and the cutting surface sharp.

Bell mouthing of the slot can be prevented by keeping the spindle end play in one direction during the grinding operation, and by not permitting the leading edge of the grinding wheel to linger at the ends of the slot.

Sharp corners can be maintained in the bottom of the slot by using a grinding wheel with a grit size of 120 and a *P* bond.

To grind a slot in a job, Fig. 13–23, which is held directly on the magnetic chuck or on an angle plate, where the slot is not held central, shape the wheel as previously outlined but undercut both sides. Then,

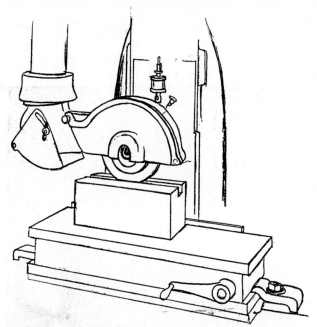

FIG. 13–23. Work held by chuck to have slot ground.

1) Check the slot for location, determine the amount of grind stock and place the work assembly on the magnetic chuck up against the back rail.

2) Centralize the grinding wheel in the slot and grind the slot to the correct depth.

3) Feed the table out and grind the one side of the slot to leave the correct thickness of wall. Be sure to hold the spindle end play in.

4) Move the table in and grind the near side of the slot to give the correct width to the slot.

Radius grinding. The surface grinder may be used for grinding radii on work by dressing the grinding wheel to the required radius. There are many fixtures used for this purpose but the one shown in Fig. 13–24 is quite adaptable for generating accurate radii.

The cradle of this fixture has a ground boss around the opening for the diamond, which is located at a definite distance, *D,* away from the axis of rotation of the cradle.

To adjust the diamond for dressing a radius, set a planer gage, or stack gage blocks, to *D* plus or minus the radius depending upon whether a concave or convex radius is required. Then, place the planer gage or gage blocks on the ground boss and adjust the diamond setting gage to this height; lock it in place, remove the planer gage or gage blocks, and insert the diamond, adjusting it to the diamond setting gage. After the diamond is adjusted, lock it in place and remove the diamond setting gage. The fixture is then ready for use.

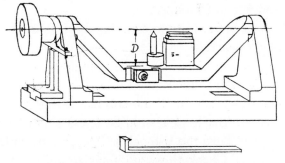

FIG. 13–24. Radius cradle.

It is absolutely necessary to have the point of the diamond set on the vertical centerline of the grinding wheel to produce the correct radius in the work, Fig. 13–25. Setting the point of the diamond to either side of the centerline will cause the wheel to cut an ellipse rather than a radius. This is sometimes necessary when grinding a form tool such as that shown in Fig. 13–26.

To grind a radius in a form tool such as that shown in Fig. 13–26.

Procedure.

1) After the radius has been roughed out, set a vernier bevel protractor to 90° minus the clearance angle.

2) With the base set on the magnetic chuck as shown in Fig. 13–27, draw a pencil line on the face of the wheel from the center of the spindle to the periphery of the wheel.

3) With the radius dresser set at the required radius, place it on the magnetic chuck and adjust the table so that the point of the diamond will contact the periphery of the wheel where the radial line ends, but in the center of the wheel (relative to the thickness).

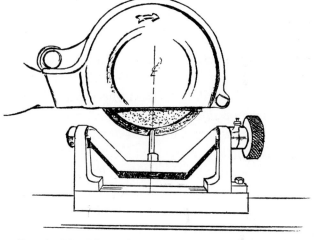

4) Raise the wheel head, start the machine, then feed the wheel down, swinging the radius dresser back and forth until the wheel is completely shaped.

5) Do not change the table setting, after it has been set as outlined, until the dressing operation has been completed.

FIG. 13–25. Diamond set on vertical centerline of wheel.

6) Set up the work, to the clearance angle, against a 90° angle plate and grind the radius required.

Surface grinder wheels. The surface grinder uses wheels of various shapes, but the ones most commonly used are the straight (disk), double recessed (gage), and thin

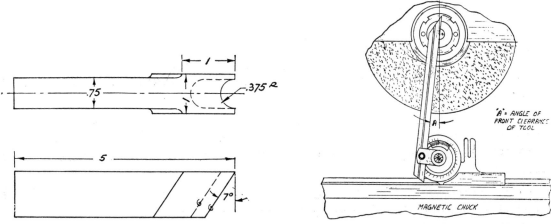

FIG. 13–26. Sketch of radius forming tool.

FIG. 13–27. Bevel protractor set up for scribing line.

6) Goggles are provided to protect your eyes. Use them on any machine or at any time when there is danger to your eyes from flying particles.

rubber slotting wheels. The sizes of these wheels may vary from very small ones of the internal class to wheels 10″ in diameter and 1″ face. They are of a grain size and hardness of bond as follows:

46-*G*; 46-*H*; 46-*I*; 46-*J*; or 46-*K*
60-*H*; 60-*I*; 60-*J*; 60-*K*; or 60-*L*.
80-*O*; 120-*P*; rubber slotting wheels
1/32" to 3/32" thick.

With the exception of the slotting wheels, they are all of vitrified bond.

GENERAL INFORMATION

Before installing a wheel on the surface grinder, it should be inspected for cracks by sounding it out. It should contain blotting paper gaskets on each side and should fit on the spindle with from .003" to .005" play. The flanges or washers used to hold the wheel should be not less than one-third of the diameter of the wheel and should be of the *recessed* or *safety* type. The nut should be tightened sufficiently to hold the wheel but should not be set up too tightly.

Many surface grinder difficulties may be avoided by selecting **"free cutting"** wheels. Generally speaking, use a hard wheel on soft materials and a soft wheel on hard materials. Do not try to use a small diameter wheel without the use of a high speed attachment, because as the wheel diameter decreases, there is a great loss of peripheral speed causing the wheel to wear away quite rapidly.

Keep the wheel clean and sharp.

Keep the machine well oiled and clean.

Keep the magnetic chuck free from nicks and burrs, and do not leave the machine for any length of time with the magnetic chuck turned on.

Be alert and observing. Many pieces of work are nearly scrapped because of the operators' lack of these qualities.

SAFETY SUGGESTIONS

1) When the machine is started after it has stood idle for quite some time, step away from the machine as the switch is closed.

2) Do not engage the grinding wheel with the work without being sure that the magnetic chuck is turned ON and the work securely held.

3) Work with a small surface exposed to the face of the magnetic chuck should be properly blocked to keep it in place.

4) When removing work from the chuck, move the table out and to the right, then pull the work off in a direction perpendicular to the work table.

5) Do not attempt to check the work without first moving it clear of the grinding wheel.

6) Goggles are provided to protect your eyes. Use them on any machine or at any time when there is danger to your eyes from flying particles.

7) Dry grinders are provided with exhaust hoods to carry away dust particles as a safeguard to the health of machine operators. See that they are correctly adjusted at all times and do not misuse them.

REVIEW QUESTIONS

1. Name two classifications of surface grinders.
2. How is the work held on the ring grinder?
3. Discuss the procedure of grinding work on the vertical spindle rotary type grinder.
4. Discuss the chief characteristics of the horizontal planer type grinder.
5. How is the work held in this grinder?
6. What is meant by grinding to clean-up?
7. What are witness marks?
8. How are thin pieces of work ground to prevent warping?
9. What is meant by blocking the work?
10. Discuss the set-up for grinding work square.
11. What are the two methods of producing angular work on the surface grinder?
12. Discuss several methods of holding the work at an angle.
13. Outline the necessary steps required to grind two opposite flats central and to size.
14. Discuss the procedure of slot grinding using a V-block.
15. What grit size and bond are used to maintain sharp corners in slot grinding?
16. Discuss the use of the radius cradle.
17. What three shapes of wheels are commonly used on the surface grinder?
18. How are grain size and bond hardness indicated on surface grinder wheels?
19. What is meant by a safety type flange?
20. Discuss the safety suggestions for the surface grinder.

CUTTER GRINDING

DEFINITION

Cutter grinding is the process of shaping and sharpening by abrasion the edges of drills, reamers, and milling cutters. The working efficiency of a cutter depends to a great extent on its keenness and, in the case of multiple tooth cutters, the concentricity of the cutting edges. Dull or poorly sharpened cutters are not capable of removing an amount of stock in keeping with the efficiency of the machine and produce an unsatisfactory finish.

Machines. A cutter grinder is a machine that supports the cutter while a suitable rotating abrasive wheel is applied to the cutting edge for the purpose of sharpening it. These machines vary in design from single purpose grinders used to sharpen cemented carbide tipped tool bits to complex universal machines capable of doing any type of cutter grinding. Fig. 14–1 shows a universal type of cutter grinder. This machine can, with the use of special attachments and specially formed grinding wheels, sharpen cutters of any geometric shape.

CUTTER GRINDING WHEELS

Shape. The wheel shapes commonly used on the cutter grinder are the **straight, flaring cup,** and **dish,** as shown in Fig. 14–2 *A, B,* and *C.* For general purpose cutter grinding, select wheels that are soft and free cutting. Take light cuts to avoid drawing the temper at the cutting edge. Do not select a wheel which is too soft, or it will wear rapidly and make it difficult to sharpen all teeth to the same height, causing the cutter to be eccentric.

Abrasive, grain size, and bond. For flaring cup wheels the grain size should be between 30 and 60, while straight wheels should have a 36 or 46 grain size. Disk wheels, used for sharpening formed cutters, should have a grain size of from 36 to 80.

These wheels are made of aluminous oxide abrasive and of vitrified bond having a hardness of from *I* to *L,* with a grain structure of 5.

In using any of these wheels the cutting faces should be kept clean and sharp by frequent dressing and should not be crowded in their cutting action. Most cutters are made of high speed steel which causes a wheel to become dirty very quickly. They

A. Hand wheel for adjusting grinding wheel to the work
B. Start and stop push buttons
C. Lower work table
D. Adjustable stops for positioning longitudinal movement of table
E. Upper work table
F. Work head center (adjustable)
G. Graduations for accurate swivel adjustment of upper table
H. Plain or disk grinding wheel
I. Wheel head swivel graduations
J. Flaring cup grinding wheel
K. Spring loaded foot stock center (adjustable)
L. Micrometer adjusting screw for swiveling table
M. Hand wheel for elevating wheel head from side of machine
N. Hand wheel for longitudinal movement of table
O. Hand wheel for elevating wheel head from front of machine

FIG. 14–1. Universal cutter and tool grinder.

give off a dull orange spark when touched to a grinding wheel; for this reason do not expect a brilliant shower of sparks and start crowding the wheel into the cutter.

Direction of rotation. Cutter grinder wheels may be rotated in a direction away from the cutting face of the cutter or onto the cutting edge, as shown in Figs. 14–3 and 14–4.

The set-up shown in Fig. 14–3 is safer because it holds the tooth down against the tooth rest and is very commonly used. It has the defect, however, of concentrating the heat at the cutting edge of the tooth thus drawing the temper, and of throwing up a burr which must be oilstoned off if the cutter is to give maximum service per grind.

The method shown in Fig. 14–4, while not so safe, gives a sharper cutting edge, free from burrs, and does not have quite the tendency to draw the temper

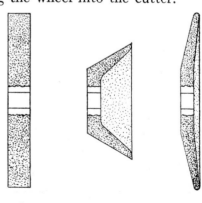

A   *B*   *C*

FIG. 14–2. Shapes of cutter grinding wheels.

A, Straight.   B, Flaring cup.   C, Saucer or dish.

of the cutting edge. If the operator will hold the tooth being ground down against the tooth rest much time will be saved and a more satisfactory job of grinding will be accomplished.

Tooth rests. As an aid to locating quickly and accurately the cutting edge of the tooth to be ground, tooth rests of three different types are used, as shown in Fig.

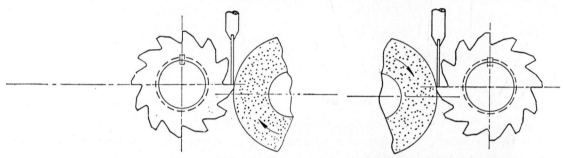

FIG. 14–3. Wheel rotating away from cutting face.   FIG. 14–4. Wheel rotating onto the cutting face.

14–5 *A, B,* and *C.* They consist of a piece of spring steel about .030″ thick, 1/2″ to 1-1/2″ wide and from 1″ to 3″ long, brazed or riveted into a shank made either from a piece of round 3/8 inch cold rolled steel or machine steel.

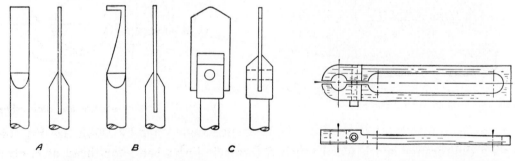

FIG. 14–5.   Types of tooth rests.   FIG. 14–6. Tooth rest bracket.
A, Plain.   B, Hook.   C, Double angle.

Tooth rests are held by means of a bracket, Fig. 14–6, which can be attached to the grinding wheel head or by a special bracket which can be clamped to the cutter grinder table.

Fig. 14–5 *A* is the type of tooth rest used to support the tooth when grinding plain, angular, side, or formed milling cutters having straight teeth. It may be mounted either on the wheel head or on the work table. Fig. 14–5 *B* shows a hook tooth rest used when the tooth must be supported from the back or top of plain, angular, or side milling cutters. It is generally mounted on the work head or work table. Fig. 14–5 *C* shows a double angle tooth rest used for supporting the tooth of any helical tooth cutter. It is always mounted on the grinding wheel head.

Cutter grinding classifications. Cutter grinding is divided into two general classifications depending on the design of the tooth and the method used to sharpen them.

The first classification includes cutters having teeth which must be sharpened on the periphery or sides, such as keyway cutters, or slab milling cutters having straight or helical teeth, side mills, face mills, end mills, machine reamers, and mill saws.

The second classification includes formed cutters; that is, those which must be sharpened by grinding the teeth radially so as not to change the contour of the tooth. Examples are concave cutters, convex cutters, gear cutters, hobs, or specially shaped cutters.

CUTTER SHARPENING
Plain milling cutters.

Procedure

1) Mount the cutter on a mandrel and place it between the work table centers.

2) Mount the tooth rest on the wheel head. If a cup wheel is being used, set the top of the tooth rest, with the tooth to be ground bearing on it, even with the horizontal centerline of the grinding wheel spindle and adjust the grinding wheel head to produce the correct clearance. The distance* to lower the wheel head is equal to the diameter

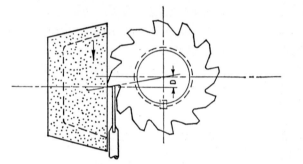

FIG. 14–7. Relation of cutter and cup wheel.

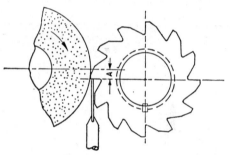

FIG. 14–8. Relation of cutter and plain wheel.

of the cutter in inches, multiplied by the clearance angle, then by .0087. See Fig. 14–7. If a straight wheel is used, the distance to raise or lower the wheel head or lower the table is equal to the diameter of the grinding wheel multiplied by the clearance angle of the cutter in inches by .0087. See Fig. 14–8.

3) Start the wheel and feed the cutter to the wheel until sparks indicate contact between the wheel and the work. Take a trial clean-up cut, holding the tooth down on the tooth rest with a slight hand pressure.

4) Move the table longitudinally, revolve the cutter one-half a revolution and, without changing the depth of cut, grind that tooth. Observe any out-of-roundness of the cutter and make any necessary adjustments.

5) Bring the next tooth to be ground to bear on the tooth rest and take the same cut as was taken on the previous tooth.

6) Repeat this process until all teeth have been sharpened and ground concentric with the cutter body. The grinding wheel must be kept sharp and clean otherwise the temper will be drawn from the cutting edge.

See that all teeth are ground concentric, by keeping the wheel wear equalized dur-

*This procedure of calculating the machine setting should be carried out especially when grinding the clearance angle on cutters being ground for the first time.

ing the grinding operation. The wheel wear can be equalized by grinding each tooth successively around the cutter then revolving the cutter one-half a revolution and starting a new light cut on this opposite tooth. This practice keeps the teeth concentric with the cutter body within the required amount of accuracy.

If a cup wheel is used, the wheel head must be swiveled about 5° from "0" to keep the opposite rim of the wheel from fouling on the cutter.

Side milling cutters. The peripheral teeth of a side milling cutter are sharpened the same as those of a plain milling cutter.

Procedure

1) To sharpen the side teeth of a side milling cutter, the cutter is mounted on a stub expansion arbor and placed either in a combination holder or a universal swivel fixture, as shown in Fig. 14–9.

2) Mount the tooth rest on the table.

3) Adjust the fixture so the face of the cutter is toward the grinding wheel. Swivel the upper section of the fixture to produce the desired clearance angle. Large diameter cutters have from 4° to 5° clearance. Small cutters up to 3″ have 6° to 7° clearance. Cutters used for cutting brass, copper, aluminum, and similar materials, should have a clearance of from 9° to 12°.

4) To reduce back drag of the side teeth on the work, set the bottom section of the swivel fixture so that the teeth will taper back about 1° on a side; that is, the teeth should be about 1° out of parallel with the side of the cutter body.

5) Raise the table or lower the wheel head so that the face of the cup wheel at the top rim will act on the tooth. Set the tooth rest to bring the cutting edge of the tooth into a horizontal plane.

6) Spot the grinding wheel on the tooth to be ground and continue as outlined for plain milling cutters.

Fig. 14–9. Sharpening the side teeth of a side mill.

End mills. The side teeth of end mills are sharpened the same as the peripheral teeth of plain milling cutters. The end teeth are sharpened the same as the side teeth of side milling cutters.

The end mill is held by placing the taper shank in the socket of the universal swivel fixture.

Face mills. Face milling cutters are sharpened in the same way as side milling cutters, but generally the corners of the teeth are given a 1/16 to 1/8 × 45° chamfer to increase the cutter life per grind, as shown in Fig. 14–10.

To chamfer the corners of the teeth, turn the universal swivel fixture so that the axis of rotation of the cutter forms a 45-degree angle with the axis of rotation of the grinding wheel. Adjust the fixture so that the chamfered land will have its edges parallel.

Helical tooth cutters. Slabbing cutters having helical teeth are sharpened nearly the same as plain cutters, with the exception that the tooth rest must be mounted on the wheel head and the cutter must be held in place. The reason for this is obvious because, as the work table traverses, the cutter must be given a twisting motion to keep the land of the teeth correctly located at the grinding wheel. If the tooth is not held down on the tooth rest, the grinding wheel will cut an irregular land and possibly spoil the tooth.

The tooth rest used for supporting the teeth of a helical tooth cutter should have the top angled off to approximately the helix angle of the cutter. This prevents the leading edge of the tooth from snagging on the

Fig. 14–10.   Set up for chamfering teeth of a face mill.

tooth rest just as the cutter gets to the grinding wheel and gives a more uniform land at the cutting edge.

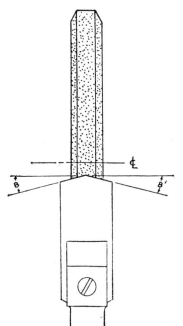

Fig. 14–11.   Tooth rest set up for staggered tooth cutter.

Staggered tooth cutters. Side milling cutters having alternate right- and left-hand helical teeth, set over similar to the set of the teeth on a wood saw, are sharpened on the side teeth in the same manner as a regular side milling cutter.

Procedure for sharpening the peripheral teeth:

1) Mount the cutter on a mandrel and place it between the work table centers.

2) Install a straight grinding wheel on the wheel head spindle and, after dressing and truing its face, put a 1/8 × 45° chamfer on the edges.

3) Select a tooth rest with the top angled off the center both ways to equal the helix angle of the cutter teeth and mount it on the wheel head, as shown in Fig. 14–11.

4) The high point of the tooth rest must be located on the center of the wheel face and the wheel head adjusted to give the correct clearance.

5) The tooth to be ground is brought to bear on that side of the tooth rest which corresponds to the helix angle of the tooth. The grinding wheel is started and the tooth

fed in until sparks indicate contact. The tooth is then ground and the table traversed so that the next tooth can be brought to bear on its corresponding side of the tooth rest, as shown in Fig. 14–12.

6) This process of bringing each successive tooth to bear on its corresponding side of the tooth rest is continued until all teeth have been sharpened and ground concentric within the required degree of accuracy.

Angular cutters. Single angle cutters have one set of teeth which are neither parallel nor perpendicular to the axis of rotation of the cutter. Sometimes these cutters have teeth on the sides like a side milling cutter. These side teeth are sharpened in the same way as the side teeth of a side milling cutter.

Fig. 14–12.   Grinding staggered tooth cutter.

Fig. 14–13.   Sharpening an angular cutter.

Procedure to sharpen the angular teeth:

1) Place the cutter on a stub expansion arbor in the universal swivel fixture.

Mount a straight grinding wheel on the wheel spindle and true it up; mount a straight tooth rest on the table, and, after adjusting the swivel fixture to the angle of the cutter, adjust the tooth rest so the face of the first tooth to be ground will be in a horizontal plane as shown in Fig. 14–13.

2) Raise the wheel head, or lower the table, to give the required clearance angle. Hold the cutter against the tooth rest by hand and feed the cutter to the grinding wheel until sparks indicate contact between the wheel and work.

3) Traverse the table, moving the cutter clear of the wheel; index the cutter 180° bringing the tooth to bear on the tooth rest; and, without changing the depth of cut, grind this tooth. Observe any irregularity relative to the depth of cut, check the tooth for correct angle, and make any necessary adjustments.

4) Bring the next tooth into position on the tooth rest and grind it. Repeat this process until all teeth have been ground as required.

5) Do not locate the top of the tooth rest in any position other than on the horizontal centerline of the cutter. Raising or lowering the tooth rest will change the angle from the one at which the swivel fixture is set.

Formed cutters. Formed cutters are those which must be ground radially on the cutting face to preserve the shape of the tooth as shown in Fig. 14–14. Two methods are commonly used to insure correct spacing of the teeth. In one, a master form having the same number of teeth as the cutter is used as a guide in connection with the tooth rest, as shown in Fig. 14–15. In another, these formed cutters are ground on a specially designed form cutter grinder or hob grinder. When neither of these methods is available, use the following procedure:

1) The machine is set up by bringing the work centers in line with the face of the grinding wheel.

2) The cutter is then mounted on a mandrel and placed between the centers and the face of the tooth located against the grinding wheel.

3) Mount the tooth rest on the table and adjust it to the back of the tooth being ground.

4) Move the work table longitudinally to clear the grinding wheel, start the machine and take a trial cut. Check the tooth for correct grinding and make any necessary adjustments.

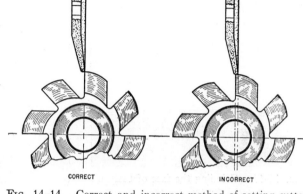

FIG. 14–14.   Correct and incorrect method of setting cutter to wheel.

5) Adjustments should be made by rotating the cutter on its axis, and changing the tooth rest setting. Do not change the position of the grinding wheel with respect to the work centers.

If the cutter is quite dull and a heavy cut is taken the grinding wheel will wear rapidly. This wear can be compensated for by adjusting the wheel radially just before the finishing cut is taken.

Taps. For the most part a tap depends on the chamfered end for its cutting action. The exception to this is the bottoming tap and pipe tap. Frequently a tap becomes dull because the leading edge of the chamfer has broken down; consequently, unless some of the first full teeth have become chipped or broken, this chamfer is all that needs to be sharpened.

FIG. 14–15.   Sharpening a formed cutter using a master form.

The chamfer is usually ground by holding the tap securely in the hand, and pressing it lightly against the grinding wheel. As the tap is pressed against the wheel it should be turned slightly from the back of the tooth to the front with the pressure diminishing as the front is approached. This action is necessary to give the chamfer the required clearance.

If the edges of the full teeth become dull or nicked the tap is sharpened by placing it between centers, as shown in Fig. 14–16, and regrinding the flutes with a straight wheel having the periphery rounded to fit the flute. The grinding wheel should be free cutting and the pressure very light to prevent drawing the temper of the teeth.

Reamers. Machine reamers are so designed that the cutting action takes place at the front end of the teeth. For this reason they are sharpened by grinding the chamfer in about the same manner as grinding the corners of the teeth of a face milling cutter. The swivel table of the machine is set at 45° and the tooth rest adjusted to produce the correct clearance angle using a flaring cup wheel.

FIG. 14-16.   Grinding the face of teeth on a tap.

Hand reamers of the solid or non-expanding type are designed so that the cutting action takes place some distance back of the front end. Since the diameters of these reamers must be held to a definite size to produce a standard size hole, it is obvious that they cannot be sharpened by grinding the clearance on them as can be done on milling cutters, because this would cause the reamer to be undersize. About the only way to sharpen them is as follows: anneal the reamer and, by means of a blunt, chisel-shaped tool driven against each tooth face, raise the cutting edge to increase the outside diameter .035″ to .040″. The reamer is then rehardened and ground on a cylindrical grinder to the correct size. The reamer is then placed between centers on the cutter grinder and the proper clearance ground on the teeth.

To grind hand reamers of the expansion type: first, adjust the expansion screw increasing the outside diameter to give the necessary grind stock; second, place the reamer in the cylindrical grinder and grind the outside diameter to the correct size; third, place the reamer between centers on the work table of the cutter grinder and grind the teeth for the proper relief, leaving a land no more than a few thousandths of an inch wide.

DO'S and DON'TS for Cutter Grinding

DO select a free, cool, cutting wheel of the correct shape.
DO mount the tooth rest correctly.
DO keep the tooth of the cutter against the tooth rest.
DO make sure that the grinding wheel follows the original relief.
DO keep the grinding wheel clean and sharp.
DON'T remove any more material from the tooth than is necessary to make it sharp.
DON'T burn the cutting edge of the tooth.
DON'T operate any cutter grinder unless the grinding wheel is properly guarded.
DON'T operate any dry cutter grinder without goggles.
DON'T mount the grinding wheel without safety washers and blotting paper gaskets.
DON'T adjust any part of the set-up while the machine is running.
DON'T attempt to hand dress the wheel without allowing plenty of clearance between
     the wheel and other parts of the work or machine.

DON'T use heavy pressure when hand dressing a wheel having a thin cross-section.

DON'T be the victim of hand or finger lacerations through careless handling of the sharpened tools.

DON'T start the machine until it has been checked as to disengagement of feed and trip levers.

DON'T start the grinding operation until the exhaust hood has been properly adjusted.

REVIEW QUESTIONS

1. Define cutter grinding.
2. Name three shapes of wheels used in cutter grinding work.
3. Discuss the effects of direction of rotation of cutter grinder wheels away from the cutting face, as well as onto the cutting face of the cutter.
4. What are tooth rests used for?
5. Name three types of tooth rests and tell what kind of work each is used for.
6. Into what two classifications does cutter grinding work fall?
7. Outline the procedure of sharpening a plain milling cutter.
8. Discuss the steps involved in sharpening the side teeth of a side mill.
9. Discuss the grinding of staggered tooth cutters.
10. Discuss the procedure of grinding angular cutters.
11. What are the important points involved in grinding formed cutters?
12. How are taps sharpened?
13. How does grinding a machine reamer differ from grinding a hand reamer?
14. List the important DON'TS of cutter grinding.

Chapter 15

GRINDING WHEELS

DEFINITION
Kind of abrasive . . . Size of abrasive . . . Kind of bond . . . Amount of bond . . . Abrasives . . . Bonds . . . Wheel Hardness

GENERAL SUGGESTIONS

DEFINITION

A grinding wheel is a cutting tool containing a vast number of cutting edges so arranged that, as they became dull, they are released and new cutting edges take their place.

Four fundamental elements are necessary in the manufacture of grinding wheels; they are: the **kind of abrasive,** the **size of abrasive,** the **kind of bond,** and the **amount of bond.**

Abrasives. Silicon carbide and aluminum oxide are the kinds of abrasive used in most grinding wheels.

Silicon carbide is the cutting element in wheels used for grinding hard, brittle materials such as cemented carbides, ceramics, and chilled cast iron. It is also used for grinding bronze, brass, copper, and aluminum.

Aluminous oxide is the cutting element in wheels used for grinding steel and other materials possessing a high tensile strength.

The size of these abrasive particles is designated by a number which corresponds to the number of meshes per lineal inch in the sieve or screen through which they will pass. For example, a No. 46 abrasive is one which will pass through a screen, having 46 openings per lineal inch, but is retained on the next smaller screen which has 60 openings per lineal inch.

COARSE	MEDIUM	FINE
12	30	70
14		80
16	46	90
20		100
24	60	120

FIG. 15–1.   Chart showing grain sizes.

The chart, Fig. 15–1, shows the grain sizes commonly used and their classification as to coarse, medium, or fine.

Bonds. The bond is the material which cements or holds the abrasive grains together to form a grinding wheel. Depending on the kind and amount used, it imparts

240

very distinct characteristics to the grinding action of the wheel. It is the bond which imparts the qualities of hardness or softness to the wheel.

The bonds commonly used are the vitrified, silicate, resinoid, rubber and shellac. Of these the vitrified and silicate are used most frequently.

The vitrified bond is used in about 75% of all grinding wheels. The reason for this is the fact that it forms a very uniform wheel which is not affected by oils, acids, water, heat, or cold. Wheels of this bond can be made dense or porous, and in considerably less time than other kinds.

The silicate bond, because of its mild cutting action, is best suited to the grinding of edged tools. It can also be used for making wheels of large diameters.

Resinoid bonded wheels are especially suited for heavy duty grinding such as snagging castings, steel billets, and so forth, and for **"cutting off"** stock. When used for snagging purposes they may be operated as fast as 9500 surface feet per minute. When installed in proper equipment they may be run as fast as 16,000 surface feet per minute for cutting-off purposes.

Rubber bonded wheels are used for grinding mill rolls and bearings where a high luster finish is required. They are capable of fast stock removal when operated at high speeds. Because of the nature of this bond, grinding wheels can be made quite thin with a high safety factor, which makes them ideal for cutting-off purposes when a coolant is used.

Shellac bonded wheels are used for grinding jobs which require a buffed or burnished surface, such as mill rolls, camshafts, and cutlery.

Wheel hardness. The hardness of a grinding wheel depends on the amount of bond used in its manufacture. To express the degrees of hardness of a wheel the letters of the alphabet are used. The Carborundum Company uses a system in which the letters at the beginning of the alphabet represent the maximum hardness, those near the middle, medium; while those near the end represent the softest bonds. The Norton Company uses a system which is the reverse of this as shown in the chart, Fig. 15–2. As can be seen from this chart, the alphabet is divided into five parts which classify the degree of hardness as *Very Soft, Soft, Medium Hard* and *Very Hard.* For tool and cutter grinding, the degrees of hardness represented in the *Very Soft* and *Very Hard* columns are seldom used.

GRADES OF BOND

VERY SOFT	SOFT	MEDIUM	HARD	VERY HARD
E	H	L	P	T
F	I	M	Q	U
G	J	N	R	W
	K	O	S	Z

FIG. 15–2. Chart of bond hardness.

In an effort to tell as nearly as possible the characteristics of a grinding wheel, the Norton Company has devised a system which tells five important things about the wheel; they are: the kind of abrasive, generally represented by the first group of two digits of the number; the size of the abrasive particles, represented by the second group of two digits; the hardness of the bond, represented by the first letter in the marking; the wheel structure, represented by the digit following the hardness of bond; and a letter or group of letters representing the kind of bond.

analysis of a typical
NORTON GRINDING WHEEL MARKING
32A46-H8VBE

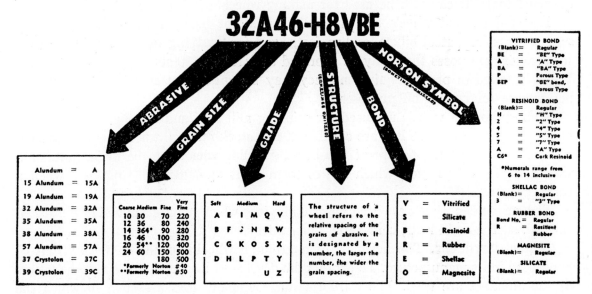

FIG. 15–3.

GENERAL SUGGESTIONS

Many suggestions have been made and a great deal of valuable information is available on the care necessary in selecting, handling, and using grinding wheels. Some of the more important suggestions follow, which, if generally practiced, will make the operator a more efficient workman.

1) All grinding wheels, except the very small ones, should be sounded for cracks. This is done by holding the wheel at the hole and tapping it with a light mallet or other non-metallic object. If the wheel is cracked, it gives off a dull, thudding sound; if it is not cracked it gives off a ringing sound.

2) Handle all wheels carefully.

3) Never put a grinding wheel on the spindle without blotting paper or other soft absorbent gaskets on each side for the flanges to bear against.

4) Do not force a wheel on the spindle. It should go on easily so that it can fit squarely against the inner safety flange.

5) Safety flanges are washers which are undercut so that they bear on the wheel

only at their outer edges. See Fig. 15–4. Do not use any other kind except on small internal grinding wheels.

6) Use safety flanges not smaller than one-third the wheel diameter.

7) Tighten the wheel nut sufficiently to hold the wheel, but not too tightly.

8) Dress the wheel frequently to keep it clean and sharp but do not remove more material than is necessary to accomplish this end.

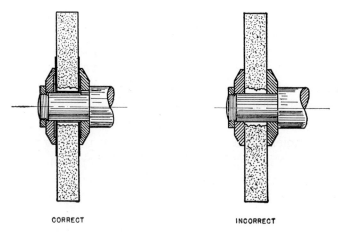

CORRECT   INCORRECT

FIG. 15–4.   Correct and incorrect methods of mounting wheel.

9) Do not use grinding wheels at higher rates of speed than recommended by the manufacturer.

Manufacturers of grinding wheels and grinding equipment publish considerable information in pamphlet form on grinding wheels and machines. To the person desiring to become proficient or acquainted with this branch of machine tool work these bulletins and pamphlets may be obtained for the asking.

REVIEW QUESTIONS

1. Define the term grinding wheel.

2. What are the four fundamental considerations in the manufacture of grinding wheels?

3. What kinds of abrasives are commonly used in grinding wheels?

4. Define the word bond as applied to grinding wheels.

5. What determines wheel hardness?

6. Name five grades of bond.

7. What letters are used for each bond?

8. In what way does the letter system employed by the Carborundum Company differ from that employed by the Norton Company in designating wheel hardness?

9. Discuss a few general suggestions in regard to the handling and uses of grinding wheels.

Chapter 16

BENCH HAND TOOLS AND THEIR OPERATION

Hammers . . . Pliers . . . Wrenches . . . Screw Drivers . . . Miscellaneous . . . Chisels . . . Files . . . Hacksaws

Hammers. The hammers used by the machinist or tool and die maker are either of the ball-peen type or soft hammers made of brass, babbitt, rawhide, and the like.

The ball-peen hammer, Fig. 16–1, is made in sizes varying from six to twenty-eight ounces in weight; the lighter sizes being used for light bench work such as layout work, while the heavier ones are used for heavy chipping or **"peening"** purposes. **"Peening"** is the act of stretching metal by means of hammer blows.

One end of this hammer has a ball-shaped head for peening purposes, from which it gets its name, while the other end has a cylindrical-shaped head, the face of which is slightly convex, and which is used for general purposes. The opening into which the handle is fitted is slightly oval in shape and is bell-mouthed at each end. This hole is

FIG. 16–1.   Ball peen hammer.

known as the **"eye"** of the hammer and the handle should be fitted to it so that it will give the best possible balance in use.

In using a hammer, grip it close to the end of the handle, raise it to a height calculated to give the desired force to the blow, then bring it down in a plane slightly inclined to the vertical. This method requires less physical effort and makes it possible to use the hammer for a longer period of time without tiring the user, and more work can be accomplished with each blow.

Form the habit of keeping the hammer blows even; learn to estimate the amount of force necessary to attain the desired end and keep your eye on the object or spot which is to receive the hammer blow.

When the ball-peen hammer is used for riveting, use a force in keeping with the size of the rivet to be peened. Heavy blows on light rivets tend to bulge or bend the rivet. Light blows upset the end of the rivet causing it to stretch over the hole.

In using a ball-peen hammer to straighten a piece of work that is warped, remember to peen it on the concave side, rather than the convex side. Warping is due to the grains of metal on one side of the work contracting faster than they do on the other side; that

244

is, the grain structure on the concave side is more compact than it is on the convex side. Therefore, to straighten the piece of metal it is necessary to stretch the metal on the concave side by peening or by a similar process.

Soft hammers, that is, those with heads made of brass, babbitt, or rawhide, shown in Fig. 16–2, are used for driving machine parts, or for seating work in a machine vise, since a steel hammer might injure the work.

FIG. 16–2. Soft hammer.

FIG. 16–3. Gas pliers.

Pliers. Common gas pliers, Fig. 16–3, are used for cutting or twisting wire, or for pulling or spreading cotter pins. They should not be used for tightening bolts or nuts; the reason for this is obvious. Sufficient pressure cannot be exerted on the handles to make the jaws grip the bolt head or nut tightly enough to hold it; the result is that the

FIG. 16–4. Diagonal wire cutters.

FIG. 16–5. Single open-end wrench.

teeth of the jaws round off the corners of the bolt head or nut making it unsafe to use a wrench on it thereafter. Fig. 16–4 shows a set of diagonal wire cutters with specially hardened jaws that are suitable for cutting music or spring wire when winding springs.

Wrenches. A wrench is a tool having suitable openings that grip the heads of bolts or nuts while they are being tightened or loosened. Wrenches are classified as being adjustable or non-adjustable, and of either the open-end or socket variety. They are named because of their shape, because of the object upon which they are used, and because of their construction.

The single or double open-end wrench, of the non-adjustable type, is used on work requiring only one or two sizes; that is, if it is a single open-end wrench, the opening is made to

FIG. 16–6. Double open-end wrench.

a definite standard size; if it is a double open-end wrench, it contains two separate standard openings, one on each end of the handle. Fig. 16–5 shows the single open-end wrench; Fig. 16–6 shows the double open-end wrench.

The adjustable open-end wrench, shown in Fig. 16–7, has one fixed jaw which is an integral part of the wrench body, while the other jaw may be adjusted by means of a screw to accommodate any size within the capacity of the wrench. The size of this wrench is determined by the length of the wrench rather than by the size of the opening as is the case in open-end wrenches.

FIG. 16–7.   Adjustable open-end wrench.

FIG. 16–8.   L-handled socket wrench.

The monkey wrench has its jaws at right angles to the handle, the lower jaw being adjustable. This wrench is used for heavy duty work and when in use should have the jaws pointing in the direction of the force applied. A Stillson or pipe wrench is used for holding or turning pipe, pipe fittings, or cylindrical pieces of work. When the adjustable

FIG. 16–9.   T-handled
socket wrench.

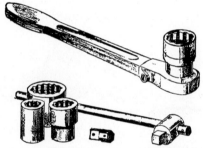

FIG. 16–10.   Ratchet socket wrench.

FIG. 16–11.   Adjustable pin face
spanner wrench.

jaw of this wrench is closed on the work and pressure is applied to the handle, the jaw opening tends to decrease in size so that the teeth of the jaw grip the work more firmly. For this reason the wrench should be used with care on thin walled pipe or tubing, and the surface of finished pipe or fittings should be protected from the teeth of the jaws.

FIG. 16–12.   Adjustable hook spanner
wrench.

Socket wrenches, Figs. 16–8, 16–9, and 16–10 have openings which contact the bolt head or nut on all sides. The handles of these wrenches may be T-shaped, L-shaped, or of the ratchet type, depending on the requirements of the work.

Spanner wrenches, Figs. 16–11 and 16–12, are those used for ring nuts having square slots cut on the periphery or drilled holes on the outer face. Fig. 16–11 shows the adjustable pin-face spanner wrench used for nuts which are countersunk in the work. The pins sticking out sideways at the end fit into the holes in the face of the nut, making it convenient to tighten or loosen nuts which could not be reached by other types of wrenches. Fig. 16–12 shows the adjustable hook spanner wrench used to tighten or loosen nuts in which square notches are cut in the periphery. This wrench, like the adjustable pin face spanner wrench, will fit a wide range of sizes of ring nuts.

Screw drivers. A screw driver is a tool or instrument having a blunt, wedge-shaped blade used for driving screws. This tool, Fig. 16–13, is usually provided with a wooden handle keyed or pinned to a tool steel shaft, the end

FIG. 16–13. Light duty screw driver.

of which is formed to fit the slot of a wood or machine screw. Large heavy duty screw drivers, Fig. 16–14, usually have a square shank to which a wrench can be fit-

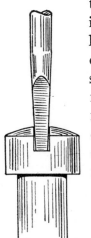

ted to aid in turning it. Fig. 16–15 shows how the working end of a screw driver should be shaped for

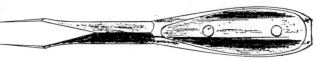

FIG. 16–14. Heavy duty screw driver.

most efficient operation. Note that the sides of the point are ground almost parallel to each other. If the sides are ground to a chisel point or edge, the blade has a tendency to slip out of the slot, damaging the head of the screw. When grinding the point or blade of a screw driver be careful not to draw the temper.

Miscellaneous hand tools. Clamps are frequently used in connection with bench work for holding parts while they are being assembled, or for holding work in the drill press. The clamps used for this purpose vary from the small light duty type to heavy duty forged types designed to clamp large pieces of work.

FIG. 16–15.
Properly shaped
screw driver blade.

Fig. 16–16 shows a parallel clamp commonly called a *Toolmaker's* clamp. These clamps have two jaws which are opened and closed by means of the two screws. The one jaw is held tightly by a spring attachment which prevents it from moving out of line when the adjusting screws are turned. This type of clamp is very useful for holding small work, but the jaws must be kept nearly parallel to each other to hold the work properly.

C-clamps, Fig. 16–17, are made in three grades: the heavy duty, general service, and light duty. These clamps are named because of their shape and find an extensive use in any shop. The size of these clamps is based on their maximum capacity, that is, a 4″ clamp will open to accommodate work 4″ wide or thick.

Punches which are frequently used on the bench are of four types: the **"pin"** punch, **"drift"** punch, **"prick"** punch, and **"center"** punch. The pin punch, Fig. 16–18, is used to dislodge taper pins, straight pins, and the like, from the work. It has a blunt point on a cylindrical stem attached to an octagonally-shaped body. The drift punch,

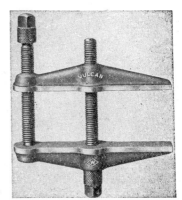

FIG. 16–16. Parallel or tool-maker's clamp.

Fig. 16–19, sometimes called a drift **"pin"** has a blunt point on the end which tapers back gradually to the full diameter of the octagonally-shaped body. It is used for aligning holes for bolts, pins, rivets, etc.

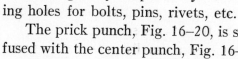

FIG. 16–17.   C-clamp.

The prick punch, Fig. 16–20, is sometimes confused with the center punch, Fig. 16–21. The prick punch has a conical point of from 30° to 45° and is used for marking small indentations on layout lines on the work in order to make the lines more apparent. The center punch has a conical point of 90° and is used to mark the location of and assist in properly starting a drill. The points of these punches are hardened while the heads are soft; the bodies are made of tool steel and are octagonal in shape to keep them from rolling when laid on the bench.

FIG. 16–18.   Pin punch.

FIG. 16–19.   Drift punch.

Chisels and their uses. The chisels used in the machine shop by the machinist or toolmaker differ from other kinds of chisels in that they do not have wooden handles and are especially made for cutting metal. The metal working chisel may be defined

FIG. 16–20.   Prick punch.

FIG. 16–21.   Center punch.

FIG. 16–22.   Flat chisel.

as a forged steel instrument with a specially shaped and hardened cutting edge at one end to facilitate the dressing, shaping, or cutting of metal. These tools are generally made from 1/2″ or 3/4″ octagonally-shaped tool steel, commonly referred to as **"chisel"** steel. Their length may vary from 3″, for fine work, to 8″ for heavy, coarse work.

The chisel most commonly used in the machine shop is the flat or **"cold"** chisel, Fig. 16–22. This chisel is **"wedge"** shaped about one-third of its length to the cutting edge, at which point it is about 3/32″ thick on the heavier chisels. For general purposes the bevel of the cutting edge should be about 70°. For cast iron and brass the angle of the cutting edge can be reduced to 45° but it should be ground so that the centerline of the chisel bisects the angle and so that the cutting edge is parallel with the flat of the wedge. The chisel is hardened from the cutting edge back about one inch. For this reason be careful not to draw the temper when sharpening it.

In using the chisel, grip it with the third and fourth fingers, with the thumb and first finger relaxed below the chisel head. It is important to keep the thumb and first finger relaxed because if the hammer should glance off the chisel and strike the hand, the blow will fall on relaxed muscles causing less injury than if it fell on contracted muscles. The hammer used to drive the chisel should be in proportion to the size of the chisel and the amount of material to be removed. The handle of the hammer should be gripped near the end and swung with a free easy motion. The cutting edge of the chisel should be held at the point where the chipping is to be done, at an angle that will produce the desired depth of cut, and so that it will cut in the direction desired. The depth of the cut will depend on the angle between the centerline of the chisel and the work; the greater the angle the deeper the cut. As the chisel approaches the edge of the work, if the cut is very heavy, it should be directed at a right angle to the former direction of cutting action.

The **"cape"** chisel, Fig. 16–23, derives its name from the fact that it is forged to produce a cape or flare for the widest flat, causing the cutting edge to be narrow in comparison to the thickness of the body. The cape is formed so that it is thicker at the cutting edge than it is at the point where the cape meets the chisel body. This chisel is used for cutting narrow slots, rectangular grooves, and keyways.

Fig. 16–23.   Round nose cape chisel.

Fig. 16–24.   Diamond point chisel.

Fig. 16–25.   Cape chisel.

A diamond-point chisel, Fig. 16–24, is used for chipping V-shaped oil grooves or for making sharp corners in holes that are square or rectangular. It gets its name from the fact that when the square-shaped working end is ground at an angle other than 90° to the centerline of the body, a diamond shape is produced. Besides using this chisel for cutting V-shaped oil grooves, it is frequently used for chipping a groove in the conical-shaped depression formed by a drill, or for drawing the drill back on center.

The round-nosed chisel, Fig. 16–25, is used for producing a concave surface. The cutting edge of this chisel is formed by grinding the tapered working end at an angle other than 90° to the centerline of the chisel body; therefore, the actual shape of the cutting face is an ellipse. The effect produced, however, is that of a concave surface.

To produce an even or flat surface with a chisel it is necessary to hold it at a constant angle of inclination to the work and keep the cutting edge up against the shoulder formed by previous blows of the hammer.

As a matter of safety, always place a chip guard ahead of and around the work to protect fellow workers. This guard, Fig. 16–26, consists of a piece of heavy canvas attached to two upright posts supported in two cast iron or aluminum bases.

To protect yourself, wear close and easy fitting safety goggles, and do not use a chisel with a **"mushroom"** head. **"Mushroom"** is the term applied to a condition in which the head of the chisel flares out due to the intermittent pressure of the hammer blows. When such a condition prevails, have the instructor demonstrate how to grind it off and recondition the head.

When using the vise to hold the work while it is being chipped, place a **"packing"** block between the work and the vise slide. This block can be any material of a size consistent with the work and will keep the work from sliding down in the vise.

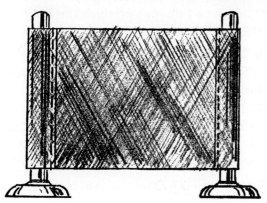

FIG. 16–26. Chip guard.

Files and their uses. A file may be defined as a piece of steel, usually tool steel, having serrations or teeth cut on the surface for the purpose of removing irregularities from the surface of work. There are many varieties of files including circular files or burring wheels.

The principal parts of a file are: the **"tang"** which is the pointed end over which the handle fits; the **"body"** which is that portion of the file containing the teeth or chisel cuts; the **"heel"** which is that portion which joins the tang and the body; and the **"point"** which is the extreme end of the file opposite the tang, as shown in Fig. 16–27.

Files may be classified into three groups according to their shape or fineness of the teeth: **single cut, double cut,** and **rasps.**

Single cut files have one series of teeth or chisel cuts on an angle with the edge of the file. These teeth may be rough, coarse, bastard, second cut, or smooth cut.

FIG. 16–27. Common mill file.

Double cut files have two series of teeth cut diagonally across each other and may be obtained in coarse, bastard, second cut, and smooth cut styles.

FIG. 16–28. Rasp.

Rasps have staggered, pointed teeth that are cut by a triangular pointed punch, as shown in Fig. 16–28.

The terms **"rough," "coarse," "bastard,"** and the like, pertain to the fineness or pitch of the file teeth; that is, a rough file usually has about 20 teeth to the lineal inch, whereas a fine cut file has approximately 120 teeth to the lineal inch. However, to express the pitch of a file, the length must be included. For example, a 12″ mill file has less chisel cuts per lineal inch than an 8″ mill file.

When a mechanic calls for a file at the tool crib, he usually refers to it with respect to the shape of the perpendicular cross section. For this reason prominent file manufacturers classify files in the same manner. Some of the more common shapes are flat, round, half-round, square, and triangular. These shapes, along with those less frequently used, are shown in Fig. 16–29.

The flat mill file derives its name from the fact that it was designed for and used extensively in sharpening wood mill saws. Today its use in machine shops and tool and die rooms is such that it might be called the indispensable file, because it is adaptable to nearly all kinds of bench and machine work.

Bastard files are those containing coarse teeth and are used when considerable stock must be removed. They do not produce a good finish, but will remove the stock very rapidly.

Smooth-cut files should be used when a small amount of material is to be removed and when a comparatively good finish is required on the work.

Safe-edge files are those which do not have chisel cuts on one or both edges. They are used for filing slots, keyways, or against shoulders where the surface adjacent to the one being filed is not to be filed. These files are properly known as **"pillar"** files.

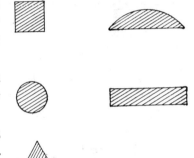

FIG. 16–29. Shapes of files.

The half-round file derives its name from the fact that one side is flat and the opposite side is convex. This file is used for general filing purposes but, when the teeth are of the mill file class, it is found to be very convenient for use on the lathe.

The round file is generally tapered and is used for enlarging holes or filing fillets or concave radii. In the smaller sizes, where it is drawn to a sharp point, it is called a **"rat tail"** file.

The three corner, or **"three-square,"** file has its sides at a 60-degree angle to each other. It is generally drawn to a sharp point and the chisel cuts meet at the edges. It is used most frequently for filing hand saw teeth. However, in the machine shop it is used for filing internal angles, for cleaning out square corners, and cleaning up damaged 60-degree screw threads.

The shape of a file to be used on a job depends on the type of surface to be filed. For example, if it is necessary to file a plane surface, it would be natural to use a flat file; if the surface was of the concave type, it would be necessary to use a round or half-round file; for filing slots or keyways or rectangular openings, a square, flat, knife, or pillar file could be used. For removing considerable material where the kind of finish produced is not important, a heavy bastard file should be used.

Using the file. Before attempting to use any file, be sure that it is equipped with a suitable handle; that is, a handle of the proper size that will fit tightly up against the heel of the file.

Cross-filing is a method of filing where the stroke is changed 90° to its former line of travel and is used to remove stock quickly but at the same time show the high points of the work and help to keep the surface flat.

In cross-filing, especially when a large file is used, the handle should be grasped so that the end will fit into and up against the fleshy part of the palm of the hand, with the thumb lying along the top of the handle and the ends of the fingers curled underneath and pointing up on the inside of the handle. The point of the file should be grasped with the thumb and first two fingers, the hand being held so that the thumb presses on the top of the file in the direction of the stroke. As more pressure is required to make the file cut, it can be applied with the thumb and fingers in this position.

The position of the feet and body should be such as to permit the file to be moved in an almost circular path, so that pressure can be applied on the forward stroke and released on the return stroke of the file. In filing surfaces of irregular form, the movement of the body must be such as to permit the blending of the strokes to produce the surface required.

Draw-filing is a method of using the file to produce a good finished surface. To do this kind of filing, it is necessary to grasp the file with both hands, the thumbs being 1/2″ to 3/4″ from each side of the work; the stock is then removed by drawing and pushing the file over the work surface. When a single-cut file is used in this manner, the teeth have a shearing action and will give a smooth finish to the work.

A common error made by many beginners is that of bearing too heavily on the file, or pushing and pulling the file over the work too fast. Learn to recognize when the file is taking the proper **"bite,"** and use, as nearly as possible, the full length of the file on the stroke. Taking short, quick strokes wears the file out in one spot; applying too much pressure on the file causes the chisel cuts to become loaded or **"pinned"** with particles of the material being filed.

If too much pressure is not being applied and the file has a tendency to **"pin,"** try rubbing chalk over the file to fill the chisel cuts. Frequent use of the file brush, or the **"scorer"** in the handle, will keep the chisel cuts clean and help to overcome pinning of the file.

As a matter of safety in filing, do not at any time use a file without a handle. File tangs are usually quite sharp and may readily puncture the hand, resulting in serious wounds. Never rub the hand over the work that is being filed. Small iron filings may prick into the skin causing infections; also oil or grease from the hand gets on the surface being filed and causes the file to score the work rather than cut it.

Hacksaws and their uses. A hacksaw is a metal blade of tool steel, high speed steel, or tungsten alloy steel with teeth formed on one edge lengthwise of the blade. The blades are from 8″ to 24″ long, from 1/2″ to 1-1/2″ wide and from .025″ to .065″ thick. The heavier hacksaw blades are used in power machines whereas the lighter blades are used in frames for hand sawing.

Power hacksaws are used where considerable stock must be cut, but they are being replaced with metal sawing bandsaws that do the work much faster because of their continuous cutting action.

Blades for hand sawing are held in frames similar to that shown in Fig. 16–30. In this frame, compensation for the different blade lengths is made by means of a wing-nut on the clip opposite handle, or by a threaded ferule in the handle.

The slotting frame holds blades of different thicknesses that are used for cutting slots in screw heads.

Hand hacksaw blades are made in two types known as **"flexible back"** and **"all hard"** blades. The flexible back blade is hardened only on the teeth, whereas the all hard blade is hardened all over. The flexible back blade should be used for cutting tubing, tin, channel iron, and copper. The all hard blade is used on steel, cast iron, and brass. These blades are made with different pitch sizes to accommodate different kinds of metal; the standard pitches being 14, 18, 24, and 32 teeth per lineal inch. Naturally, the greatest economy is obtained by

FIG. 16–30.   Hack saw.

selecting a blade of the correct number of teeth per inch for the work to be done. For example, a coarse tooth blade such as a 14-pitch, will cut fast and free; therefore, it should be used on such materials as machine steel, structural steel or other mild, free cutting materials, but it leaves a rough, jagged finish.

For general purposes an 18-pitch blade is most satisfactory because it can be used for high speed steel, tool steel, babbitt, cast iron or aluminum. Finer pitches than this are used for cutting tubing, conduit, and thin sheet metal.

All hacksaw blades have the teeth set to provide clearance between the work and the blade. In coarse tooth blades, one tooth is bent over to the right, the next tooth to the left and so on until all have been staggered. This is known as **"regular alternate"** and permits the teeth to cut a slot a little wider than the thickness of the blade body. Fine tooth blades are set **"double alternate"**; that is, the teeth are set over in pairs, first to the right and then the left.

After the correct hacksaw blade has been selected for the job, place it in the frame so that the teeth point down and away from the handle. For cutting a long piece of material having a width almost equal to the frame depth, the clips can be turned to permit the blade to be used at right angles to the frame. In tightening the blade in the frame, turn the handle enough to hold the blade firmly but not too tightly.

Start the blade in the work by holding the thumb alongside the blade to guide it at the sawing point. After taking a series of short quick strokes to seat the teeth, place one hand conveniently on the outer end of the frame to help guide the blade through the work.

When the sawing operation is fully started, be sure to lift the blade on the return stroke and operate it at a speed of from 30 to 50 strokes per minute, depending on the kind of material being cut. Sufficient pressure should be applied to make the blade cut rather than to have it slide over the work. This pressure can best be gaged by the flow of chips and the action of the blade on the work. The recommended pressure is from 20 to 30 pounds per inch of contact area of the teeth. Too much pressure will cause the blade to buckle, heat up, and dull quickly. It is important to use, as nearly as possible, the full length of the blade in each stroke in order to get the maximum usefulness.

Extremely thin sheet metal can be cut by means of a hacksaw by clamping the metal between two pieces of board, then sawing through all three of them. To avoid breaking or dulling hacksaw blades:

DON'T use a coarse blade on thin material.

DON'T draw the blade too tightly in the frame.

DON'T use too much pressure.

DON'T cut too fast.

DON'T saw the work at a point too far away from its support.

DON'T **"cant"** or twist the blade after it has completely entered the work.

REVIEW QUESTIONS

1. Name several types of hammers used by machinists and tool- and die-makers and describe each one.

2. What is meant by the word peening?

3. Discuss the important considerations involved in using a hammer.

4. Upon which side of a warped piece of metal should the blows be delivered, the convex side or concave side? Why?

5. Should pliers be used to tighten nuts or bolts? Why?

6. How many kinds of wrenches can you name? Describe each.

7. Should a screw driver be sharpened to a fine edge? Why?

8. What are parallel clamps?

9. How many grades of C-clamps are commonly found?

10. Name four types of punches and discuss the purpose of each.

11. Discuss several types of chisels.

12. How should a chisel be held in the hand?

13. What safety factors should be observed in chipping relative to the operator and others around him?

14. What are the principal parts of a file?

15. Files are classified into what three groups?

16. Name several common shapes of files.

17. Why should a handle be used on a file?

18. What is meant by cross-filing?

19. What is meant by draw-filing?

20. Discuss several points in the use of the hacksaw.

~~~~~~

Chapter 17

BENCH
MATERIALS — ROUTING — INSPECTION

MATERIALS

*Aluminum . . . Copper . . . Brass and Bronze . . . Cast Iron . . . Cold rolled . . . SAE
Chromium . . . Chrome Vanadium . . . Tool Steel . . . High Speed Steel*

JOB PROCESSING

Stock order . . . Routing card

GAGES AND INSPECTION

Kinds . . . Use

MATERIALS

Besides knowing how to use common hand tools, the bench worker is frequently required to make such tools as special gages, milling cutters, small dies, punches, jigs, fixtures and templates. The production of these tools, where parts are manufactured under the interchangeable system and any tools that have the effect of lowering the cost of manufacture of those parts, forms the major part of the toolmaker's work at the bench.

Many times, in the execution of these duties it is the task of the toolmaker to devise ways and means of making these tools and it becomes his responsibility to select the material from which they are to be made. The efficiency of the tool and its cost will depend to a great extent on how wisely this material is selected. The following information is given to act as a guide, but remember that the characteristics of these materials can be varied by the manufacturing methods employed, such as forging, heat treatment, and so on.

Aluminum. This material should be used for parts that must be of light weight but which have no moving members in direct contact with them. Such parts are housings for small electric motors, pistons, hand wheels, machine pulleys, and the like.

Copper. Because of its softness and flexibility, the use of this material is confined almost entirely to electrical conductors such as contact tips, slides and fittings for electric welders.

Brass and bronze. Brass, because of its resistance to oxidation, is used for water and steam fittings. Bronze is used for bushings, bearings, and special gears. It is also used for ornamental purposes such as plaques and medals.

Cast iron. This material should be used for parts where compressive strength is the main requirement. It is not to be used for parts which will be subjected to torque or bending strains. Parts for which cast iron is commonly used are die bolsters, surface plates, machine bases or housings, jig and fixture bases, and various supporting members of machines.

Cold rolled or machine steel. Because of its low carbon content this steel is not generally satisfactory for parts that must have high wearing qualities. When carbon is injected into the surface by certain heat-treating processes, it acquires a hard surface which makes it usable for such parts as clamps, locating gages, stock guides, small stripper plates and wear plates on punch presses. Lacking this heat treatment it can be used for small screws, bolts, studs, nuts and washers and miscellaneous small parts for machines.

SAE chromium or Ford "AAA" steel. SAE steels of the 5100 series or Ford "AAA" steel is used for Acme or square thread screws, milling machine arbors, axles, spindles, collets, spindle heads, punch retainers, armature shafts and boring bars. This steel can be given heat treatments that will give it either a hard surface and a soft core, or toughness and accuracy.

Chrome vanadium steel has high torque resisting qualities which make it an ideal material to be used for wrenches and similar tools.

Tool steel—Ford "RR" or SAE 1095. Because of its carbon content this steel is used when maximum hardness is desired on such parts as forming dies, punches, locating pins, forming and knurling rolls, machine hammers, screw drivers, plug and snap gages, parallels and V-blocks.

High speed steel. This steel is used almost entirely for making cutting tools such as milling cutters, broaches, reamers, forming tools, drills, counterbores, spot facers, countersinks, thread chasers and tool bits.

JOB PROCESSING

Under modern manufacturing methods, when new tools or parts are to be made, or if changes are to be made in existing equipment, drawings or blue prints are sent to the bench with a written order requesting these tools or changes in equipment to be made. The drawing or blue print contains such information as the dimensions for the part or parts, the detail or pattern number of each part, the kind of stock from which it is to be made and the heat treatment. Besides this information, the drawing contains other data relative to the finish, whether it is to be ground or filed, the degrees of hardness, and a stock list that gives the detail number, name of part and kind of material.

With this information as a beginning the bench man must first study the blue print to familiarize himself with the requirements; then a stock order is made out in duplicate, stating the work order number, account number, department to which the cost is to be charged; and the number of pieces, the size of each piece, the kind of material and the location to which the stock is to be sent.

The following illustration is a typical stock order form:

After the stock is received it should be checked for size and kind of material against the duplicate stock order; then a sketch of the detail, or the detail clipped from an extra blue print, is attached to a machining order, and with the stock for that detail, it is sent to the machine shop. Generally it is the bench man's duty to determine the sequence of the machining operations and to route the job accordingly. For example, the detail may require turning, milling, boring, drilling, tapping, heat treating and

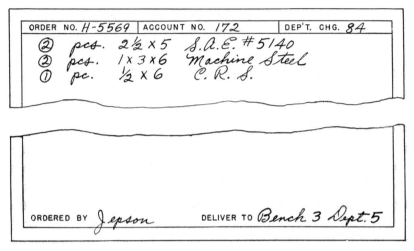

ORDER NO. *H-5569*	ACCOUNT NO. *172*	DEP'T. CHG. *84*

② *pcs.* 2½ × 5   *S.A.E. # 5140*
② *pcs.* 1 × 3 × 6   *Machine Steel*
① *pc.* ½ × 6   *C. R. S.*

ORDERED BY *Jepson*   DELIVER TO *Bench 3 Dept. 5*

FIG. 17–1.   Stock order list.

grinding. It is the bench man's responsibility to determine in what order these manufacturing operations are to be done for the greatest efficiency.

Where the bench man has several orders all working at the same time, it is necessary to keep a record of the location of each detail, and orders which are on a **"time and material"** basis require that an accurate record be kept of the time involved. Some

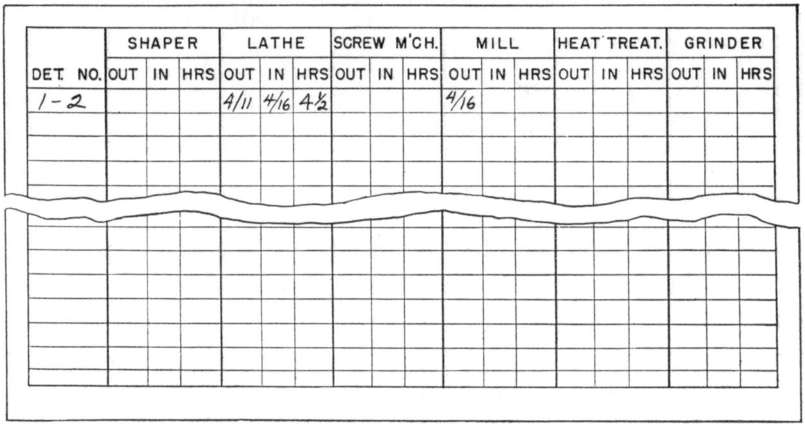

DET. NO.	SHAPER			LATHE			SCREW M'CH.			MILL			HEAT TREAT.			GRINDER		
	OUT	IN	HRS	OUT	IN	HRS	OUT	IN	HRS	OUT	IN	HRS	OUT	IN	HRS	OUT	IN	HRS
1-2				4/11	4/16	4½				4/16								

FIG. 17–2.   Routing card.

factories have regular forms, routing cards, with spaces marked for detail number, machine, date sent out, date returned and machining time. These forms should be filled out for each separate work order number; then as a detail or pattern is sent to the machine shop, the number of that detail and the date sent out is entered in the proper column. When the detail and machining order are returned to the bench, the date returned and machining time are entered in the proper column. Since the same detail is sent out for other manufacturing operations, entries are made in the correct columns on the back of the routing card.

After each machining operation, when the work is returned to the bench, it should be inspected to make sure that it is ready for the next operation. This prevents added operations from being done in the event that the previous operation has not been carried out properly.

Gages and inspection. A gage may be defined as any standard of comparison or measurement. The three fundamental units of measurement are mass, time and length. Mass is gaged in terms of weight; time is gaged in terms of seconds, minutes, hours; length is gaged in terms of inches or multiples of the inch, or in metric units.

Under the American system, linear measurements are taken in terms of the inch or multiples of it. The inch may be defined as a standard unit of measurement of length equal to 1/36th of the British Imperial yard or 2.54 centimeters. The unit of measurement of length used in machine shops or tool and die rooms is the thousandth part of an inch (.001″). Most measurements taken in tool room work are of the precision type; that is, they are very exacting and have a high degree of accuracy. It is because of the fact that piece after piece can be made to the same exacting dimensions that the **"interchangeable system"** of manufacture is possible. The interchangeable system is that property of parts which permits them to be interchanged without having to change their shape or size.

FIG. 17–3. Plug gage.   FIG. 17–4. Ring gage.

These exacting or highly accurate measurements are made possible because of gages which permit the taking of measurements within designated limits, the limits being an intentional or permissible variation from the specified size.

Gages may be classified as master, inspection, and working gages. Master gages are kept as a standard of reference for other gages. Inspection gages are those which are used entirely for checking the finished part and working gages are those which the machine operator uses directly on the part during the manufacturing process.

Working gages are of two types, fixed and adjustable. Fixed gages are those the measuring portion of which cannot be varied, except through wear or expansion and contraction due to temperature change. Plug, ring, snap, and caliper gages and gage blocks are examples of the fixed working gage. Adjustable gages are those the measuring portion of which can be varied to suit the conditions under which the part is being manufactured. Micrometers, verniers, dial or fan type indicators, amplifiers, and comparators are adjustable gages. Certain limit gages of the snap gage variety have

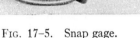

FIG. 17–5. Snap gage.

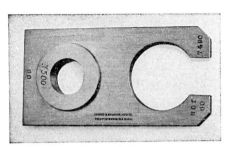

FIG. 17–6. Combination gage.

FIG. 17–7. Johansson gage block.

anvils that can be adjusted to compensate for wear; however, these are not classed as adjustable gages because they cannot be varied to suit the job during the manufacturing process.

Gage blocks, Fig. 17–12, are small, rectangular blocks of special alloy tool steel 3/8″ by 1-3/8″ by the specified size. These blocks are hardened, ground, effectively seasoned and finished to within a few millionths of an inch of the specified size.

Carl Edward Johansson made the first gage blocks while employed as a master mechanic in an arsenal at Eskilstuna, Sweden. In the manufacture of these blocks he overcame four universally recognized metallurgical and mechanical problems. First, **"nearly"** flat surfaces in steel; that is, the surfaces are not absolutely flat from a scientific standpoint of view, but are flat enough for all practical purposes, being plane within a very few millionths of an inch. Second, **"nearly"** parallel surfaces in steel. The measuring surfaces

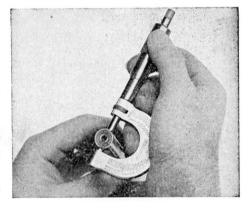

FIG. 17–8. Micrometer.

of Johansson gage blocks are parallel within a very few millionths of an inch as illustrated in Fig. 17–13. Any block in a given combination may be turned end for end without affecting either the size of the combination or the parallelism of the faces of the end blocks. Third, methods of heat treating and stabilization of the molecular structure such that the established size of the block can be guaranteed within the limits of accuracy of the set. Fourth, accuracy as to dimensions in steel; that is, the size of each block will remain within the designated accuracy for the set at 68° Fahrenheit.

Gage blocks are classified according to the purposes for which they are intended, as follows:

Laboratory set (used for reference purposes) "AA" quality, accuracy .000002".
Inspection set (used for inspection purposes) "A" quality, accuracy .000004".
Working set (used directly on the work) "B" quality, accuracy .000008".

The accuracy of each of the above sets is guaranteed to be true only at 68° Fahrenheit.

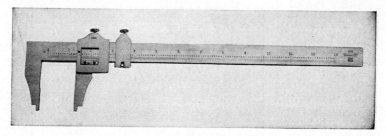

FIG. 17–9. Vernier caliper.

FIG. 17–10. Dial indicator.

FIG. 17–11. Amplifier.

Each standard set, Fig. 17–14, contains 81 blocks consisting of four series, each series containing blocks of the following sizes:

First series contains blocks from .1001" to .1009" in steps of ten-thousandths of an inch.

Second series contains blocks from .101" to .149" in steps of thousandths of an inch.

Third series contains blocks from .050" to .950" in steps of 50 thousandths.

Fourth series contains blocks from 1" to 4" in steps of one inch.

The blocks from any one series may be combined with any other series to get the required dimension; that is, the blocks of the first series may be combined with any other series to obtain any dimension, in tenths of thousandths within the capacity of the

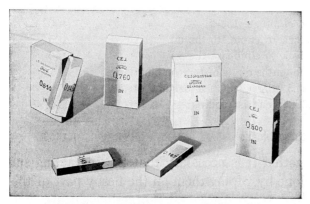

FIG. 17–12.   Miscellaneous gage blocks.

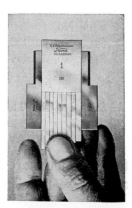

FIG. 17–13.   Combination of 9 blocks checked against 1 block.

set; the blocks from the second series can be combined with any other series to get dimensions varying by thousandths, and so on. It is possible to make over 120,000

FIG. 17–14.   Set No. 1 Johansson gage blocks.

different size gages, in steps of .0001″, from .200″ to more than 12″, with the standard 81-block set.

The size of the individual blocks required to make a given dimension within the capacity of the standard set can best be determined as follows:

1) Get thoroughly acquainted with the sizes of the blocks contained in the set.
2) Select a block the last digit of which will eliminate the last digit of the specified size.
3) Continue to select blocks such that the last digit of each block will be the last remaining digit of the specified size, until the required dimension is satisfied.
4) Use as few blocks as possible in building any combination.

Example.

Suppose that it is necessary to use gage blocks to check a dimension of 1.1463".

Solution.

STEP No. 1.	Select a block to eliminate the 3	— .1003
STEP No. 2.	Select another block to eliminate the 6	— .106
STEP No. 3.	Select another block to eliminate the 4	— .140
	The sum of the tenths digits of the combination so far equals .3 which leaves a balance of .8	
STEP No. 4.	Therefore, an .800 block is required	— .800
	The sum of these blocks	1.1463

Before the blocks are stacked together it is necessary that the contacting surfaces be thoroughly cleaned. This can be done by wiping them on the fleshy part of the base of the thumb or wrist. To stack the blocks, place one contacting surface crosswise of the other and with a slight inward pressure, twist the blocks around so that their edges are parallel.

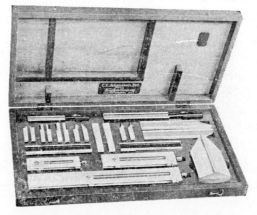

FIG. 17–15.   Gage block accessories.

This process is repeated for each succeeding block that is added to the stack to complete the required combination.

The set of accessories shown in Fig. 17–15 makes possible the use of gage blocks as compasses Fig. 17–16, inside and outside calipers, Figs. 17–17 and 17–18, height gage, trammels and similar devices.

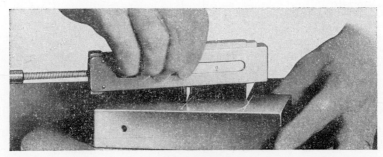

FIG. 17–16.

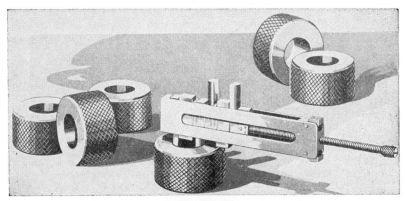

FIG. 17–17.

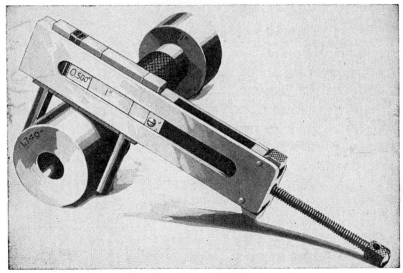

FIG. 17–18.

REVIEW QUESTIONS

1. What are some of the principal points pertaining to materials that a toolmaker is expected to know?

2. Discuss the more common metals used in tool and die work.

3. What is meant by job processing?

4. Why are routing cards needed?

5. Define an inch?

6. What is meant by the interchangeable system?

7. Discuss two types of working gages.

8. What are gage blocks?

9. Why do they adhere when "wrung" together?

10. What is the significance of the principle demonstrated in Fig. 13?

11. What is the accuracy of the "working set" of Jo-blocks?

12. How many different size gages is it possible to combine using an 81-piece set of Jo-blocks?

13. What method is used in selecting blocks to build a given size such as 1.3468"?

14. For what purposes can the accessories be used?

Chapter 18

~~~~~~

BENCH
LAYOUT — DRILLING — THREADING — SCRAPING
HEAT TREATING

Layout . . . Drills . . . Reamers . . . Counterbores . . . Countersinks . . . Threads . . .
Scraping . . . Heat treating — Manganese, Silicon, Chromium, Nickel, Vanadium,
Tungsten . . . Molybdenum

GENERAL SUGGESTIONS

Layout. Lines scribed on a piece of metal to indicate in full scale size the top, side, end or other view of the article to be manufactured, or machining operations to be performed, is called the **"layout."**

Operations to be performed on the drill press, shaper, planer, slotter, or mill are frequently laid out as a guide to the operator. The position of the layout lines should be sharp, distinct, and conform to the dimensions for that work operation as specified on the blue print or sketch.

As an aid to making the lines distinct, finished or machined surfaces should be covered with a suitable paint, ink, or similar substance so that the scribed line forms a marked contrast in the background. A suitable ink that does not rub off, but which can be readily removed, can be made by adding Gentian violet dye to orange shellac, then adding sufficient wood alcohol to make a thin paint. It is applied to the surface to be laid out by means of a small flat paint brush or dauber. Another substance commonly used as layout ink is copper sulfate solution ($CuSO_4$) frequently called **"blue vitriol."** A quantity of this solution can be made by adding 8 ounces of copper sulfate crystals to one pint of water, then adding 5 or 6 drops of sulfuric acid.

For rough work such as castings or forgings, water is added to calcimine to make it a thick paint consistency; then it can be applied with a paint brush to the surface to be laid out.

After the surface has been properly prepared, the job to be laid out should be set up on a surface plate, Fig. 18–1, or **"layout plate."** This plate is made of cast iron, heavily ribbed underneath to give it strength and to prevent distortion. The top, sides, and ends of the plate are accurately machined and scraped to give as nearly as possible a flat surface. When this plate is located level on a bench it is referred to as a **"bench"** plate; when it is of large size, that is, 6′ by 10′ approximately, it is leveled up on the floor and referred to as a **"floor"** plate.

In laying out work, the following tools are commonly used, descriptions of which may be found by referring to the index at the back of the text: Angle plates, fixed and

264

adjustable; clamps, C- and toolmaker's; hardened and ground parallels; the surface gage and its attachments; height gage; combination square, center head and bevel protractor; rules, 12″ to 60″ long; dividers, hermaphrodite caliper, and trammel; scriber, prick and center punches, and a ball-peen hammer.

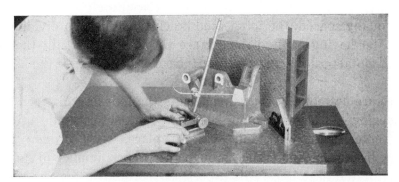

FIG. 18–1.

The job to be laid out should be placed on the surface plate so that all the parallel lines necessary can be scribed in relation to the same surface. If the lines fall inconveniently low on the surface, the job can be raised up by placing it on parallels on the surface plate. Where several parallel lines must be scribed, a temporary line can be placed near the bottom of the job to act as a base line, from which other lines may be located if it becomes necessary to move the job before the layout is completed. If these lines are to be located quite accurately, gage blocks and a height gage of convenient size should be used to set up the required dimensions. However, if the dimensions for the lines do not have to be very accurate, quick results can be obtained by setting the scriber point of a surface gage to the graduations on the blade of a combination square.

If other lines are required to intersect the lines already scribed, they can be laid out by working from the surface of a box angle plate or cube that has been located with respect to a definite point on the working surface of the job.

If these intersecting lines locate the center of a radius or hole, the prick punch and ball-peen hammer should be used to make a small indentation where the two lines cross. The divider can then be set to the required size by means of the graduations on a rule and with one leg point nested in the indentation, the required radius or circle can be scribed with the other point. After the circle has been scribed, enlarge the prick punch hole by driving the point of a center punch into it.

Sometimes it is necessary to locate the center of a cored hole or a hole previously formed. When such an occasion arises all that is necessary is to take a piece of pencil solder (round solder about the size of a lead pencil), flatten it somewhat with a hammer, cut it a trifle larger than the diameter of the hole and then drive it into the hole to act as a bridge to carry the lines.

Where it is necessary to lay out several holes, all on the same circle, for example four holes equally spaced, all that is necessary is to scribe two lines at right angles to each other such that their intersection coincides with the location specified on the blue print or sketch. Using the intersection of these lines as the center, draw the required circle; the centers for the required holes will be at the point where the lines cut the circumference of the circle.

Where a series of holes must be laid out quite accurately, whether these holes are equally or unequally spaced, the job should be chucked up on a dividing head so that it runs true. After having painted the surface with layout ink, .tilt the dividing head spindle in a horizontal position and set it for the correct indexing if the holes are equally spaced.

If the holes are not equally spaced, calculate the indexing for each hole according to angular indexing. With the dividing head and work set correctly use a height gage to locate the center of the work and lock it in place. After scribing the center line, index the work by turning the crank through the proper number of holes and correct circle, then scribe the next line. This process is repeated, using the proper indexing, until the layout has been completed.

When it is necessary to lay out an angle, a bevel protractor can be used if the angle does not require an accuracy greater than five minutes. Greater accuracy than this can be obtained by setting the work up on a sine bar or by using a dividing head.

Drills. A drill as used in a tool and die or machine shop is a cylindrical bar of steel having rounded spiral grooves running its length and a conical point with cutting edges formed by the termination of the spiral grooves.

Fig. 18–2 shows a twist drill and its parts. The parts which are most important to the user are the point and the shank.

FIG. 18–2. Twist drill and point.

The **"point"** is the entire conical shape at the cutting end of the drill; it contains the **"dead center"** and the cutting lips. The **"dead center"** is the sharp edge at the extreme tip end of the point and is formed by the intersection of the cone shaped surfaces that make up the point. The **"cutting lips"** are the edges which remove the stock or material when a hole is originated by drilling and are formed by the termination of the spiral flutes at the point. These cutting lips derive their cutting ability from the fact that the surface of the point is ground away or **"relieved"** to provide clearance back of the cutting edge; the angle of this relief should be about 12°, as indicated in Fig. 18–3.

In grinding this angle of relief on the point, the line of the dead center should form an angle of from 120° to 135°, as shown in Fig. 18–4. The two cutting edges should be the same length and they should form equal angles with the axis of rotation or center line of the drill body. For general purpose drilling, this angle should be 59° as shown in Fig. 18–5.

The **"shank"** of the drill is that part which fits into the spindle or chuck of the mechanism used for revolving the drill. If the shank is badly nicked or burred, it is difficult to get the drill running true; it will cause heating of the drill and put the drilling

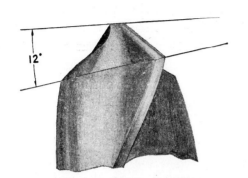

FIG. 18–3. Angle of relief back of edge.

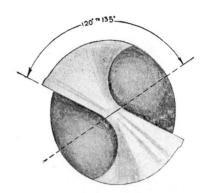

FIG. 18–4. Lip clearance angle.

machine under unwarranted strain. Fig. 18–6 shows the types of shanks commonly used by metal workers. *A* is the straight shank for drills that are to be used in drill chucks; *B* is the taper shank drill which employs the Morse taper system to adapt it to the sockets of drill presses and other drilling machines. Drills varying by 1/64" in diameter from 1/8" to 9/16" have a No. 1 Morse Standard taper; from 37/64" to 29/32" a No. 2 Morse taper; from 59/64" to 1-1/4" a No. 3 Morse taper; from 1-17/64" to 2" a No. 4 Morse taper; and from 2-1/32" to 3" they have a No. 5 Morse taper. Drill sizes are specified in four different ways as follows:

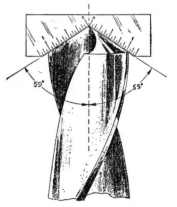

By numbers from 80 to 1, the decimal sizes of which run from .0135" to .228".

By letters from "A" to "Z," the decimal sizes of which run from .234" to .413".

By fractions from 1/64" to 4" and over by 64ths of an inch.

By millimeters from .5 to 10 mm. by .1 mm.; those drills larger than 10 mm. vary in steps of .5 mm.

FIG. 18–5. Correctly ground lips.

The distance, measured in fractions of an inch, that a drill penetrates the work for each revolution is called the **"feed."** To make the drill feed into the work, force or pressure must be applied to its end either by hand or power. The amount of power required to keep the drill working at its greatest efficiency is governed by many factors, such as the type of material being drilled, how the material is supported, the cutting ability of the drill and the condition of the mechanism used to drive or hold the drill.

By the **"speed"** of the drill is meant the distance the drill would travel if it were laid on its side and rolled for one minute at its given number of revolutions per minute. This speed is governed by many factors and opinions as to what is the correct speed are at variance; for this reason the correct speed and feed of a drill can be determined only by sound judgment and experience. The following tables are only approximate and should be used as a starting point; if conditions indicate this speed to be too fast, it should be decreased to a speed that is satisfactory. Chapter 19 contains tables of cutting speeds which can be referred to for all fractional size drills; for decimal size drills, use the nearest corresponding fraction.

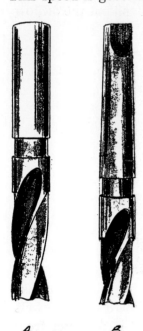

FIG. 18–6. Commonly used types of shanks.

A — Straight shank.
B — Taper shank.

Alloy Steels	— 50 to 70 FPM
Machine or Cold Rolled Steel	— 70 to 100 FPM
Cast Iron	— 70 to 150 FPM
Brass, Bronze, Aluminum	— 200 to 300 FPM

In preparing the work to be drilled, lay out the hole or holes to be drilled first, then mount the work correctly on the drill press table. To mount the work properly, support it close to the location of the hole, then clamp it to the table or in a drill press vise. In any event do not try to hold it by hand. If the work is laid flat on the table be sure that it is properly blocked against the drill action.

After the work is properly set up, place a drill chuck in the drill press spindle and, using a center drill in proportion to the size of the hole, center drill the work at the center punch mark; then remove the center drill. If the hole to be drilled is 1″ or larger, run a smaller drill through first; generally the **pilot drill** is equal to, or slightly larger than, the web thickness at the point of the final drill size. Bring the drill down to the work by hand and feed it in slowly, observing whether or not it is drilling to conform to the hole layout; if the conical hole formed by the point of the drill is not concentric with the layout, the drill will have to be drawn over.

To draw the drill over, use a round nose cape chisel of a size consistent with the

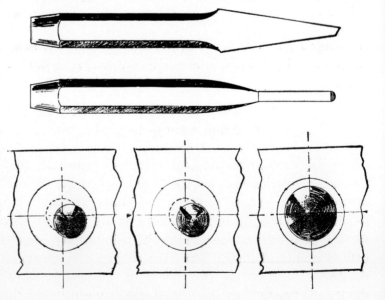

FIG. 18–7. Drawing a drill back on center.

drill and cut a small groove, starting at the top of the conical hole and chipping clear to the center, on the side toward which the drill is to be drawn, as shown in Fig. 18–7. This procedure may have to be repeated several times in order to get the edge of the conical hole concentric with the layout.

After the drill has been properly started, throw in the power feed and permit the drill to originate the hole. The feed should be proportionate to the diameter of the drill, which, generally speaking, is as follows:

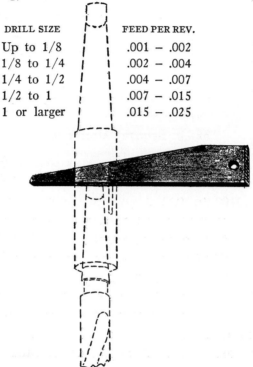

DRILL SIZE	FEED PER REV.
Up to 1/8	.001 – .002
1/8 to 1/4	.002 – .004
1/4 to 1/2	.004 – .007
1/2 to 1	.007 – .015
1 or larger	.015 – .025

FIG. 18–8.   Drill drift and its use.

To keep a drill cutting at its highest efficiency, it is necessary to use a good cutting lubricant. The following recommendations prove very satisfactory in the majority of cases:

> For mild, free cutting steels, use soda water or lard oil.
> For carbon or alloy steels, use soda water, or kerosene oil.
> For brass or bronze, drill dry or use lard oil.
> For aluminum or soft alloys, use soda water or kerosene.
> For cast iron, drill dry.

After the drilling operation has been completed, carefully remove the drill chuck or drill from the drill press spindle. Do not use anything to remove them except a drill drift, Fig. 18–8, otherwise the tang or drill spindle socket may be badly damaged. As the chuck or drill is drifted out, be careful that they do not drop on the table and damage themselves or the table. Do not insert dirty, oily or nicked shanks in the drill spindle socket. Be sure to clean the drill press and leave it in good condition when through using it. Keep your sleeves rolled up above the elbow when operating a drill press and keep your hands away from the drill while it is revolving.

FIG. 18–9. Solid hand reamer.

Reamers and reaming. A reamer is a cutting tool similar to the drill in that it has flutes running the length of the body; however, it is used for perfecting holes that have been previously originated by drilling or boring. The amount of stock left for

FIG. 18–10. Adjustable hand reamer.

reaming depends on the diameter of the hole and the quality of work desired; it should not be greater than .010″ to .012″.

Reamers can be classified as end cutting or side cutting, each of which can be obtained with either solid or adjustable teeth. Fig. 18–9 shows the solid hand reamer while Fig. 18–10 shows the adjustable hand reamer.

The solid fluted hand reamer is made tapering in diameter, starting at the front end and running back about one-fourth its length, being about .010″ smaller at the starting end than at the body diameter. The body diameter tapers back toward the shank at the rate of about .0002″ per inch of length. For this reason, when checking the diameter of a hand reamer with a micrometer, be sure to measure it at the high point of the body rather than at the front or back ends.

The hand reamer shown in Fig. 18–10 is commonly called an **"expansion"** reamer. Contrary to general opinions this reamer was not intended for perfecting odd sized holes, but rather one that could be sharpened and then adjusted back to standard size. Perhaps if more mechanics understood this fact fewer of these reamers would be broken in use.

The limits of expansion for the standard sizes are as follows and any attempt to exceed these limits may result in the unwarranted breaking of the blades:

REAMER SIZE	LIMITS OF EXPANSION
1/4 to 15/32	.005 of an inch
1/2 to 31/32	.008 " " "
1 to 1-23/32	.010 " " "
1-3/4 to 2-1/2	.012 " " "

Be careful not to turn a reamer backwards; this practice destroys the cutting edge of the teeth and causes the reamer to be undersized. Machine reamers are made in a variety of shapes and types but the kinds commonly used are the **"chucking"** reamer and **"rose"** reamer. Both are available in either straight or Morse taper shank.

The **fluted chucking reamer,** Fig. 18–11, differs from the rose reamer, Fig. 18–12, in that the body diameter has no back taper and the teeth are backed off with

FIG. 18–11.   Fluted chucking reamer (taper shank).

radial relief. In the case of the straight tooth chucking reamer there is a tendency for the teeth to cut on the sides, toward the back end, which causes it to cut oversize. This condition is relieved somewhat if the teeth are of left-hand helix with an angle of 8° to 10°.

FIG. 18–12.   Rose chucking reamer (taper shank).

The **rose reamer** gets its name from the fact that the leading edge of the teeth are given a back-off chamfer of 45° causing the end view of the reamer to appear like a rose. The lands of the teeth are ground radially without relief, but tapering back toward the shank so that the cutting action takes place at the front end of the teeth; for this reason the size of this reamer should be measured at the front end.

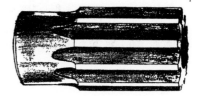

FIG. 18–13.   Shell reamer.

The shell reamer, Fig. 18–13, is a reamer head with a hole having 1/8″ taper per foot to fit a special arbor as shown in Fig. 18–14. The back end of this reamer head has a square slot cut in it to fit over the drivers of the arbor. The advantage of having reamers of this sort lies in the fact that there is a great saving in the cost of material, since one arbor suffices for several different sizes of heads. However, the saving in material is partially offset by the cost of making and finishing the hole and slot. These reamers are used primarily for sizing and finishing operations and may be obtained with either straight or helical teeth.

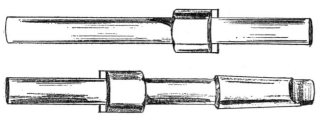

FIG. 18–14.   Two types of shell reamer arbors.

For making taper sockets for milling machine, lathe, grinder or drill press spindles, or holes for taper pins, a **taper reamer,** Figs. 18–15 and 18–16, must be used. This reamer is a side cutting tool and is made for roughing and finishing purposes. The roughing taper reamer differs from the finishing reamer in that the teeth at the cutting edges are notched to relieve the broad cutting surface that would ordinarily be bearing on the work. These reamers are obtainable for hand reaming or for machine reaming.

Taper pin reamers, Fig. 18–17, are made with a standard taper of 1/4″ to the foot. Since taper pins are used to hold two machine sections in alignment, these reamers are made for hand use only. However, they can be used in a machine if they are placed in a drill chuck. These reamers are made with either straight or helical teeth.

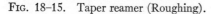

FIG. 18–15. Taper reamer (Roughing).

FIG. 18–16. Taper reamer (Finishing).

Counterbores and countersinks. A counterbore or **"spotfacer"** is a tool similar to a shell end mill, but is used to bore a larger hole on the same axis as a previously originated hole for the purpose of bringing a section of a mating part, bolt, or set screw head flush with a given surface.

FIG. 18–17. Taper pin reamer.

FIG. 18–18. Countersink.

A **countersink,** Fig. 18–18, is a multiple toothed cutter with the teeth formed on an angular surface and is used for beveling the mouth of a hole, either as a chamfer or as a seat for a flat or oval head machine screw.

Counterbores are of three types: solid, interchangeable, or inverted.

The **solid counterbore,** Fig. 18–19, has the pilot, cutter head and shank as one piece, and is a part of standard tap sets. The cutter diameter is usually .010″ larger

FIG. 18–19. Solid counterbore.

FIG. 18–20. Interchangeable counterbore.

than the diameter of the screw head and the pilot is equal to the body diameter of the screw body or the tap drill size for the screw. These counterbores are made with either straight or Morse standard taper shanks.

Interchangeable counterbores, Fig. 18–20, consist chiefly of a special taper shank holder of several standard sizes with provisions for holding different sizes of cutter heads and pilots.

An **"inverted"** or **"upside-down"** counterbore, Fig. 18–21, commonly called a spotfacer, is one that fits an arbor having a pin through it to fit the slot in the back of the cutter head. This tool is used to machine seats for washers on the flanged bases of machines that cannot be done conveniently by the other types of counterbores.

Threads and threading. Besides forming threads by means of a single pointed tool on the lathe, they can also be formed by a tap, die, or special rolling process.

A **tap** is a hardened cylindrical bar of steel with threads formed on its surfaces and grooves or flutes running lengthwise, intersecting with the threads to form cutting edges. It is used to form threads on an internal cylindrical or tapered surface.

A **die** is usually a flat piece of hardened steel with a fluted, cylindrical hole, such that the flutes intersect with threads cut on the surface of the cylindrical hole to form cutting edges.

The parts of a thread which are important to the average mechanic are as follows:

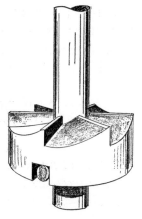

Fig. 18–21.   Inverted counterbore.

Major Diameter. The larest diameter of the thread of the screw or nut.

Pitch Diameter. On a straight thread, the diameter of an imaginary cylinder the surface of which would pass through the thread at such points as to make equal the width of the spaces cut by the surface of the cylinder.

Minor Diameter. The smallest diameter of the screw or nut.

Pitch. The distance from a point on a screw thread to a corresponding point on the next consecutive thread measured parallel to the axis of the screw body.

Angle of Thread. The angle included between the sides of the thread measured in an axial plane.

Lead. The distance a screw thread advances in one complete revolution measured parallel to the axis of rotation of the screw body. In a **single thread,** the lead is equal to the pitch. In a **double thread** the lead equals twice the pitch. In a **triple thread** the lead equals three times the pitch, and so on.

Depth. The distance from the top of the thread to the **minor diameter** measured perpendicular to the axis.

The **American National Coarse thread** series is the title given to the old United States Standard (USS) thread. The title for the old SAE (Society of Automotive Engineers) thread has been changed to the **American National Fine thread** series. Fig. 18–22 shows a screw and a cross section of its mating part with the important parts labeled.

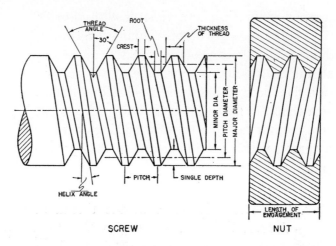

FIG. 18–22.   Screw thread and cross section of nut.

The following formulas and symbols are used for calculating the various parts of threads:

$$C = \text{Clearance} = 2\,H \div 6$$
$$D = \text{Major diameter}$$
$$E = \text{Pitch diameter} = D - H$$
$$F = \text{Flat, crest, root} = P \div 8$$
$$G = \text{Diameter of best wire} = .57735 \div N$$
$$H = \text{Single depth} = .6495 \div N$$
$$2H = \text{Double depth} = 1.299 \div N$$
$$K = \text{Minor diameter} = D - 2\,H$$
$$L = \text{Lead of thread} = 1 \div N'$$
$$M = \text{Measurement over 3 wires} = D + 3\,G - (1.5155 \div N)$$
$$N' = \text{Number of turns of thread in one inch}$$
$$N = \text{Number of threads per inch}$$
$$P = \text{Pitch} = 1 \div N$$
$$s = \text{Helix angle}$$
$$\text{Tangent } s = L \div (3.1416\,E)$$
$$T = \text{Tap drill for 75\% thread} = D - (.97 \div N)$$

FIG. 18–23.   Taper, Plug, and Bottoming taps.

Internal threads are produced at the bench by means of a tap driven by hand, by using one of several kinds of tap wrenches, two of which are shown in Figs. 18–24

FIG. 18–24.   Standard tap wrench.

and 18–25. The kinds of taps commonly used, shown in Fig. 18–23, are known as *Taper, Plug,* and *Bottoming* taps. In order to understand better the process of tapping, consider the following:

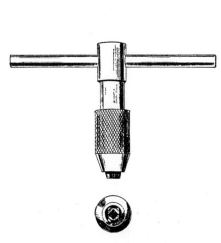

FIG. 18–25.   T-Handle tap wrench.

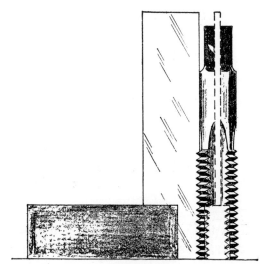

FIG. 18–26.   Checking a tap for squareness with the work.

Example.

Required a 7/16—14 NC tapped hole.

Solution.

STEP No. 1. Layout the location for the hole and center punch it.

STEP No. 2. Calculate the tap drill size as follows:
$T = D — (.97 \div N) = .4375 — (.97 \div 14) = .4375 — .0693 = .3682.$
.3682 corresponds to a letter "U" drill.
If a table of "Basic Thread Dimensions and Tap Drill Sizes" is available, the correct tap drill may be found in it, eliminating the calculation.

STEP No. 3. Get a letter "U" size drill, a 7/16—14 taper tap (if the hole is blind and must be tapped to the bottom, get a 7/16—14 bottoming tap also), and a center drill from the crib.

STEP No. 4. Set up the work properly on the drill press table, insert the center drill in the drill chuck, then center drill the work at the center punch mark.

STEP No. 5. Replace the center drill with the tap drill and bring it into contact with the work, making sure that the conical hole made by the drill point, is concentric with the layout. Drill the hole through or to the proper depth as required.

STEP No. 6. Remove the work and drills from the machine and clean the machine before leaving it.

STEP No. 7. At the bench, place the work so that the hole can be conveniently tapped without its moving; then, with the taper tap placed in the tap wrench, start it in the hole using a good grade of tapping compound.

STEP No. 8. To start the tap square with the work, remove the wrench from the tap and place a solid square against the body of the tap, in two positions 90° apart, each time noting any variation between the tap and square, as shown in Fig. 18–26.

STEP No. 9.   Place the wrench back on the tap and as it is turned force the tap in the direction required to make it square with the work.

STEP No. 10.   Each time the tap is turned forward slightly it should be backed up to break the chips, otherwise they will pack in the flutes and break the tap.

STEP No. 11.   After making sure that the tap is started square, continue working it as in Step No. 10 until the tap has either passed through the hole or seated itself on the bottom of the hole. Be careful not to force the tap too much or it might break off in the work.

STEP No. 12.   After the hole has been tapped, clean out the chips and dirt and test it with a male thread gage.

If a tap should break off in the hole, it can possibly be removed by means of a **tap extractor,** Fig. 18–27. In using this tool be sure to clean out all the loose broken

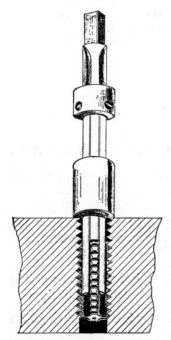

chips first; then force the wire jaws down into the flutes of the tap so that they grip it firmly and then push the re-enforcing collar down over the jaws as close to the work or tap as possible; place the tap wrench on the squared end of the extractor and gently but firmly work it back and forth to loosen the tap. Do not force it too hard, otherwise the jaws of the extractor might twist, bend, or break off.

Bolts, screws, studs or piping that have broken off in the work can be removed by means of an **"Ezy-Out"** shown in Fig. 18–28. To remove a broken bolt or stud, get an Ezy-out of a size consistent with the bolt or stud, and a drill slightly larger than the small end of the Ezy-out; drill through the center of the broken bolt; then insert the Ezy-out and using a tap wrench turn it counter-clockwise so that the taper spirals grip the sides of the broken bolt and back it out.

Scraping. Scraping is the act

FIG. 18–27. Tap extractor and application.

of producing nearly flat surfaces by means of a file-shaped gouge. It is done for the purpose of increasing the life of sliding machine parts or providing accurate gaging surfaces. Scraping may also be done for the purpose of producing nearly cylindrical surfaces by employing a crescent shaped gouge.

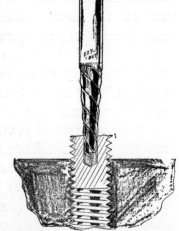

FIG. 18–28. Ezy-out and its use.

Nearly flat surfaces may be produced by three methods: grinding, lapping, or scraping.

Surfaces produced by grinding, while very smooth, are not exactly flat as may be proved by checking a ground surface against a master surface plate. Ground surfaces also contain imbedded particles of abrasive grit and dust which hasten their wear against contacting surfaces.

Lapping produces a much smoother and flatter surface than either grinding or scraping; however, it gives a surface possessing high cohesive qualities and is more expensive. This cohesive quality is undesirable in surface plates and cubes as it causes the inspectors' squares, height gages, and the like to stick, thereby preventing the smooth sliding action necessary for taking delicate tests and measurements. These difficulties are avoided in a scraped surface.

Industrial history is not very definite as to the person who was responsible for the first accurately scraped surfaces. It is well known, however, that Henry Maudslay (1771–1831) produced flat surfaces by the three plate method. This method consists of scraping two plates to fit each other. Then plate No. 2 is laid aside and a third plate scraped to No. 1. After plates 1 and 3 are scraped to each other, plate 1 is laid aside and plates 3 and 2 are scraped to fit. This process of alternately scraping one plate to another is continued until any two plates placed together in any direction will show a perfect bearing. A perfect bearing is defined as a surface having 25 to 30 bearing spots per square inch, the spots being about 1/16″ in diameter. A surface scraped to these specifications makes the best bearing because the lower sections between the bearing spots act as pockets to retain a supply of lubricant.

The surface to be scraped is best prepared by planing or milling. It should not be ground. The ground surface contains particles of abrasive grit which nick and dull the edges of the scraper, thus causing the work to have heavy scratches in it.

After the surface has been planed or milled, it is first roughly cross-scraped to remove the burrs and tool marks left by machining. Then it is given a light coat of red lead and the surface plate is given a light coat of Prussian blue or lamp-black. In the case of small jobs the work is placed face down on the surface plate. In larger jobs the surface plate is placed face down on the job and rubbed back and forth. When the work and the surface plate are separated, the surface to which the plate was applied discloses black and blue spots. These spots are the high points of the surface and are removed with the scraping tool.

The operation of spotting and scraping is continued until the desired quality of surface is obtained. Each time a cut is taken the operator should change the direction of the cut to eliminate chattering of the tool, and, as the surface becomes flatter, the amount of Prussian blue or lamp-black applied to the surface plate should be cut down to a very light film so as to show only the highest points. At this juncture shorter cutting strokes should be taken. This shortening of the stroke causes the bearing spots to come closer together, giving a better bearing and a neater appearance.

The actual scraping operation is dependent on three important factors: (1) the kind of material to be scraped; (2) the condition in which the operator keeps the scraper; and (3) the manner in which the operator uses the scraper.

Some machine parts are made of a good grade of gray iron which is soft and flaky and upon which a good scraping job can be done. Other machine parts are cast from an inferior grade of iron having a high slag content or many blow holes. These parts in turn may contain many hard and soft spots due to irregular cooling during the normalizing operation. This type of iron is difficult to scrape, not only because of the hard and soft spots but also because the slag content nicks the scraper and keeps it from cutting.

The tool used for scraping flat bearing surfaces is made of a piece of high carbon steel, usually 12″ to 15″ long, 1″ to 1-1/2″ wide and tapering from 1/4″ to 1/16″ at the cutting edge. Opposite the cutting end a file tang is provided to take a handle. The scraper is hardened from the cutting end back for about 2-1/2″ and has a double cutting edge. The sizes of scrapers vary to suit the ideas of the individual users. Some mechanics prefer long slender scrapers while others prefer a shorter one having little or no flexibility to it. These scrapers are frequently made from salvaged flat files because of the suitability of the steel.

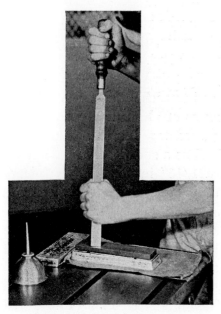

Fig. 18–29.   Stoning a scraper.

The hardening of the scraper, as well as the grinding and stoning of it, are very important. The tool must be hard enough to hold its cutting edge over a long period of time and yet be tough enough so that the edge does not chip and break down easily. In grinding, the sides of the tool must be ground smooth to remove the peaks and valleys incident to forging; then the end must be ground flat and square with the sides. In both of these operations care must be taken to avoid overheating the tool so as not to draw the temper.

The matter of holding and moving the scraper in the stoning operation is very much a matter of individual choice. Generally, the scraper is held in an upright position about 5° or 10° from the vertical with the flat side toward the operator while the right hand grasps the handle and the left hand grasps the scraper body near the center. See Fig. 18–29. In this position the edge of the scraper is passed back and forth over the oilstone with a long sweeping motion, so that the thickness of the blade travels parallel with the length of the stone to produce a radial cutting edge which will be 5° to 10° out of square with the scraper body. This procedure is repeated on the other side of the scraper body to give a double cutting edge. When both sides have been properly sharpened, the flat sides are stoned slightly to remove any burrs.

In using the scraper, the handle is held by the right hand for pushing purposes, while the left hand bears down in the center of the scraper body. The scraper is usually held at about a 30-degree angle with the work as in Fig. 18–30. There is no hard and fast rule that the scraper must be held at 30°, but mechanics who do much scraping are agreed that this angle is about right to avoid excessive gouging and yet permit fast cutting.

Many machine parts as well as the bases of jigs and fixtures are made of cast iron because it is cheaper than steel and holds its shape well. Frequently, however, machine parts made of brass, copper, babbitt, or steel are used. On all these materials, with the exception of steel, the same scraper as was employed for cast iron is used. On steel, a scraper having a single cutting edge is used so that it will lead into the work.

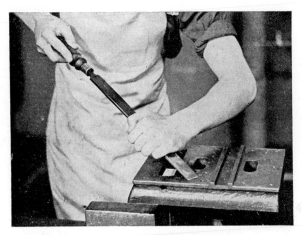

Fig. 18–30.   Using a scraper.

Scraped surfaces are generally provided where one part of a machine must slide accurately on another part. However, before any scraping operations are done on a machine bed or frame, it must be leveled. This is usually accomplished by driving tapered wedges under the base so that the machine will test level in two perpendicular

Fig. 18–31.   Straight edge, angle plate, and cube on a surface plate.

directions. Bench surface plates are equipped with three adjustable legs so that they may be easily leveled on the bench.

Besides sliding machine parts, there are pieces of equipment which, though not scraped for accuracy with respect to sliding action, are scraped to facilitate the accurate laying-out, setting-up, and checking of machine parts and tools. Among the more common of such pieces are angle plates, cubes, and various sizes and shapes of surface plates as shown in Fig. 18–31.

Scraping is not always done for the purpose of providing nearly flat surfaces. Finished parts of machines which are conspicuous are usually scraped or **"flaked"** to give them a pleasing appearance. This decorative effect consists of a series of crescent-shaped spots covering the entire exposed surface and, besides requiring skill, calls for some artistic ability on the part of the operator. Since no two mechanics do this work exactly alike, flaked surfaces and designs become peculiar to a particular operator much the same as hand writing does.

In this kind of scraping, the operator holds the scraper at an angle with the work with both hands below the handle which rests against his body. The scraping tool is then given a rocking motion and at the same time is pulled across the work. Some mechanics rock the scraper from the center to either side, resulting in a series of chain-like designs. Others push the scraper in the conventional scraping manner with a series of short strokes to form rows of crescents about 1/2″ apart and inclined at 45° to each other. Any of these methods will produce a pleasing effect but require a great deal of patience and practice for proper execution.

Scraping hints.

1) In handling a surface plate or straight edge, be very careful not to bump or drop it. It takes very little to destroy its truth and accuracy, but a great deal to restore them.

2) Surface plates, or straight edges, should not be stored beside steam pipes or in any place where they might be subjected to extreme temperature changes. Wide variations of temperature cause these tools to warp, thus destroying their accuracy.

3) All plates, regardless of their size, rest on three adjustable legs. These legs are provided for leveling purposes and to equalize the strain on the plate. Keep these legs adjusted properly, and the accuracy of the plate will be retained over a long period.

4) When leveling the work, use wedges or the three point suspension plan. This method keeps the work from twisting and rocking and makes for greater efficiency in completing the job.

5) Before placing the work and the surface plate together, make sure that both parts are free from dirt and chips. Do not use a towel for wiping off the plate; use the palm of the hand. It can detect small particles of dust or dirt which would otherwise not be cleaned off by a towel.

6) Never clamp work in a vise to check it with a plate. If it is necessary to hold it in a vise to scrape it, do so, but be sure to take it out for checking, otherwise it will be sprung out of shape.

7) Never press on a plate or straight edge while spotting the work. This practice gives a false impression on the work and is apt to bend or warp the straight edge.

8) Always try to use a surface plate of a size as close as possible to that of the

work. Small plates on large work produce low and high areas on the surface of the work. Small jobs on large plates produce low areas on the surface plate.

9) In starting the work, always check it to make sure that there is sufficient stock to get the job square and flat, but not excessive stock to require extra time and expense, and which could be removed more readily by machining. This is particularly true when working to close limits.

10) Lamp-black is better to use as a spotting medium than Prussian blue. Prussian blue is a concentrated oil paint and becomes gummy, thus adhering to the plate and causing inaccuracies in the spotting operation. Lamp-black is a mineral oil containing soot which does not dry readily. It can be left on the plate permanently to prevent tarnishing and rusting of the plate.

11) In finishing a job, do not try to remove all of the black spots. Remove only those that shine from the friction of the surface plate.

12) The finished work should not be too smooth; otherwise it takes on the same effect as a lapped surface.

13) When a piece of work is finished, the bearing should be slightly heavier at the edges than at the center. This keeps dirt and dust from getting under it and scoring the surface.

14) Surface plates, straight edges, cubes, and scraping parallels are the most important gaging tools used in scraping. Use them carefully and they will pay big dividends by way of satisfaction in producing an accurate piece of work with a minimum of effort.

Heat treating. Heat treating is a method of changing the physical properties of a metal by the proper application of heat. Different metals, especially steel, can be given desirable qualities in this process.

Steel is an alloy of iron and one or more elements. When iron is alloyed with carbon without substantial amounts of other alloying elements, it is called **"carbon"** steel. When the carbon content is less than .20% (read twenty-hundredths of one per cent) the steel is known as low carbon steel; steel having .20% to .60% carbon is known as medium carbon steel; when the carbon content is over .60% it is known as high carbon steel. The medium and high straight carbon steels are commonly called **"tool"** steel. **"Alloy"** steels are those to which some element other than carbon has been added to give the steel certain desirable qualities.

Some of the more common elements added with carbon to make alloy steels are: manganese, silicon, chromium, nickel, vanadium, tungsten and molybdenum.

Carbon is the principal hardening element in most alloy steels and has about the same effect on the mass as it would have in steels which contain no other alloying elements. Alloy steels containing not more than .20% carbon are used for carburizing or case hardening. (Carburizing means forcing carbon into the surface of iron base alloys by heating them in contact with carbonaceous material at a temperature below their melting point.) Steels containing carbon in excess of .20% are used where the steel is to be heat treated by quenching and drawing.

Manganese is a constituent of all steels and where it does not exceed .80% is used as a purifier by helping to offset the effects of impurities in the metal. When added to steel in amounts from 1% to 15% it is used to produce hardness and resistance to wear.

Silicon has about the same effect on steel as manganese, in that it acts as a purifier and cleanser. When silicon is added to steel in large quantities it imparts definite electrical properties. In tool steel it imparts hardening and toughening qualities.

When **chromium** is alloyed with steel, it acts as a hardening agent and increases the strength of the mass. For this reason, steel alloys of this type are used for axle shafts and armor plate. When the chromium percentage is from 12% to 30% the steel tends to resist oxidation. Consequently rustless steel is high in chromium content.

Nickel is used as an alloying element in steel to increase the strength and toughness and to resist certain heat treatment strains. For general use the amount varies from 1% to 4%. When added to steel in quantities of from 24% to 36% it causes the steel to become practically non-magnetic and reduces the coefficient of expansion.

Vanadium is alloyed with steel to act as a deoxidizer and cleanser and produces a fine grained steel. When used with tool steel it resists jar and shock better than straight carbon steel.

Tungsten added to straight carbon steel produces a fine, dense, grain structure and when used in small quantities helps cutting tools to retain a sharp cutting edge. When tungsten is added in amounts from 17% to 20%, with certain other elements, it produces a steel that is capable of retaining its hardness at speeds far in excess of those for which tool steel cutters can be used.

Molybdenum increases the endurance limit and yield point of steel and is added in quantities of from .10% to .40%.

For recognizing the different kinds of steel, four methods can be used. In the steel stock yard where bars of steel are stored, the ends are painted various single colors or combinations of colors. For example, tool steel may have the ends painted brown; high speed steel, red; SAE 4620 aluminum and red. When these bars are cut so that they do not show the painted ends, the pieces are stamped either with the SAE number or letters of the Ford system designating the particular kind of steel.

When none of these identifying characters appear on the stock, the type of steel may be identified by holding it against a rotating abrasive wheel and observing the spark characteristics. For example, low carbon steel of the straight carbon series shows long club-shaped sparks, smooth light lines, light yellow in color with no starry formations. High carbon steel of the straight carbon series shows numerous yellow star-shaped sparks on the end of small clubs. High speed steel shows several interrupted brownish-red spark lines with ball-shaped sparks of a dark red color. The spark characteristics of some of the more common steels are shown in Fig. 18–32. It must be remembered that the spark characteristics simply act as a guide in identifying different steels; considerable practice and experience are required before one can become proficient at it.

At room temperature, steel can exist in four different states. First, it can exist in the condition in which it comes from the rolling mill, a normal or natural condition;

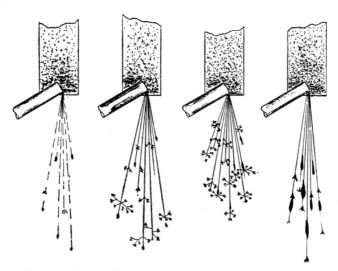

FIG. 18–32.   Spark characteristics of commonly used steels.

second, it can exist in the annealed condition; third, the fully hardened condition; and fourth, the tempered or semi-hard condition.

The basic principles of **hardening steel** consist briefly of the following:

1) The steel must be heated to a point on the temperature scale at which it undergoes a definite physical change. The point on the temperature scale at which this change starts to take place is called the **"lower critical point."**

2) The steel must be heated above the lower critical point to give the physical properties desired. How high the temperature must be raised above this point depends on the analysis of the steel.

3) In order to make these changes permanent the steel must be cooled by quenching or some other process more rapidly than the changes can reverse themselves.

4) Immediately after quenching or cooling, the steel will be in its hardest or most brittle state. Therefore, in order to increase the toughness it is necessary to let down on the hardness by tempering or drawing.

It should be remembered that in order to harden a piece of steel successfully, it must be in the normal state or condition.

Normalizing is the heating of a piece of metal to about 100° above the critical temperature on the Fahrenheit scale and cooling it in still air at ordinary room temperature for the purpose of restoring the steel to a natural or normal physical condition.

Annealing consists of heating and cooling solid material to remove hardness, and to make it softer, to refine the structure, change its ductility or make it machineable.

Tempering (drawing) is the process of reheating a piece of metal after it has been hardened, to a temperature below the critical point and then cooling, for the purpose of letting down on the hardness or removing brittleness.

Quenching is cooling a piece of metal rapidly by immersing it in oil, water, or a blast of cold air.

Carburizing is the process of injecting carbon into the surface of a piece of steel by heating it, at a temperature below its melting point, in an atmosphere of carbonaceous materials such as leather scraps, bone dust, charcoal, and the like.

Cyaniding is a process similar to carburizing, where the metal is heated to a suitable temperature in contact with molten cyanide salt and then quenched. This is a common case hardening operation where the thickness of the case seldom exceeds .008″.

Typical heat treatments for some of the more commonly used steels are as follows:

Machinery or Cold Rolled Steel. Heat the piece in cyanide to 1500 or 1550°F, soaking it for about 10 minutes; then quench it in brine if the part is large, or in oil if it is small.

Tool Steel. Heat the piece in a closed furnace to 1400 or 1450°F, then quench in brine after which it can be tempered in oil at 350 to 375°F.

High Speed Steel. Heat the part to 1400 to 1450°F; then superheat it to a minimum of 2350°F, after which, quench in oil. Temper in furnace at 1050 to 1100°F so that it will test 62–64 on the Rockwell "C" scale.

The hardness of metals can be checked by one of several methods. One of the oldest methods that is still in use is that of trying to cut into the piece with the corner of a file and judging the hardness by the depth of the mark left by the file. This method is not as reliable as some of the hardness testing machines, but by it one can determine whether a piece is hard or soft.

One of the more common hardness testing machines is the **Rockwell** instrument, Fig. 18–33. It consists of a 120° diamond cone for hard metals or a 1/16″ steel ball for softer materials, which is impressed into the surface to be tested by means of a weight acting through a series of levers. The softer the piece, the deeper will be the impression. Hardness is indicated on a direct reading scale graduated in terms of the Rockwell "B" or Rockwell "C" rating.

The **Brinell** testing machine, Fig. 18–34, measures the hardness by the resistance offered to the penetration of a steel ball under pressure. The degrees of hardness are found by measuring the distance the ball is forced into the piece. The greater this distance, the softer the work and the higher the Brinell number.

The **Scleroscope** tests the hardness of a piece of metal by checking the distance which a diamond pointed hammer will rebound when dropped through a glass guiding tube. The distance the hammer rebounds is checked on a scale inside the glass tube. The accuracy of this machine is based on the fact that the harder the metal, the higher the rebound.

FIG. 18–33.   FIG. 18–34.

General suggestions

1) Use pieces of wire and fire clay to prevent cracking of thin sections or sharp edges.

2) Long slender pieces of work should be quenched by holding them vertically over the quenching tank and plunging them straight down. This prevents warping of the job.

3) Generally speaking, a piece of steel should be heated in the furnace one hour for each square inch of cross-sectional area to insure even heating.

4) Be careful not to put damp or wet articles in lead or cyanide pots because violent explosions might occur.

5) Goggles should be worn when working on lead, nitrate, and cyanide furnaces.

6) Hot tongs should be cooled by quenching before hanging them up or laying them down.

7) Pieces which are hot should not be permitted to lay around where some one is apt to be burned by them. Mark with chalk the word HOT on the piece or close to it.

REVIEW QUESTIONS

1. What is a layout?

2. How is a piece of work prepared to have a layout made upon it?

3. What is a layout plate?
4. Name the tools commonly used in layout work.
5. When is a dividing head employed in layout operations?
6. Define a drill.
7. Name the important parts of a drill.
8. What is meant by the angle of relief?
9. What are the important angles to be observed in grinding a drill?
10. What range of drill sizes is specified by number? By letter? By fractions?
11. Define the term feed as applied to drilling.
12. List the approximate speeds recommended for the commonly used metals.
13. Discuss the necessary steps in layout and drilling a hole.
14. What is meant by "drawing a drill back on center"? Discuss.
15. What is a drill drift? How should it be used? When?
16. How much stock should be left for reaming?
17. Discuss several types of reamers.
18. What is a taper reamer? Discuss two types.
19. Taper pin reamers have what TPF?
20. What is a counterbore? Name three types.
21. What is a countersink?
22. When is an inverted counterbore used?
23. What is a tap? Name three kinds.
24. What is a die?
25. Name the important parts of a thread.
26. Discuss the process of tapping a hole.
27. What is a tap extractor? How is it used?
28. How is an "Ezy-Out" used?
29. For what purpose is scraping employed?
30. Name three methods of producing nearly flat surfaces.
31. How is a surface prepared for scraping? Why?
32. Describe a scraper.
33. How should a scraper be held?
34. What is meant by the word flaking?
35. Define the term heat treat.
36. What is carbon steel? Tool steel? Alloy steel?
37. Name several common elements used with carbon to make alloy steel.
38. Discuss four methods of distinguishing the common steels.
39. Discuss the spark characteristics of the commonly used steels.
40. In what four different "states" does steel exist at room temperature?
41. What is meant by the term lower critical point?
42. Define the following terms:

Normalizing	Quenching
Annealing	Carburizing
Tempering	Cyaniding

43. Discuss several methods of testing the hardness of metals.
44. Discuss general safety rules to be observed in heat treating.

Chapter 19

FORMULAS AND TABLES

Circles . . . Areas . . . Solids . . . Decimal equivalents — Inches to millimeters . . . Diameters of numbered drills . . . Diameters of lettered drills . . . Allowance for machine fits . . . Table of cutting speeds . . . Taper pins and reamers . . . SAE standard taper dimensions . . . Standard taper dimensions . . . American National Coarse and Fine thread dimensions and tap drill sizes . . . Woodruff key seat cutter sizes . . . Table of coordinates for the jig borer

TABLE I

PROPERTIES OF CIRCLES.

Circumference of circle = diameter × 3.1416

Diameter of circle = circumference × .3183

Side of square inscribed in circle = diameter of circle × .70711

Diameter of circle circumscribed about a square = side of square × 1.4142

Diameter of a circle circumscribed about a hexagon = distance across flat × **1.1547**

Length of arc = number of degrees × diameter × .008727

Circumference of circle of unity = 3.14159265.

AREA OR SURFACE.

Triangle = base × one-half the altitude.

Parallelogram = base × perpendicular height.

Trapezoid = half the sum of the parallel sides × perpendicular height.

Circle = diameter squared × .7854 or radius squared × 3.1416.

Sector of a circle = length of arc × half the radius.

Segment of a circle less than a semi-circle = area of sector minus area of triangle.

Segment of circle greater than a semi-circle = area of sector + area of triangle.

Side of square having same area as circle = diameter of circle × .8862.

Diameter of circle having same area as square = side of square × 1.1284.

Parabola = base × 2/3 perpendicular height.

Ellipse = long diameter × short diameter × .7854.

Regular polygon = sum of sides × half perpendicular distance from center to sides.

Cylinder = (circumference × height) + area of both ends.

Sphere = diameter squared × 3.1416.

Segment of sphere = (height of segment × circumference of sphere of which it is a part) + area of base.

Right pyramid or cone = periphery or circumference of base × 1/2 slant height, + area of base.

Frustum of a regular right pyramid or cone = (sum of peripheries or circumferences of the two ends × half slant height) + area of both ends.

SOLID CONTENTS OR VOLUME.

Cube, or rectangular solid = length × width × height.

Prism, right or oblique, = area of base × perpendicular height.

Cylinder, right or oblique, = area of section at right angles to sides × length of side.

Sphere = diameter cubed × .5236.

Segment of sphere = (height of segment squared + three times the square of radius of base of segment) × height of segment × .5236.

Side of cube having same volume as sphere = diameter of sphere × .806.

Length of cylinder having same volume and same diameter as sphere = diameter of sphere × .66667.

Pyramid or cone, right or oblique, regular or irregular, = area of base × 1/3 perpendicular height.

Frustum of cone = multiply area of two ends together and extract the square root; add to this square root the sum of the areas of both ends and then multiply the total sum by 1/3 the perpendicular distance between the ends.

Courtesy of Atlas Press, Kalamazoo, Mich.

TABLE II

DECIMAL EQUIVALENTS

INCHES TO MILLIMETERS

Inches		Inches	m/m	Inches		Inches	m/m
	1/64	.01563	.397		33/64	.51563	13.097
1/32		.03125	.794	17/32		.53125	13.494
	3/64	.04688	1.191		35/64	.54688	13.890
1/16		.0625	1.587	9/16		.5625	14.287
	5/64	.07813	1.984		37/64	.57813	14.684
3/32		.09375	2.381	19/32		.59375	15.081
	7/64	.10938	2.778		39/64	.60938	15.478
1/8		.125	3.175	5/8		.625	15.875
	9/64	.14063	3.572		41/64	.64063	16.272
5/32		.15625	3.969	21/32		.65625	16.669
	11/64	.17188	4.366		43/64	.67188	17.065
3/16		.1875	4.762	11/16		.6875	17.462
	13/64	.20313	5.159		45/64	.70313	17.859
7/32		.21875	5.556	23/32		.71875	18.256
	15/64	.23438	5.953		47/64	.73438	18.653
1/4		.25	6.350	3/4		.75	19.050
	17/64	.26563	6.747		49/64	.76563	19.447
9/32		.28125	7.144	25/32		.78125	19.844
	19/64	.29688	7.541		51/64	.79688	20.240
5/16		.3125	7.937	13/16		.8125	20.637
	21/64	.32813	8.334		53/64	.82813	21.034
11/32		.34375	8.731	27/32		.84375	21.431
	23/64	.35938	9.128		55/64	.85938	21.828
3/8		.375	9.525	7/8		.875	22.225
	25/64	.39063	9.922		57/64	.89063	22.622
13/32		.40625	10.319	29/32		.90625	23.019
	27/64	.42188	10.716		59/64	.92188	23.415
7/16		.4375	11.113	15/16		.9375	23.812
	29/64	.45313	11.509		61/64	.95313	24.209
15/32		.46875	11.906	31/32		.96875	24.606
	31/64	.48438	12.303		63/64	.98438	25.003
1/2		.5	12.700	1		1.00000	25.400

TABLE III

DIAMETERS OF NUMBERED DRILLS

Drill No.	Diameter Inches	Drill No.	Diameter Inches	Drill No.	Diameter Inches
80	.0135	53	.0595	26	.1470
79	.0145	52	.0635	25	.1495
78	.0160	51	.0670	24	.1520
77	.0180	50	.0700	23	.1540
76	.0200	49	.0730	22	.1570
75	.0210	48	.0760	21	.1590
74	.0225	47	.0785	20	.1610
73	.0240	46	.0810	19	.1660
72	.0250	45	.0820	18	.1695
71	.0260	44	.0860	17	.1730
70	.0280	43	.0890	16	.1770
69	.0292	42	.0935	15	.1800
68	.0310	41	.0960	14	.1820
67	.0320	40	.0980	13	.1850
66	.0330	39	.0995	12	.1890
65	.0350	38	.1015	11	.1910
64	.0360	37	.1040	10	.1935
63	.0370	36	.1065	9	.1960
62	.0380	35	.1100	8	.1990
61	.0390	34	.1110	7	.2010
60	.0400	33	.1130	6	.2040
59	.0410	32	.1160	5	.2055
58	.0420	31	.1200	4	.2090
57	.0430	30	.1285	3	.2130
56	.0465	29	.1360	2	.2210
55	.0520	28	.1405	1	.2280
54	.0550	27	.1440		

TABLE IV

DIAMETERS OF LETTERED DRILLS

Drill Letter	Diameter Inches
A	.2340
B	.2380
C	.2420
D	.2460
E	.2500
F	.2570
G	.2610
H	.2660
I	.2720
J	.2770
K	.2810
L	.2900
M	.2950
N	.3020
O	.3160
P	.3230
Q	.3320
R	.3390
S	.3480
T	.3580
U	.3680
V	.3770
W	.3860
X	.3970
Y	.4040
Z	.4130

TABLE V

ALLOWANCES FOR MACHINE FITS

In all work requiring running, push, drive or forced fits, the diameter of the hole should be exact as specified within the limits given, while the diameter of the shaft shall be such that it will fit the hole according to the given allowances for various fits.

Nominal Diameter Inches	Hole Tolerance	Allowances for Different Fits			
		Running Fit	Push Fit	Drive Fit	Forced Fit
Up to 1/2″	+.0005 −.0005	−.001 −.002	−.0003 −.0008	+.0005 +.0003	+.001 +.0005
1/2″ to 1″	+.001 −.0005	−.0015 −.003	−.0003 −.0008	+.001 +.0008	+.002 +.0015
1″ to 2″	+.001 −.0005	−.002 −.004	−.0003 −.0008	+.0015 +.001	+.004 +.003
2″ to 3″	+.0015 −.001	−.0025 −.0045	−.0005 −.001	+.0025 +.0015	+.006 +.0045
3″ to 4″	+.0015 −.001	−.003 −.005	−.0005 −.001	+.003 +.002	+.008 +.006

TABLE VI

TABLE OF CUTTING SPEEDS

(Fraction Size Drills)

Feet per Min.	30	40	50	60	70	80	90	100	110	120	130	140	150
Diameter Inches	REVOLUTIONS PER MINUTE												
1/16	1833	2445	3056	3667	4278	4889	5500	6111	6722	7334	7945	8556	9167
1/8	917	1222	1528	1833	2139	2445	2750	3056	3361	3667	3973	4278	4584
3/16	611	815	1019	1222	1426	1630	1833	2037	2241	2445	2648	2852	3056
1/4	458	611	764	917	1070	1222	1375	1528	1681	1833	1986	2139	2292
5/16	367	489	611	733	856	978	1100	1222	1345	1467	1589	1711	1833
3/8	306	407	509	611	713	815	917	1019	1120	1222	1324	1426	1528
7/16	262	349	437	524	611	698	786	873	960	1048	1135	1222	1310
1/2	229	306	382	458	535	611	688	764	840	917	993	1070	1146
5/8	183	244	306	367	428	489	550	611	672	733	794	856	917
3/4	153	203	255	306	357	407	458	509	560	611	662	713	764
7/8	131	175	218	262	306	349	393	436	480	524	568	611	655
1	115	153	191	229	267	306	344	382	420	458	497	535	573
1-1/8	102	136	170	204	238	272	306	340	373	407	441	475	509
1-1/4	92	122	153	183	214	244	275	306	336	367	397	428	458
1-3/8	83	111	139	167	194	222	250	278	306	333	361	389	417
1-1/2	76	102	127	153	178	204	229	255	280	306	331	357	382
1-5/8	70	94	117	141	165	188	212	235	259	282	306	329	353
1-3/4	65	87	109	131	153	175	196	218	240	262	284	306	327
1-7/8	61	81	102	122	143	163	183	204	224	244	265	285	306
2	57	76	95	115	134	153	172	191	210	229	248	267	287
2-1/4	51	68	85	102	119	136	153	170	187	204	221	238	255
2-1/2	46	61	76	92	107	122	137	153	168	183	199	214	229
2-3/4	42	56	69	83	97	111	125	139	153	167	181	194	208
3	38	51	64	76	89	102	115	127	140	153	166	178	191

TABLE VII

TAPER PINS AND REAMERS

Size No.	Dia. of Small End of Reamer	Dia. of Large End of Reamer	Size Drill for Reamer	Maximum Length of Pin	Dia. of Large End of Pin
0	.135	.162	28	1	.156
1	.146	.179	25	1-1/4	.172
2	.162	.200	19	1-1/2	.193
3	.183	.226	12	1-3/4	.219
4	.208	.257	3	2	.250
5	.240	.300	1/4	2-1/4	.289
6	.279	.354	9/32	3-1/4	.341
7	.331	.423	11/32	3-3/4	.409
8	.398	.507	13/32	4-1/2	.492
9	.482	.609	31/64	5-1/4	.591
10	.581	.727	19/32	6	.706

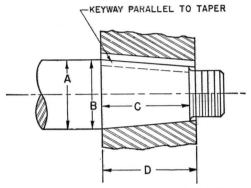

KEYWAY PARALLEL TO TAPER

TAPER PER FOOT = 1.500 ± 0.005 IN.

FIG. 19-1. (SAE standard taper dimensions.)

TABLE VIII

SAE STANDARD TAPER DIMENSIONS

Diam. in Inches (nominal)	Diam. of Shaft A		Diam. of Hole B		Length of Shaft C	Length of Hole D
	Max.	Min.	Max.	Min.		
1/4	0.250	0.249	0.248	0.247	5/16	3/8
3/8	0.375	0.374	0.373	0.372	7/16	1/2
1/2	0.500	0.499	0.498	0.497	11/16	3/4
5/8	0.625	0.624	0.623	0.622	11/16	3/4
3/4	0.750	0.749	0.748	0.747	15/16	1
7/8	0.875	0.874	0.873	0.872	1-1/8	1-1/4
1	1.001	0.999	0.997	0.995	1-3/8	1-1/2
1-1/8	1.126	1.124	1.122	1.120	1-3/8	1-1/2
1-1/4	1.251	1.249	1.247	1.245	1-3/8	1-1/2
1-3/8	1.376	1.374	1.372	1.370	1-7/8	2
1-1/2	1.501	1.499	1.497	1.495	1-7/8	2
1-5/8	1.626	1.624	1.622	1.620	2-1/8	2-1/4
1-3/4	1.751	1.749	1.747	1.745	2-1/8	2-1/4
1-7/8	1.876	1.874	1.872	1.870	2-3/8	2-1/2
2	2.001	1.999	1.997	1.995	2-7/8	3
2-1/4	2.252	2.248	2.245	2.242	2-7/8	3
2-1/2	2.502	2.498	2.495	2.492	3-3/8	3-1/2
2-3/4	2.752	2.748	2.745	2.742	3-3/8	3-1/2
3	3.002	2.998	2.995	2.992	3-7/8	4
3-1/4	3.252	3.248	3.245	3.242	4-1/8	4-1/4
3-1/2	3.502	3.498	3.492	3.492	4-3/8	4-1/2
4	4.002	3.998	3.995	3.992	5-3/8	5-1/2

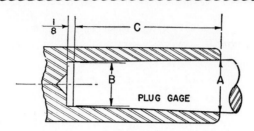

Fig. 19–2. (Standard taper dimensions.)

TABLE IX

STANDARD TAPER DIMENSIONS

JARNO

Number of Taper	A Diam. at End of Socket	B Diam. of Plug at Small End	C Standard Plug Depth
1	0.125	0.10	1/2
2	0.250	0.20	1
3	0.375	0.30	1-1/2
4	0.500	0.40	2
5	0.625	0.50	2-1/2
6	0.750	0.60	3
7	0.875	0.70	3-1/2
8	1.000	0.80	4
9	1.125	0.90	4-1/2
10	1.250	1.00	5
11	1.375	1.10	5-1/2
12	1.500	1.20	6
13	1.625	1.30	6-1/2
14	1.750	1.40	7
15	1.875	1.50	7-1/2
16	2.000	1.60	8
17	2.125	1.70	8-1/2
18	2.250	1.80	9
19	2.375	1.90	9-1/2
20	2.500	2.00	10

MORSE

Number of Taper	A Diam. at End of Socket	B Diam. of Plug at Small End	C Standard Plug Depth
0	0.356	0.252	2
1	0.475	0.369	2-1/8
2	0.700	0.579	2-9/16
3	0.938	0.778	3-3/16
4	1.231	1.020	4-1/16
5	1.748	1.475	5-3/16
6	2.494	2.116	7-1/4
7	3.270	2.750	10

BROWN AND SHARPE

Number of Taper	A Diam. at End of Socket	B Diam. of Plug at Small End	C Standard Plug Depth
1	0.239	0.200	15/16
2	0.299	0.250	1-3/16
3	0.375	0.312	1-1/2
3	0.385	0.312	1-3/4
3	0.395	0.312	2
4	0.402	0.350	1-1/4
4	0.420	0.350	1-11/16
5	0.523	0.450	1-3/4
5	0.533	0.450	2
5	0.539	0.450	2-1/8
6	0.599	0.500	2-3/8
6	0.635	0.500	3-1/4
7	0.725	0.600	3
8	0.898	0.750	3-9/16
8	0.917	0.750	4
9	1.067	0.900	4
9	1.077	0.900	4-1/4
10	1.260	1.044	5
10	1.289	1.044	5-11/16
10	1.312	1.044	6-7/32
11	1.498	1.250	5-15/16
11	1.531	1.250	6-3/4
12	1.797	1.500	7-1/8
13	2.073	1.750	7-3/4
14	2.344	2.000	8-1/4
15	2.615	2.250	8-3/4
16	2.885	2.250	9-1/4
17	3.156	2.750	9-3/4
18	3.427	3.000	10-1/4

TABLE X

AMERICAN NATIONAL COARSE AND FINE THREAD DIMENSIONS AND TAP DRILL SIZES

$$p = \text{pitch} = \frac{1}{\text{No. thrd. per in.}}$$

$$d = \text{depth} = p \times .649519$$

$$f = \text{flat} = \frac{p}{8}$$

Size		Threads per Inch			Outside Diameter Inches	Pitch Diameter Inches	Single Depth	Tap Drill Approx. 75% Full Thread	Diam. of Best Wire	Mic. Reading Over 3 Wires
		NC	NF	NS						
0		..	80	..	.0600	.0519	.00812	3/64	.00721	.06269
1		..	..	56	.0730	.0614	.0116	54	.01030	.07684
1		64	..	..	.0730	.0629	.0101	53	.00902	.07639
1		..	72	..	.0730	.0640	.0090	53	.00801	.07599
2		56	..	..	.0860	.0744	.0116	50	.01030	.08984
2		..	64	..	.0860	.0759	.0101	49	.00902	.08939
3		48	..	..	.0990	.0855	.0135	47	.01202	.10349
3		..	56	..	.0990	.0874	.0116	45	.01030	.10284
4		..	..	32	.1120	.0917	.0203	45	.01804	.11877
4		..	..	36	.1120	.0940	.0180	44	.01603	.11800
4		40	..	..	.1120	.0958	.0162	43	.01443	.11741
4		..	48	..	.1120	.0985	.0135	42	.01203	.11649
5		..	..	36	.1250	.1070	.0180	40	.01603	.13100
5		40	..	..	.1250	.1088	.0162	38	.01443	.13041
5		..	44	..	.1250	.1102	.0147	37	.01312	.12992
6		32	..	..	.1380	.1177	.0203	35	.01804	.14477
6		..	..	36	.1380	.1200	.0180	34	.01603	.14400
6		..	40	..	.1380	.1218	.0162	33	.01443	.14341
8		..	..	30	.1640	.1423	.0216	30	.01924	.17121
8		32	..	..	.1640	.1437	.0203	29	.01804	.17077
8		..	36	..	.1640	.1460	.0180	29	.01603	.17001
8		..	..	40	.1640	.1478	.0162	28	.01443	.16941
10		24	..	..	.1900	.1629	.0270	25	.02405	.19901
10		..	..	28	.1900	.1668	.0232	23	.02061	.19771
10		..	..	30	.1900	.1684	.0217	22	.01924	.19721
10		..	32	..	.1900	.1697	.0203	21	.01804	.19677
12		24	..	..	.2160	.1889	.0270	16	.02405	.22501
12		..	28	..	.2160	.1928	.0232	14	.02061	.22371
12		..	..	32	.2160	.1957	.0203	13	.01804	.22277
	1/4	20	..	..	.2500	.2175	.0325	7	.02886	.26083
	1/4	..	28	..	.2500	.2268	.0232	3	.02061	.25771
	5/16	18	..	..	.3125	.2764	.0361	F	.03207	.32452
	5/16	..	24	..	.3125	.2854	.0270	I	.02405	.32151
	3/8	16	..	..	.3750	.3344	.0406	5/16	.03608	.38853
	3/8	..	24	..	.3750	.3479	.0270	Q	.02405	.38401
	7/16	14	..	..	.4375	.3911	.0464	U	.04123	.45294
	7/16	..	20	..	.4375	.4050	.0325	25/64	.02886	.44831

TABLE X — Continued

Size	Threads per Inch			Outside Diameter Inches	Pitch Diameter Inches	Single Depth	Tap Drill Approx. 75% Full Thread	Diam. of Best Wire	Mic. Reading Over 3 Wires
	NC	NF	NS						
1/2	13	..	..	.5000	.4500	.0500	27/64	.04441	.51666
1/2	..	20	..	.5000	.4675	.0325	29/64	.02886	.51081
9/16	12	..	..	.5625	..5084	.0541	31/64	.04811	.58054
9/16	..	18	..	.5625	.5264	.0361	33/64	.03207	.63702
5/8	11	..	..	.6250	.5660	.0590	17/32	.05248	.64468
5/8	..	18	..	.6250	.5889	.0361	37/64	.03207	.58146
3/4	10	..	..	.7500	.6850	.0650	21/32	.05773	.77164
3/4	..	16	..	.7500	.7094	.0406	11/16	.03608	.76853
7/8	9	..	..	.8750	.8028	.0722	49/64	.06415	.89907
7/8	..	14	..	.8750	.8286	.0464	13/16	.04123	.89044
7/8	..	..	18	.8750	.8389	.0361	53/64	.03207	.88702
1	8	..	..	1.0000	.9188	.0812	7/8	.07216	1.02705
1	..	14	..	1.0000	.9536	.0464	15/16	.04123	1.01545
1-1/8	7	..	..	1.1250	1.0322	.0928	63/64	.08247	1.15591
1-1/8	..	12	..	1.1250	1.0709	.0541	1- 3/64	.04811	1.14304
1-1/4	7	..	..	1.2500	1.1572	.0928	1- 7/64	.08247	1.28091
1-1/4	..	12	..	1.2500	1.1959	.0541	1-11/64	.04811	1.26804
1-3/8	6	..	..	1.3750	1.2667	.1083	1- 7/32	.09622	1.41108
1-3/8	..	12	..	1.3750	1.3209	.0541	1-19/64	.04811	1.39304
1-1/2	6	..	..	1.5000	1.3917	.1083	1-11/32	.09622	1.53608
1-1/2	..	12	..	1.5000	1.4459	.0541	1-27/64	.04811	1.51804
1-3/4	5	..	..	1.7500	1.6201	.1299	1- 9/16	.11547	1.79331
2	4-1/2	..	..	2.0000	1.8557	.1443	1-25/32	.12830	2.04813
2-1/4	4-1/2	..	..	2.2500	2.1057	.1443	2- 1/32	.12830	2.29813
2-1/2	4	..	..	2.5000	2.3376	.1624	2- 1/4	.14433	2.55412
2-3/4	4	..	..	2.7500	2.5876	.1624	2- 1/2	.14433	2.80412
3	4	..	..	3.0000	2.8376	.1624	2- 3/4.	.14433	3.05412
3-1/4	4	..	..	3.2500	3.0876	.1624	3-	.14433	3.30412
3-1/2	4	..	..	3.5000	3.3376	.1624	3- 1/4	.14433	3.55412
3-3/4	4	..	..	3.7500	3.5876	.1624	3- 1/2	.14433	3.80412
4	4	..	..	4.0000	3.8376	.1624	1- 3/4	.14433	4.05412

TABLE XI

CONVERSION TABLE FOR WOODRUFF KEY-SEAT CUTTER SIZES

Old	SAE	ASA	Dia	Thk	Depth
1	10	204	1/2	1/16	.1718
2	20	304	1/2	3/32	.1561
3	30	404	1/2	1/8	.1405
4	40	305	5/8	3/32	.2031
5	50	405	5/8	1/8	.1875
6	60	505	5/8	5/32	.1719
7	70	406	3/4	1/8	.2505
8	80	506	3/4	5/32	.2349
9	90	606	3/4	3/16	.2193
10	100	507	7/8	5/32	.2969
11	110	607	7/8	3/16	.2813
12	. . .	. . .	7/8	7/32	.2715
A	115	807	7/8	1/4	.250
13	130	608	1	3/16	.344
14	. . .	. . .	1	7/32	.329
15	150	808	1	1/4	.313
B	155	1008	1	5/16	.2818
16	160	609	1-1/8	3/16	.390
17	. . .	. . .	1-1/8	7/32	.380
18	180	809	1-1/8	1/4	.359
C	185	1009	1-1/8	5/16	.3278
19	. . .	. . .	1-1/4	3/16	.4376
20	. . .	. . .	1-1/4	7/32	.427
21	210	810	1-1/4	1/4	.422
D	215	1010	1-1/4	5/16	.3908
E	225	1210	1-1/4	3/8	.3595
22	. . .	811	1-3/8	1/4	.469
23	230	1010	1-3/8	5/16	.4378
F	235	1211	1-3/8	3/8	.4065
24	240	812	1-1/2	1/4	.516
25	250	1012	1-1/2	5/16	.4848
G	255	1212	1-1/2	3/8	.4535

ASA is the American Standards Association system for notating key and cutter sizes. The last two digits give the nominal diameter in eighths of an inch, and the digits preceding the last two give the thickness in thirty-seconds of an inch.

SAE is the Society of Automotive Engineers.

TABLE XII

TABLE OF CO-ORDINATES FOR THE JIG BORER.   BASED ON $1''$ DIAMETER CIRCLE

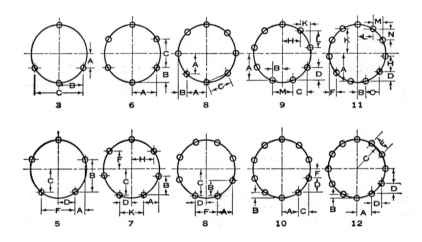

Holes	Chord	A	B	C	D	F	H	K	L	M	N
3	.86603	.25000	.43302	.86603							
5	.58779	.18164	.55902	.40451	.29389	.58779					
6	.50000	.43302	.25000	.50000							
7	.43388	.27052	.33920	.45049	.21694	.31175	.39090	.43388			
8	.38268	.35355	.14650	.38268							
8	.38268	.27059	.27059	.46194	.19134	.38268					
9	.34202	.46985	.17101	.26200	.21985	.38302	.32139	.17101	.29170	.34202	
10	.30901	.29389	.09549	.18464	.25000	.15451					
11	.28173	.47975	.14087	.23701	.15232	.11704	.25627	.42063	.27032	.18449	.21319
12	.25882	.25000	.06699	.48297	.18301	.25882					

Multiply the value required by the diameter of the given circle.   Example: To find "C" for 9 holes equally spaced on a 5.25 dia. circle, multiply .26200 by 5.25.   Result, 1.3755.

The values given in the following Table XIII under R and T are for **ONE**-diametral pitch gears. The values for any other diametral pitch will be in the ratio of one to the new pitch size. That is, if a 24-tooth gear is 5-diametral pitch, the corrected addendum will be one-fifth as large as a 24-tooth gear of one-diametral pitch. In like manner the chordal thickness will be one-fifth as large.

The following example is given as an illustration:

Example.

Calculate the corrected addendum and chordal thickness of a gear having 31 teeth and of 9-diametral pitch.

Solution.

In the column headed N select the nearest number to 31. In this case 35.

Opposite 35, in the column headed R find the value 1.0176 which is the corrected addendum of a 35-tooth gear, one-diametral pitch.

Then 1.0176 ÷ 9 = .1130 + or the corrected addendum of a 31-tooth gear of 9-diametral pitch.

Opposite 35, under T find 1.5702. This is the chordal thickness of a 35-tooth gear of one-diametral pitch.

Then 1.5702 ÷ 9 = .1744 + or the chordal thickness of a 31-tooth 9-diametral pitch gear.

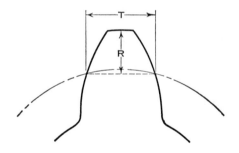

TABLE XIII

CHORDAL THICKNESS AND CORRECTED ADDENDUM CHART

(For Diametral Pitch = 1)

N	R	T	N	R	T
8	1.0769	1.5607	17	1.0362	1.5686
9	1.0648	1.5628	21	1.0294	1.5694
10	1.0616	1.5643	26	1.0237	1.5698
11	1.0559	1.5654	35	1.0176	1.5702
12	1.0514	1.5663	55	1.0112	1.5706
14	1.0440	1.5675	135	1.0046	1.5708

INDEX